Distances and Domination in Graphs

Distances and Domination in Graphs

Editor

Ismael González Yero

MDPI • Basel • Beijing • Wuhan • Barcelona • Belgrade • Manchester • Tokyo • Cluj • Tianjin

Editor
Ismael González Yero
Universidad de Cádiz
Spain

Editorial Office
MDPI
St. Alban-Anlage 66
4052 Basel, Switzerland

This is a reprint of articles from the Special Issue published online in the open access journal *Mathematics* (ISSN 2227-7390) (available at: https://www.mdpi.com/journal/mathematics/special_issues/Distances_Domination_Graphs).

For citation purposes, cite each article independently as indicated on the article page online and as indicated below:

LastName, A.A.; LastName, B.B.; LastName, C.C. Article Title. *Journal Name* **Year**, *Article Number*, Page Range.

ISBN 978-3-03943-515-9 (Hbk)
ISBN 978-3-03943-516-6 (PDF)

Contents

About the Editor

Ismael González Yero is an Associate Professor of Applied Mathematics at the University of Cadiz, Spain. He earned his Ph.D. in Mathematics (2010) from Rovira I Virgili University, Spain. His research work focuses on graph theory, specifically on parameters related to distances and domination in graphs, metric graph theory and products of graphs, and their applications in computer science, with some emphasis on privacy in social networks and community detection. He is the author of about 100 research papers on these topics.

Preface to "Distances and Domination in Graphs"

In graph theory, a large number of topics related to distances in graphs is being investigated in several studies. The most typical and known ones are perhaps the diameter, the radius, and the eccentricity. However, there is a large number of other interesting distance-related topcis in graphs that are frequently used in applied and/or theoretical investigations. Some of the most common ones are related to well-known indexes that measure the properties of graphs, for example, the centrality, the closeness, and the betweenness centrality. One interesting fact that allows us to deal with such problems is that the matrix of distances in a graph can be computed in polynomial time, using, for example, the well-known Floyd–Warshall algorithm. Another interesting case in problems concerning distances in graphs is the degree–diameter problem, which basically involves the determination of the largest possible graph (in terms of the size of its vertex set) such that the largest degree of any of the vertices in the graph is, at most, the specified diameter. This problem has been extensively studied, and there is a huge background of literature on it. Some other examples of distance-related parameters are the convexity number, the geodetic number, and the metric dimension. During the last 30 years, with the increase in investigations in several areas like computer science, computer engineering, operational research and social networks, graph theory has become an important tool for researching many of the mentioned areas. On the other hand, one of the most important topics in graph theory is the theory of domination and related problems, such as independence, covering and matching. The growth of studies on domination in graphs can be partly attributed to its applicability in diverse theoretical fields, such as linear algebra, communication networks, social sciences, computational complexity and algorithm design. The significant increase in interest in this topic has resulted in an enormous quantity of published papers—around 1600 papers, a significant number of monographs and theses, and several books. Based on this increased interest, this Special Issue was developed at the journal *Mathematics* under the title of "Distance and Domination in Graphs", in order to gather some relavant and recent investigations concerning distances and domination in graphs.

Ismael González Yero
Editor

Article

A Review of and Some Results for Ollivier–Ricci Network Curvature

Nazanin Azarhooshang †, Prithviraj Sengupta † and Bhaskar DasGupta *,†

Department of Computer Science, University of Illinois at Chicago, Chicago, IL 60607, USA;
nazarh2@uic.edu (N.A.); psengu4@uic.edu (P.S.)
* Correspondence: bdasgup@uic.edu; Tel.: +1-312-355-1319
† These authors contributed equally to this work.

Received: 31 July 2020; Accepted: 18 August 2020; Published: 24 August 2020

Abstract: Characterizing topological properties and anomalous behaviors of higher-dimensional topological spaces via notions of curvatures is by now quite common in mainstream physics and mathematics, and it is therefore natural to try to extend these notions from the non-network domains in a suitable way to the network science domain. In this article we discuss one such extension, namely Ollivier's discretization of Ricci curvature. We first motivate, define and illustrate the Ollivier–Ricci Curvature. In the next section we provide some "not-previously-published" bounds on the exact and approximate computation of the curvature measure. In the penultimate section we review a method based on the linear sketching technique for efficient approximate computation of the Ollivier–Ricci network curvature. Finally in the last section we provide concluding remarks with pointers for further reading.

Keywords: network science; network curvature; discrete Ricci curvature; earth-mover's distance

MSC: 68Q17; 68W40

1. Introduction

It is by now quite common in mainstream physics and mathematics [1,2] to characterize topological properties and anomalous behaviors of higher-dimensional topological spaces via notions of (local and global) curvatures of these spaces, e.g., in general relativity, extreme variations of four dimensional space-time curvatures via geodesic incompleteness lead to characterizations of black-holes [3]. It is therefore natural to try to extend these notions from the non-network domains e.g., from continuous metric spaces or from higher-dimensional geometric objects) in a suitable way to the network science domain so that non-trivial new topological characteristics of networks can be captured. There are several ways this can be achieved; we briefly mention two other approaches before proceeding with the approach that is the main topic of this paper. Note that such extensions need to overcome at least two key challenges, namely that (i) networks are discrete (non-continuous) objects, and that (ii) networks may not necessarily have an associated natural geometric embedding.

One notion of network curvature that has been well-studied in the network theory literature, first suggested by Gromov in a non-network group theoretic context [4], is the Gromov-hyperbolic curvature. First defined for infinite continuous metric space [2], the measure was later adopted for finite graphs. Usually the measure is defined via properties of geodesic triangles or via equivalent (in a sense that can be made precise) 4-node conditions, though Gromov originally defined the measure using Gromov-product nodes in [4]. Informally any infinite metric space has a finite Gromov-hyperbolicity measure if it behaves metrically in the large scale as a negatively curved Riemannian manifold, and thus the value of this measure can be correlated to the standard scalar curvature of a hyperbolic manifold. Intuitively, for a finite network the measure is based on the properties of the set of exact and approximate geodesics of the network. There is a large body of research works dealing with theoretical and empirical aspects of this measure, e.g., see [5–10] for theoretical aspects, and see [11–13] for empirical aspects with applications to real-world networks.

A second notion of curvature is the applying Forman's discretization of Ricci curvature for (polyhedral or CW) complexes (the "Forman–Ricci curvature") [14] to networks. Informally, one applies the Forman-Ricci curvature to networks by topologically associating components (sub-graphs) of the given graphs with higher-dimensional objects. The topological association itself can be carried out several ways. Although this type of curvature originated relatively recently, there are already a number of papers investigating properties of these measures and applying them to real-world networks, e.g., see [8,15–18].

The network curvature discussed in this paper is another discretization of Ricci curvature, namely Ollivier's discretization [19–22], henceforth dubbed as the "Ollivier–Ricci curvature". Both Ollivier–Ricci curvature and Forman-Ricci curvature assign measures that assign a number to each edge of the given network, but the numbers are calculated in quite different ways in these two curvatures since they capture different metric properties of a Riemannian manifold. The reader is referred to the paper by [15] for a comparative analysis of these two measures. In addition to the network curvatures measures discussed above, researchers have also explored other notions of curvature, such as the one based on circle packings by Chow and Luo [23].

Basic Notations and Terminologies

To simplify exposition, we assume in this paper that the given network (In this paper the terms "graph" and "network" will be used interchangeably.) $G = (V, E)$ is an undirected unweighted connected graph; generalization of the corresponding definitions and concepts to the case of non-negative edge weights is mostly straightforward. The following notations will be used in the rest of this paper.

▷ For a node $v \in V$, $\mathsf{Nbr}(v) = \{ u \mid \{v, u\} \in E \}$ denotes the set of neighbors of v, and $\deg(v) = |\mathsf{Nbr}(v)|$ denotes the degree of v.

▷ $\mathsf{dist}_G(u, v)$ (or simply $\mathsf{dist}(u, v)$) denote the distance (i.e., number of edges in a shortest path) between the nodes u and v in G.

2. Ollivier–Ricci Curvature: Motivation, Definition and Illustration

In this section, we provide the formal definition of the Ollivier–Ricci curvature. First, we need to define the so-called Earth Mover's Distance (EMD) (also known as the L_1 transportation distance, the L_1 Wasserstein distance and the Monge-Kantorovich-Rubinstein distance) [24–27]. For the purpose of this paper, it suffices to define the distance in the discrete setting of a network as follows. Suppose that we have two probability distributions $\mathbb{P}_1$ and $\mathbb{P}_2$ on a subset $\varnothing \subset V' \subseteq V$ of nodes, i.e., two real numbers $0 \le \mathbb{P}_1(v), \mathbb{P}_2(v) \le 1$ for every node $v \in V'$ with $\sum_{v \in V'} \mathbb{P}_1(v) = \sum_{v \in V'} \mathbb{P}_2(v) = 1$. We can think of every number $\mathbb{P}_1(v)$ as the maximum total amount of "earth" (dirt) at node v that can be moved to other nodes, and every number $\mathbb{P}_2(v)$ as the maximum total amount of earth node v can store in its storage. The cost of transporting one unit of earth from node u to node v is $\mathsf{dist}_G(u, v)$, and the goal is to satisfy the storage requirement of all nodes by moving earths as needed while minimizing the total transportation cost. Letting the variable $z_{u,v} \in [0, 1]$ denote the amount of shipment from node u to node v in an optimal solution, EMD for the two probability distributions $\mathbb{P}_1$ and $\mathbb{P}_2$ on V' can be formulated as the linear programming (LP) problem shown in Figure 1 which can be solved in polynomial time. One can also think of the EMD solution as the distance between two probability distributions $\mathbb{P}_1$ and $\mathbb{P}_2$ on the set of nodes V' based on the shortest-path metric on G. We will use the notation $\widehat{\mathsf{EMD}}(V', \mathbb{P}_1, \mathbb{P}_2)$ to denote the value of the objective function in an optimal solution of the LP in Figure 1.

---

variables: $z_{u,v}$ for every pair of nodes $u, v \in V'$

minimize $\quad \sum\limits_{u \in V'} \sum\limits_{v \in V'} \text{dist}(u, v) \, z_{u,v}$ $\qquad$ (* minimize total transportation cost *)

subject to

$\qquad\quad \sum\limits_{v \in V'} z_{u,v} = \mathbb{P}_1(u)$, for each $u \in V'$ $\qquad$ (* take from u as much as it has *)

$\qquad\quad \sum\limits_{u \in V'} z_{u,v} = \mathbb{P}_2(v)$, for each $v \in V'$ $\qquad$ (* ship to v as much as it needs *)

$\qquad\quad z_{u,v} \geq 0$, for all $u, v \in V'$

Figure 1. LP-formulation for EMD on the set of nodes $|V'|$ with $|V'|^2$ variables. Comments are enclosed by (* and *). Note that the constraints $z_{u,v} \leq 1$ are unnecessary and therefore omitted.

For an intuitive understanding of the connection of EMD to Ollivier–Ricci curvature for networks, we informally recall one way of defining Ricci curvature measure for a smooth Riemannian manifold. The Ricci curvature at a point x in the manifold along a direction can be thought of transporting a small ball centered at x along that direction and measuring the "distortion" of that ball. The role of the direction is captured by the edge $\{u, v\}$, the roles of the balls at the two nodes are played by the distributions $\mathbb{P}_1$ and $\mathbb{P}_2$, and the role of the distortion due to transportation is captured by the EMD measure. More precisely, given our input graph $G = (V, E)$ and an edge $\{u, v\} \in E$, the paper [20] uses the EMD measure to define the "course Ricci curvature" $\text{RIC}(u, v)$ along the edge $\{u, v\}$ in the following manner (see Figure 2 for an illustration):

▶ Let V' be the set of nodes $V_{u,v} \overset{\text{def}}{=} \{u, v\} \cup \text{Nbr}(u) \cup \text{Nbr}(v)$.

▶ Let the probability distributions $\mathbb{P}_1$ and $\mathbb{P}_2$ be uniform distributions (If the given graph is non-negative node weights then another option is to normalize the restrictions of these node weights to the sub-graph $H_{u,v}$ and use them for the distributions $\mathbb{P}_1$ and $\mathbb{P}_2$.) $\mathbb{P}_u$ and $\mathbb{P}_v$, respectively, over the nodes in $\{u\} \cup \text{Nbr}(u)$ and $\{v\} \cup \text{Nbr}(v)$, respectively, i.e.,

$$\mathbb{P}_u(x) \overset{\text{def}}{=} \mathbb{P}_1(x) = \begin{cases} \dfrac{1}{|\{u\} \cup \text{Nbr}(u)|}, & \text{if } x \in \{u\} \cup \text{Nbr}(u) \\ 0, & \text{otherwise} \end{cases}$$

$$\mathbb{P}_v(x) \overset{\text{def}}{=} \mathbb{P}_2(x) = \begin{cases} \dfrac{1}{|\{v\} \cup \text{Nbr}(v)|}, & \text{if } x \in \{v\} \cup \text{Nbr}(v) \\ 0, & \text{otherwise} \end{cases} \qquad (1)$$

▶ Remembering that $\text{dist}_G(u, v) = 1$ for an edge $\{u, v\} \in E$, we can then define the course Ricci curvature as (*cf.* [20] (Definition 3)):

$$\text{RIC}(u, v) = 1 - \frac{\text{EMD}(V_{u,v}, \mathbb{P}_u, \mathbb{P}_v)}{\text{dist}_G(u, v)} \equiv \text{RIC}(u, v) = 1 - \text{EMD}(V_{u,v}, \mathbb{P}_u, \mathbb{P}_v) \qquad (2)$$

The measure can easily be extended for graphs with non-negative edge weights; redefine $\text{dist}(u, v)$ to be minimum total weight over all possible paths between u and v and use the equation:

$$\text{RIC}(u, v) = 1 - \frac{\text{EMD}(V_{u,v}, \mathbb{P}_u, \mathbb{P}_v)}{\text{dist}_G(u, v)}$$

Some authors also define the discrete Ricci curvature $\text{RIC}(u)$ for a node $u \in V$ by taking the average of the discrete Ricci curvarure over all edges incident on u, e.g., by letting $\text{RIC}(u) = \frac{\sum_{\{u,v\} \in E} \text{RIC}(u,v)}{\deg(u)}$.

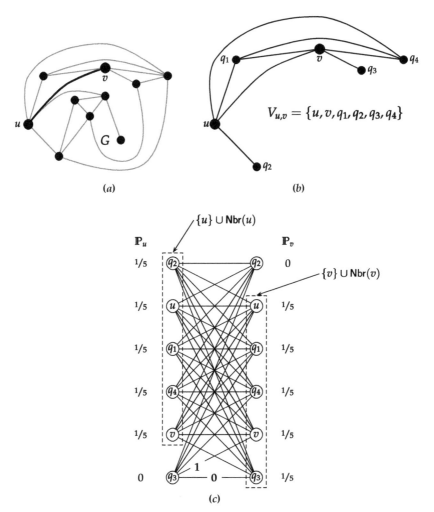

Figure 2. A pictorial illustration of calculation of $\text{RIC}(u, v)$. (**a**) The given graph G; (**b**) The subset of nodes $V_{u,v}$; (**c**) The distributions $\mathbb{P}_u$ and $\mathbb{P}_v$. For visual clarity, only two distances $\text{dist}(q_3, q_3) = 0$ and $\text{dist}(v, q_3) = 1$ are shown.

An Illustration of Computing the Value of $\text{RIC}(u, v)$ For a Two-dimensional Grid

Consider an infinite two-dimensional grid on the plane and any edge $\{u, v\}$ of the grid as shown in Figure 3. Note that any node of the grid has exactly 4 neighbors, thus $\mathbb{P}_u(x) =$
$\begin{cases} 1/5, & \text{if } x \in \{u\} \cup \text{Nbr}(u) \\ 0, & \text{otherwise} \end{cases}$ and $\mathbb{P}_v(x) = \begin{cases} 1/5, & \text{if } x \in \{v\} \cup \text{Nbr}(v) \\ 0, & \text{otherwise} \end{cases}$. Moreover, the set of nodes $\text{Nbr}(u) \setminus \{v\}$ and $\text{Nbr}(v) \setminus \{u\}$ are disjoint, thus it is easy to see that $\text{EMD}(V_{u,v}, \mathbb{P}_u, \mathbb{P}_v) = 1$ (see Figure 3). Using (2) we therefore get $\text{RIC}(u, v) = 0$.

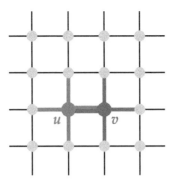

Figure 3. A pictorial illustration of calculation of $\textsc{Ric}(u,v)$ for a two-dimensional grid. The blue edges, when shifted to the left by one unit, coincide with the red edges, giving $\textsc{Emd}(V_{u,v}, \mathbb{P}_u, \mathbb{P}_v) \le 1$. It can also be argued that $\textsc{Emd}(V_{u,v}, \mathbb{P}_u, \mathbb{P}_v) \ge 1$ (e.g., see [20] (Example 5) with $N = 2$), thus giving $\textsc{Emd}(V_{u,v}, \mathbb{P}_u, \mathbb{P}_v) = 1$.

3. Exact and Approximate Computation of Ric(u, v)

Note that any node $x \in V_{u,v}$ with either $\mathbb{P}_u(x) = 0$ or $\mathbb{P}_v(x) = 0$ can be ignored in the calculation of $\textsc{Emd}(V_{u,v}, \mathbb{P}_u, \mathbb{P}_v)$. Thus, a straightforward calculation of $\textsc{Ric}(u,v)$ requires the following two steps:

▷ Find the pair-wise distances between the nodes in $\mathrm{Nbr}(u)$ and $\mathrm{Nbr}(v)$. This can be done in $O(n^\omega \log n)$ using Seidel's algorithm [28] where n is the number of nodes and ω be the value such that two $n \times n$ matrices can be multiplied in $O(n^\omega)$ time; the smallest current value of ω is slightly less than 2.373 [29].

▷ Solve an LP with $O(\deg(u)\deg(v))$ variables and $O(\deg(u)\deg(v))$ constraints via standard LP solvers such as the interior-point method. Alternatively, the LP can be solved by minimum-cost network flow algorithms by viewing it as a transportation problem, e.g., see [30].

However, the calculation of $\textsc{Emd}(V_{u,v}, \mathbb{P}_u, \mathbb{P}_v)$ (and therefore $\textsc{Ric}(u,v)$) can be further simplified if we make some more observations.

Consider a pair of nodes $u' \in \mathrm{Nbr}(u)$ and $v' \in \mathrm{Nbr}(v)$ for an edge $\{u,v\} \in E$. Note that there are only four possible values of $\mathrm{dist}_G(u',v')$: $\mathrm{dist}_G(u',v') = 0$ if $u' = v'$, $\mathrm{dist}_G(u',v') = 1$ if $\{u',v'\} \in E$, $\mathrm{dist}_G(u',v') = 2$ if there is a path of length 2 between u' and v', and $\mathrm{dist}_G(u',v') = 3$ for all other cases. Thus, to to find all pair-wise distances between the nodes in $\mathrm{Nbr}(u)$ and $\mathrm{Nbr}(v)$ we only need to check for paths up to length 3, which can be done faster in $O(n^\omega)$ time using Seidel's algorithm [28] again.

For further discussion, consider the total variation distance (TVD) between the two distributions $\mathbb{P}_u$ and $\mathbb{P}_v$ on the set of nodes in $V_{u,v}$:

$$
|| \mathbb{P}_u - \mathbb{P}_v ||_{\textsc{TVD}} \overset{\text{def}}{=} \frac{1}{2} \left(\sum_{v' \in V_{u,v}} \left(|\mathbb{P}_u(v') - \mathbb{P}_v(v')| \right) \right)
$$

Note that $|| \mathbb{P}_u - \mathbb{P}_v ||_{\textsc{TVD}}$ can be trivially computed in $O(\deg(u) + \deg(v))$ time.

Proposition 1. $1 - 3|| \mathbb{P}_u - \mathbb{P}_v ||_{\textsc{TVD}} \le \textsc{Ric}(u,v) \le 1 - || \mathbb{P}_u - \mathbb{P}_v ||_{\textsc{TVD}}$.

Proof. Since every pair of non-identical nodes $u', v' \in V_{u,v}$ satisfy $1 \le \mathrm{dist}_G(u',v') \le 3$, we have $|| \mathbb{P}_u - \mathbb{P}_v ||_{\textsc{TVD}} \le \textsc{Emd}(V_{u,v}, \mathbb{P}_u, \mathbb{P}_v) \le 3|| \mathbb{P}_u - \mathbb{P}_v ||_{\textsc{TVD}}$ which imply the claimed result via definition of $\textsc{Ric}(u,v)$. $\square$

The bound in Proposition 1 may not necessarily be a tight approximation for $\textsc{Ric}(u,v)$; for example, for the grid in Figure 3 we get $|| \mathbb{P}_u - \mathbb{P}_v ||_{\textsc{TVD}} = 3/5$ giving $-4/5 \le \textsc{Ric}(u,v) \le 2/5$ as an approximation to the actual value of $\textsc{Ric}(u,v) = 0$.

For development of further bounds, consider the edge $\{u, v\} \in E$. Assume without loss of generality that $\deg(u) \leq \deg(v)$ and G has 4 or more nodes, thus $\deg(v) \geq 2$. Suppose that u and v have $0 \leq \ell \leq \deg(u)$ common neighbour nodes as shown pictorially below:

$$\overbrace{\text{Nbr}(u) = \{ \ p_1, p_2, \ldots, p_k, q_1, q_2, \ldots, q_\ell \ \}}^{k+\ell=\deg(u)-1 \geq \ell+1 \text{ nodes}}$$

$$\{ \ \underbrace{q_1, q_2, \ldots, q_\ell}_{\substack{\ell \geq 0 \text{ common} \\ \text{neighbours}}}, r_1, r_2, \ldots, r_m \ \} = \text{Nbr}(v)$$

$$\underbrace{}_{m+\ell=\deg(v)-1 \geq \ell+1 \text{ nodes}}$$

Note that the two probability vectors $\mathbb{P}_u$ and $\mathbb{P}_v$ for the edge $\{u, v\}$ are as shown below:

	p_1	$\cdots$	p_k	q_1	$\cdots$	q_ℓ	u	r_1	$\cdots$	r_m	v
$\mathbb{P}_u =$	$\frac{1}{\deg(u)+1}$	$\cdots$	$\frac{1}{\deg(u)+1}$	$\frac{1}{\deg(u)+1}$	$\cdots$	$\frac{1}{\deg(u)+1}$	$\frac{1}{\deg(u)+1}$	0	$\cdots$	0	$\frac{1}{\deg(u)+1}$
$\mathbb{P}_v =$	0	$\cdots$	0	$\frac{1}{\deg(v)+1}$	$\cdots$	$\frac{1}{\deg(v)+1}$	$\frac{1}{\deg(v)+1}$	$\frac{1}{\deg(v)+1}$	$\cdots$	$\frac{1}{\deg(v)+1}$	$\frac{1}{\deg(v)+1}$

By our assumption $\frac{1}{\deg(u)+1} \geq \frac{1}{\deg(v)+1}$, and thus a straightforward calculation gives the following value for $\| \mathbb{P}_u - \mathbb{P}_v \|_{\text{TVD}}$:

$$\begin{aligned} \| \mathbb{P}_u - \mathbb{P}_v \|_{\text{TVD}} &= \frac{1}{2} \times \left(\frac{k}{\deg(u)+1} + \frac{m}{\deg(v)+1} + (\ell+2) \times \left(\frac{1}{\deg(u)+1} - \frac{1}{\deg(v)+1} \right) \right) \\ &= \frac{\frac{k+\ell}{2}+1}{\deg(u)+1} + \frac{\frac{m-\ell}{2}-1}{\deg(v)+1} = \frac{1}{2} + \frac{(\deg(v)+1) - 2(\ell+2)}{2(\deg(v)+1)} = 1 - \frac{\ell+2}{\deg(v)+1} \end{aligned} \quad (3)$$

Proposition 2. $-2 + 3\frac{\ell+2}{\deg(v)+1} \leq \text{RIC}(u, v) \leq \frac{\ell+2}{\deg(v)+1}$, and in particular it always holds that $-2 < \text{RIC}(u, v) \leq 1$.

Proof. Plugging the bound (3) in Proposition 1 proves the first claim. To prove the second claim, note that $0 < \frac{\ell+2}{\deg(v)+1} \leq 1$. $\square$

For further bounds, suppose that there exists a $\gamma \in \{1, 2, 3\}$ such that for any two distinct nodes $u' \in \text{Nbr}(u)$ and $v' \in \text{Nbr}(v)$ we have $\text{dist}(u', v')$ is exactly γ. In that case, it follows that

$$\text{EMD}(V_{u,v}, \mathbb{P}_u, \mathbb{P}_v) = \gamma \times \| \mathbb{P}_u - \mathbb{P}_v \|_{\text{TVD}} \Rightarrow \text{RIC}(u, v) = 1 - \gamma \times \| \mathbb{P}_u - \mathbb{P}_v \|_{\text{TVD}} = 1 - \gamma + \frac{\gamma(\ell+2)}{\deg(v)+1}$$

Now, suppose that G has no cycles of 5 of fewer edges containing the edge $\{u, v\}$ (a tree is a trivial example of such a graph). This implies $\gamma = 3$ and $\ell = 0$, giving the following bound.

Proposition 3. *If G has no cycles of 5 of fewer edges containing the edge $\{u, v\}$ then $\text{RIC}(u, v)$ is precisely $-2 + \frac{6}{\deg(v)+1} \leq 0$ and can be computed in $O(\deg(u) + \deg(v))$ time.*

4. Review of Efficient Approximate Computation of Ric(u, v) via Linear Sketching

It is clear that a crucial bottleneck in computing $\text{RIC}(u, v)$ for an arbitrary graph $G = (V, E)$ is the computation of $\text{EMD}(V_{u,v}, \mathbb{P}_u, \mathbb{P}_v)$ since it seems to require solving a linear program with $O(\deg(u) \deg(v))$ variables and $O(\deg(u) \deg(v))$ constraints (note that in the worst case $\deg(u) \deg(v)$ can be as large as $\Theta(n^2)$ when n is the number of nodes of G). In this section we review a non-trivial approach for computing $\text{EMD}(V_{u,v}, \mathbb{P}_u, \mathbb{P}_v)$ provided we settle for a *slightly* non-optimal solution for $\text{EMD}(V_{u,v}, \mathbb{P}_u, \mathbb{P}_v)$.

Linear sketching is a popular method to perform approximate computations on large data sets using dimensionality reduction [31]. The general (informal) intuition behind linear sketching is to take linear projections of the given data set and then use these projections to provide solutions to the original problem. Significant research has been done on the problem of estimating EMD using linear sketches for general metric spaces [32–36]. In this section, we discuss the results by McGregor and Stubbs [37] to approximately estimate EMD on a graph metric (i.e., metric induced by inter-node distances in a graph, as is the case for computing $\text{RIC}(u, v)$). Recall that our bottleneck is the computation of $\text{EMD}(V_{u,v}, \mathbb{P}_u, \mathbb{P}_v)$ for the given graph G.

The first step is to transform the problem of computing $\text{EMD}(V_{u,v}, \mathbb{P}_u, \mathbb{P}_v)$ by standard techniques to the following equivalent problem which will be denoted by EMD_d. Given two multi-sets $\mathcal{A}, \mathcal{B} \subseteq \mathcal{X}$ over a ground set $\mathcal{X}$ with $|\mathcal{A}| = |\mathcal{B}| = k$, and a metric $\mathsf{d} : \mathcal{X} \times \mathcal{X} \mapsto \mathbb{R}^+$ on $\mathcal{X}$, compute minimum-cost of perfect matching between $\mathcal{A}$ and $\mathcal{B}$, i.e., using $\pi_{\mathcal{A},\mathcal{B}}$ to denote a 1-1 mapping from $\mathcal{A}$ to $\mathcal{B}$, we need to compute

$$\text{EMD}_\mathsf{d}(\mathcal{A}, \mathcal{B}) = \min_{\pi_{\mathcal{A},\mathcal{B}}} \left\{ \sum_{a \in \mathcal{A}} \mathsf{d}(a, \pi_{\mathcal{A},\mathcal{B}}(a)) \right\}$$

For the purpose of measuring approximation quality, we say that an algorithm is an (ϵ, δ)-algorithm for computing a quantity of value Q if the value Q' returned by the algorithm satisfies $\Pr[|Q - Q'| < \epsilon Q] \geq 1 - \delta$.

The basic approach of McGregor and Stubbs in [37] is to define two vectors $\mathbf{x}, \mathbf{y} \in \mathbb{R}^{|E|}$ corresponding to the set $\mathcal{A}$ and $\mathcal{B}$. We then estimate $\text{EMD}_\mathsf{d}(\mathcal{A}, \mathcal{B})$ by posing it as a ℓ_1-regression problem using the vectors $\mathbf{x}, \mathbf{y}$ and a set of other vectors defined by the structure of the underlying graph. The idea is take some random projections of these vectors to a smaller dimensional space and then perform ℓ_1-regression on these projections to save space and time. The following result by Kane et al. [38] is crucial to the analysis of this approach (the notation $\Pr_{M \sim \nu}$ is the standard notation for denoting that the entries of M are drawn from the distribution ν):

($\star$) There exists a distribution ("q-dimensional sketch") ν over linear maps from $\mathbb{R}^n \mapsto \mathbb{R}^q$ where $q = O(\varepsilon^{-2} \log n \log \delta^{-1})$ and a "post-processing" function $f : \mathbb{R}^q \mapsto \mathbb{R}$ such that for any $\mathbf{x} \in \mathbb{R}^n$ with polynomially-bounded entries, it holds that

$$\Pr_{M \sim \nu} \left[\, | \, \| \mathbf{x} \|_1 - f(M\mathbf{x}) \, | \leq \varepsilon \| \mathbf{x} \|_1 \, \right] \geq 1 - \delta$$

To understand how the above result relates to the calculation of $\text{EMD}_\mathsf{d}(\mathcal{A}, \mathcal{B})$, first consider the case when the given instance of $\text{EMD}_\mathsf{d}(\mathcal{A}, \mathcal{B})$ is one dimensional, i.e., let $G = (V, E)$ be a path with n nodes $V = \{1, \ldots, n\}$ and $n - 1$ edges $E = \{e_1, \ldots, e_{n-1}\}$ where $e_i = \{i, i+1\}$, let $A, B \subseteq V$, and let $\mathsf{d}(i, j) = \text{dist}_G(i, j)$ for all $i, j \in V$. Then we can associate computation of $\text{EMD}_\mathsf{d}(\mathcal{A}, \mathcal{B})$ to a norm estimation problem in the following manner. Assume that we have vectors $\mathbf{x} = (x_1, \ldots, x_{n-1}) \in \mathbb{R}^{n-1}$ and $\mathbf{y} = (y_1, \ldots, y_{n-1}) \in \mathbb{R}^{n-1}$ such that for all $i \in \{0, 1, n-1\}$ the following assertions hold: $x_i = |\{a \in \mathcal{A} \,|\, i \geq a\}|$ and $y_i = |\{b \in \mathcal{B} \,|\, i \geq b\}|$. Then, it can be shown that $\text{EMD}_\mathsf{d}(\mathcal{A}, \mathcal{B}) = \| \mathbf{x} - \mathbf{y} \|_1$ and thus we can use the result of Kane et al. [38] as stated in ($\star$) directly.

As a second illustration of the above point, suppose that the graph G in the previous example is now a cycle of n nodes $V = \{1, \ldots, n\}$ and n edges $E = \{e_1, \ldots, e_n\}$ where $e_i = \{i, i+1\}$ for $i \in \{1, \ldots, n-1\}$ and $e_n = \{n, 1\}$. Suppose that we simply ignore the last edge e_n so that the graph becomes a path and we can apply the previous approach. However, this omission of e_n changes the distance between the nodes $i \in \mathcal{A}$ and $j \in \mathcal{B}$ from $\mathsf{d}(i, j) = \min \{|i - j|, |i - n| + 1 + |1 - j|, |i - 1| + 1 + |n - j|\}$ to a new distance $\mathsf{d}'(i, j) = |i - j|$. To resolve this issue, we make a sequence of guesses for the number of pairs of nodes that will be joined using the edge e_n. More precisely, for $\lambda \in \{-k, -k+1, \ldots, k-1, k\}$ let $\mathcal{C}_\lambda$ be the multi-set consisting of λ copies of "1" if $\lambda > 0$ and $|\lambda|$ copies of "n" if $\lambda < 0$. Then, one can show that

$$\text{EMD}_d(\mathcal{A}, \mathcal{B}) \leq |\lambda| + \text{EMD}_{d'}(\mathcal{A} \uplus \mathcal{C}_\lambda, \mathcal{B} \uplus \mathcal{C}_{-\lambda})$$

with equality for some $\lambda \in \{-k, -k+1, \ldots, k-1, k\}$, where $\uplus$ denotes the union for multi-sets. Thus, we can use the result in $(\star)$ in the following manner. First define two vectors $\mathbf{x} = (x_1, \ldots, x_n) \in \mathbb{R}^n$ and $\mathbf{y} = (y_1, \ldots, y_n) \in \mathbb{R}^n$ where $x_i = |\{a \in \mathcal{A} \mid i \geq a\}|$ and $y_i = |\{b \in \mathcal{B} \mid i \geq b\}|$ for $i \in \{1, \ldots, n-1\}$, and $x_n = y_n = 0$. Let $\mathbf{z} = \mathbf{x} - \mathbf{y}$ and $\mathbf{c} = (1, \ldots, 1) \in \mathbb{R}^n$. Then, it follows that

$$\text{EMD}_d(\mathcal{A}, \mathcal{B}) = \min_{\lambda \in \{-k, -k+1, \ldots, k-1, k\}} \{ \| \mathbf{z} + \lambda \mathbf{c} \|_1 \}$$

Define the function $f : \mathbb{R} \mapsto \mathbb{R}$ as $f(\lambda) = \| \mathbf{z} + \lambda \mathbf{c} \|_1$; clearly $\text{EMD}_d(\mathcal{A}, \mathcal{B}) = \min_{\lambda \in \{-k, -k+1, \ldots, k-1, k\}} \{f(\lambda)\}$. For a specific $\lambda \in \{-k, -k+1, \ldots, k-1, k\}$, we can use $(\star)$ to find an approximation $\widetilde{f}_\lambda$ of f_λ using a $O(\varepsilon^{-2} \log n \log(k\delta^{-1}))$-dimensional sketch of $\mathbf{z}$ such that $\Pr\left[|\widetilde{f}_\lambda - f(\lambda)| > \varepsilon f(\lambda)\right] < \frac{\delta}{2k+1}$. Iterating the process $2k+1$ times and using the union bound for probabilities, we get

$$\Pr\left[\forall \lambda \in \{-k, \ldots, k\} : |\widetilde{f}_\lambda - f(\lambda)| \leq \varepsilon f(\lambda)\right] \geq 1 - \sum_{\lambda=-k}^{k} \Pr\left[|\widetilde{f}_\lambda - f(\lambda)| > \varepsilon f(\lambda)\right]$$

$$> 1 - (2k+1) \times \frac{\delta}{2k+1} = 1 - \delta$$

It is possible to design a more careful approach that iterates only $O(\log k)$ times instead of $2k+1$ times. The ideas behind this approach as described above can be extended to trees with some non-trivial effort.

Finally the approach can indeed be generalized to the case when G is an arbitrary graph (which applies to computing $\text{RIC}(u, v)$) in the following manner. The basic idea to calculate $\text{EMD}_d(\mathcal{A}, \mathcal{B})$ for an arbitrary graph G is to reduce it in an approximate sense to that of computing EMD for a tree. Let $T = (V, E_T)$ be an arbitrary spanning tree of G, and let $F = E \setminus E_T$. The tree T defines a natural tree metric d' where $d'(a, b)$ is the length of the shortest path between a and b in T for all $a, b \in V$. One can then express $\text{EMD}_d(\mathcal{A}, \mathcal{B})$ in terms of $\text{EMD}_{d'}(\mathcal{A}', \mathcal{B}')$ for some $\mathcal{A}' \supseteq \mathcal{A}$ and $\mathcal{B}' \supseteq \mathcal{B}$ in the following manner. For $f = (u, v) \in F$ and $\lambda_f \in \{-k, -k+1, \ldots, k-1, k\}$, let $\mathcal{C}_{\lambda_f}^f$ be the multi-set consisting of λ_f copies "u" if $\lambda_f > 0$ and $|\lambda_f|$ copies of "v" if $\lambda_f < 0$. Then the following bound holds:

$$\text{EMD}_d(\mathcal{A}, \mathcal{B}) \leq \sum_{f \in F} |\lambda_f| + \text{EMD}_{d'}\left(\mathcal{A} \uplus \sum_{f \in F} \mathcal{C}_{\lambda_f}^f, \mathcal{B} \uplus \sum_{f \in F} \mathcal{C}_{-\lambda_f}^f\right)$$

The above inequality leads to the following approach. Fix an arbitrary node $r \in V$ as the root of the spanning tree T, and let $\mathcal{P}_T(u, v)$ denote the set of edges in the unique path in T between nodes u and v. Define the two vectors $\mathbf{x}, \mathbf{y} \in \mathbb{R}^{|E|}$ as follows (x_e and y_e denote the component of $\mathbf{x}$ and $\mathbf{y}$, respectively, indexed by the edge $e \in E$):

$$x_e = \begin{cases} |\{a \in \mathcal{A} \mid e \in \mathcal{P}_T(a, r)\}|, & \text{if } e \in E_T \\ 0, & \text{otherwise} \end{cases} \qquad y_e = \begin{cases} |\{b \in \mathcal{B} \mid e \in \mathcal{P}_T(b, r)\}|, & \text{if } e \in E_T \\ 0, & \text{otherwise} \end{cases}$$

and let $\mathbf{z} = \mathbf{x} - \mathbf{y}$. For each $f = (u, v) \in F$, define a vector $\mathbf{c}^f \in \mathbb{R}^{|E|}$ where the component c_e^f of $\mathbf{c}^f$ indexed by the edge $e \in F$ is given by:

$$
c_e^f = \begin{cases}
1, & \text{if } e \in \mathcal{P}_T(u,r) \setminus \mathcal{P}_T(v,r) \\
-1, & \text{if } e \in \mathcal{P}_T(v,r) \setminus \mathcal{P}_T(u,r) \\
1, & \text{if } e = f \\
0, & \text{otherwise}
\end{cases}
$$

This leads to the following optimization problem:

$$
\text{EMD}_\mathbf{d}(\mathcal{A},\mathcal{B}) = \min_{\forall f \in F : \lambda_f \in \{-k,-k+1,\dots,k-1,k\}} \| \mathbf{z} + \sum_{f \in F} \lambda_f \, \mathbf{c}^f \|_1
$$

The above optimization problem can be solved using several approaches, e.g., using a recursive regression algorithm that exploits the convexity of f or using some recent results on robust regression via sub-space embeddings [39,40].

5. Discussion

In this paper we have reviewed some computational aspects of the Ollivier–Ricci curvature for networks, and shown a few simple computational bounds. As already mentioned in Section 1, there are other notions of network curvature that is also used by researchers and therefore this review should not be viewed as championing the Ollivier–Ricci curvature over other curvatures. We hope that this review will motivate further research on the exciting interplay between notions of curvatures from network and non-network domains. Some applications of network curvatures for real-world networks appear in references such as [11,13,15,16,18].

We conclude our article by mentioning an interesting application of the Ollivier–Ricci curvature for Markov chains for graph coloring and other problems (recise technical descriptions of these results are beyond the scope of this introductory review). The probability distributions on nodes used to compute EMD in the Ollivier–Ricci curvature can be naturally associated with a Markov process on the given graph (as a very simplified illustration, one can use a "normalized version" of $\text{EMD}(V_{u,v}, \mathbb{P}_u, \mathbb{P}_v)$ as the probability of transition between the states corresponding to nodes u and v). Such associations have a long history in the Markov chain literature under various names such as path coupling [41] and the values of $\text{RIC}(u,v)$'s have been used (explicitly or implicitly) to prove useful properties of the Markov chain, such as fast convergence to its stationary distribution, in many settings such as graph colouring [41] and sampling of paths with constraints [42].

Author Contributions: The author contributions are as follows: Conceptualization, N.A., P.S. and B.D.; methodology, N.A., P.S. and B.D.; software, N.A., P.S. and B.D.; validation, N.A., P.S. and B.D.; formal analysis, N.A., P.S. and B.D.; investigation, N.A., P.S. and B.D.; resources, N.A., P.S. and B.D.; data curation, N.A., P.S. and B.D.; writing–original draft preparation, N.A., P.S. and B.D.; writing–review and editing, N.A., P.S. and B.D.; visualization, N.A., P.S. and B.D.; supervision, B.D.; project administration, B.D.; funding acquisition, B.D. All authors have read and agreed to the published version of the manuscript.

Funding: This research was funded by NSF grant number IIS-1814931.

Conflicts of Interest: The authors declare no conflict of interest.

Abbreviations

The following abbreviations are used in this manuscript:

EMD   Earth Mover's Distance
RIC   Ricci curvature

References

1. Berger, M. *A Panoramic View of Riemannian Geometry*; Springer: Berlin/Heidelberg, Germany, 2012.
2. Bridson, M.R.; Haefliger, A. *Metric Spaces of Non-Positive Curvature*; Springer: Berlin/Heidelberg, Germany, 1999.
3. Schutz, B.F. *A First Course in General Relativity*; Cambridge University Press: Cambridge, UK, 1990.
4. Gromov, M. Hyperbolic groups. *Essays Group Theory* **1987**, *8*, 75–263.
5. Benjamini, I. Expanders are not hyperbolic. *Isr. J. Math.* **1998**, *108*, 33–36. [CrossRef]
6. Chalopin, J.; Chepoi, V.; Dragan, F.F.; Ducoffe, G.; Mohammed, A.; Vaxès, Y. Fast approximation and exact computation of negative curvature parameters of graphs. In Proceedings of the 34th International Symposium on Computational Geometry, Budapest, Hungary, 11–14 June 2018.
7. Chepoi, V.; Dragan, F.F.; Estellon, B.; Habib, M.; Vaxès, Y. Diameters, centers, and approximating trees of δ-hyperbolic geodesic spaces and graphs. In Proceedings of the 24th Annual Symposium on Computational Geometry, College Park, MD, USA, 9–11 June 2008; pp. 59–68.
8. DasGupta, B.; Janardhanan, M.V.; Yahyanejad, F. How did the shape of your network change? (On detecting network anomalies via non-local curvatures). *Algorithmica* **2020**, *82*, 1741–1783. [CrossRef]
9. DasGupta, B.; Karpinski, M.; Mobasheri, N.; Yahyanejad, F. Effect of Gromov-hyperbolicity Parameter on Cuts and Expansions in Graphs and Some Algorithmic Implications. *Algorithmica* **2018**, *80*, 772–800. [CrossRef]
10. Fournier, H.; Ismail, A.; Vigneron, A. Computing the Gromov hyperbolicity of a discrete metric space. *Inf. Process. Lett.* **2015**, *115*, 576–579. [CrossRef]
11. Albert, R.; DasGupta, B.; Mobasheri, N. Topological implications of negative curvature for biological and social networks. *Phys. Rev. E* **2014**, *89*, 032811. [CrossRef] [PubMed]
12. Jonckheere, E.; Lou, M.; Bonahon, F.; Baryshnikov, Y. Euclidean versus hyperbolic congestion in idealized versus experimental networks. *Internet Math.* **2011**, *7*, 1–27. [CrossRef]
13. Papadopoulos, F.; Krioukov, D.; Boguna, M.; Vahdat, A. Greedy Forwarding in Dynamic Scale-Free Networks Embedded in Hyperbolic Metric Spaces. In Proceedings of the IEEE Conference on Computer Communications, San Diego, CA, USA, 15–19 March 2010; pp. 1–9.
14. Forman, R. Bochner's method for cell complexes and combinatorial ricci curvature. *Discret. Comput. Geom.* **2003**, *29*, 323–374. [CrossRef]
15. Samal, A.; Sreejith, R.P.; Gu, J.; Liu, S.; Saucan, E.; Jost, J. Comparative analysis of two discretizations of Ricci curvature for complex networks. *Sci. Rep.* **2018**, *8*, 8650. [CrossRef] [PubMed]
16. Sreejith, R.P.; Jost, J.; Saucan, E.; Samal, A. Systematic evaluation of a new combinatorial curvature for complex networks. *Chaos Solitons Fractals* **2017**, *101*, 50–67. [CrossRef]
17. Sreejith, R.P.; Mohanraj, K.; Jost, J.; Saucan, E.; Samal, A. Forman curvature for complex networks. *J. Stat. Mech. Theory Exp.* **2016**, *2016*, 063206. [CrossRef]
18. Weber, M.; Saucan, E.; Jost, J. Characterizing complex networks with Forman-Ricci curvature and associated geometric flows. *J. Complex Netw.* **2017**, *5*, 527–550. [CrossRef]
19. Ollivier, Y. Ricci curvature of metric spaces. *Comptes Rendus Math.* **2007**, *345*, 643–646. [CrossRef]
20. Ollivier, Y. Ricci curvature of Markov chains on metric spaces. *J. Funct. Anal.* **2009**, *256*, 810–864. [CrossRef]
21. Ollivier, Y. A survey of Ricci curvature for metric spaces and Markov chains. In *Probabilistic Approach to Geometry*; Kotani, M., Hino, M., Kumagai, T., Eds.; Mathematical Society of Japan: Tokyo, Japan, 2010; pp. 343–381.
22. Ollivier, Y. A visual introduction to Riemannian curvatures and some discrete generalizations. In *Analysis and Geometry of Metric Measure Spaces*; Lecture Notes of the 50th Séminaire de Mathématiques Supérieures, Montréal, 2011; Dafni, G., McCann, R.J., Stancu, A., Eds.; American Mathematical Society: Providence, RI, USA, 2013; pp. 197–219.
23. Chow, B.; Luo, F. Combinatorial Ricci flows on surfaces. *J. Differ. Geom.* **2003**, *63*, 97–129. [CrossRef]
24. Mallows, L. A note on asymptotic joint normality. *Ann. Math. Stat.* **1972**, *43*, 508–515. [CrossRef]
25. Rubner, Y.; Tomasi, C.; Guibas, L.J. A metric for distributions with applications to image databases. In Proceedings of the 6th International Conference on Computer Vision, Bombay, India, 4–7 January 1998; pp. 59–66.

26. Rubner, Y.; Tomasi, C.; Guibas, L.J. The earth mover's distance as a metric for image retrieval. *Int. J. Comput. Vis.* **2000**, *40*, 99–121. [CrossRef]
27. Villani, C. Topics in optimal transportation. In *Graduate Studies in Mathematics*; American Mathematical Society: Providence, RI, USA, 2003; p. 58
28. Seidel, R. On the All-Pairs-Shortest-Path Problem in Unweighted Undirected Graphs. *J. Comput. Syst. Sci.* **1995**, *51*, 400–403. [CrossRef]
29. Williams, V.V. Multiplying matrices faster than Coppersmith-Winograd. In Proceedings of the 44th ACM Symposium on Theory of Computing, New York, NY, USA, 20–22 May 2012; pp. 887–898.
30. Ahuja, R.K.; Magnanti, T.L.; Orlin, J.B. *Network Flows: Theory, Algorithms, and Applications*; Prentice-Hall, Inc.: Upper Saddle River, NJ, USA, 1993.
31. Cormode, G.; Garofalakis, M.N.; Haas, P.J.; Jermaine, C. Synopses for massive data: Samples, histogram, wavelets, sketches. *Found. Trends Databases* **2012**, *4*, 1–294. [CrossRef]
32. Andoni, A.; Ba, K.D.; Indyk, P.; Woodruff, D.P. Efficient sketches for earth-mover distance, with applications. In Proceedings of the 50 thAnnual IEEE Symposium on Foundations of Computer Science, Atlanta, GA, USA, 25–27 October 2009; pp. 324–330.
33. Brody, J.; Liang, H.; Sun, X. Space-efficient approximation scheme for circular earth mover distance. In *LATIN 2012*; Fernández-Baca, D., Ed.; Lecture Notes in Computer Science; Springer: Berlin/Heidelberg, Germany, 2012; Volume 7256; pp. 97–108
34. Indyk, P. A near linear time constant factor approximation for euclidean bichromatic matching (cost). In Proceedings of the 18th annual ACM-SIAM symposium on Discrete algorithms, New Orleans, LA, USA, 7–9 January 2007; pp. 39–42.
35. Indyk, P.; Price, E. K-median clustering, model-based compressive sensing, and sparse recovery for earth mover distance. In Proceedings of the 43rd Annual ACM Symposium on Theory of Computing, San Jose, CA, USA, 6–8 June 2011; pp. 627–636.
36. Verbin, E.; Zhang, Q. Rademacher-sketch: A dimensionality-reducing embedding for sum-product norms, with an application to earth-mover distance. In Proceedings of the International Colloquium on Automata, Languages, and Programming, Warwick, UK, 9–13 July 2012; pp. 834–845.
37. McGregor, A.; Stubbs, D. Sketching earth-mover distance on graph metrics. In *International Workshop on Approximation Algorithms for Combinatorial Optimization*; Springer: Berlin/Heidelberg, Germany, 2013; pp. 274–286.
38. Kane, D.M.; Nelson, J.; Porat, E.; Woodruff, D.P. Fast moment estimation in data streams in optimal space. In Proceedings of the 43rd annual ACM symposium on Theory of computing, San Jose, CA, USA, 6–8 June 2011; pp. 745–754.
39. Clarkson, K.L.; Drineas, P.; Magdon-Ismail, M.; Mahoney, M.W.; Meng, X.; Woodruff, D.P. The fast cauchy transform and faster robust linear regression. In Proceedings of the 24th annual ACM-SIAM Symposium on Discrete algorithms, New Orleans, LA, USA, 6–8 January 2013; pp. 466–477.
40. Kane, D.M.; Nelson, J.; Porat, E.; Woodruff, D.P. Subspace embeddings for the ℓ_1-norm with applications. In Proceedings of the 43rd Annual ACM Symposium on Theory of Computing, San Jose, CA, USA, 6–8 June 2011; pp. 755–764.
41. Bubley, R.; Dyer, M.E. Path coupling: A technique for proving rapid mixing in Markov chains. In Proceedings of the 38th Annual Symposium on Foundations of Computer Science, Miami Beach, FL, USA, 20–22 October 1997; pp. 223–231.
42. Gerin, L. Random sampling of lattice paths with constraints, via transportation. In Proceedings of the 21st International Meeting on Probabilistic, Combinatorial, and Asymptotic Methods in the Analysis of Algorithms, Vienna, Austria, 28 June–2 July 2010; pp. 317–328.

Article

On a Relation between the Perfect Roman Domination and Perfect Domination Numbers of a Tree

Zehui Shao [1], Saeed Kosari [1,*], Mustapha Chellali [2], Seyed Mahmoud Sheikholeslami [3] and Marzieh Soroudi [3]

[1] Institute of Computing Science and Technology, Guangzhou University, Guangzhou 510006, China; zshao@gzhu.edu.cn

[2] LAMDA-RO Laboratory, Department of Mathematics, University of Blida, Blida B.P. 270, Algeria; m_chellali@yahoo.com

[3] Department of Mathematics, Azarbaijan Shahid Madani University, Tabriz 51368, Iran; s.m.sheikholeslami@azaruniv.ac.ir (S.M.S.); ma.soroudi95@gmail.com (M.S.)

* Correspondence: saeedkosari38@yahoo.com

Received: 23 April 2020; Accepted: 7 June 2020; Published: 12 June 2020

Abstract: A *dominating set* in a graph G is a set of vertices $S \subseteq V(G)$ such that any vertex of $V - S$ is adjacent to at least one vertex of S. A *dominating set* S of G is said to be a *perfect dominating set* if each vertex in $V - S$ is adjacent to exactly one vertex in S. The minimum cardinality of a *perfect dominating set* is the perfect domination number $\gamma^p(G)$. A function $f : V(G) \rightarrow \{0, 1, 2\}$ is a perfect Roman dominating function (PRDF) on G if every vertex $u \in V$ for which $f(u) = 0$ is adjacent to exactly one vertex v for which $f(v) = 2$. The weight of a PRDF is the sum of its function values over all vertices, and the minimum weight of a PRDF of G is the perfect Roman domination number $\gamma_R^p(G)$. In this paper, we prove that for any nontrivial tree T, $\gamma_R^p(T) \geq \gamma^p(T) + 1$ and we characterize all trees attaining this bound.

Keywords: Roman domination number; perfect Roman domination number; tree

---

1. Introduction

In this paper, only simple and undirected graph without isolated vertices will be considered. The set of vertices of the graph G is denoted by $V = V(G)$ and the edge set is $E = E(G)$. The order of a graph G is the number of vertices of the graph G and it is denoted by $n = n(G)$. The size of G is the cardinality of the edge set and it is denoted by $m = m(G)$. For a vertex $v \in V$, the *open neighbourhood* $N(v)$ is the set $\{u \in V(\Gamma) : uv \in E(G)\}$, the *closed neighbourhood* of v is the set $N[v] = N(v) \cup \{v\}$, and the *degree* of v is $\deg_G(u) = |N(v)|$. Any vertex of degree one is called a *leaf*, a *support vertex* is a vertex adjacent to a leaf, a *strong support vertex* is a support vertex adjacent to at least two leaves and an *end support vertex* is a support vertex such that all its neighbors, except possibly one, are leaves. For a graph G, let $L(G) = \{v \in V(G) \mid \deg_G(v) = 1\}$ and $L_v = N(v) \cap L(G)$. The *distance* $d_G(u, v)$ between two vertices u and v in a connected graph G is the length of a shortest $u - v$ path in G. The *diameter* of G, denoted by $\text{diam}(G)$, is the maximum value among distances between all pair of vertices of G. For a vertex v in a rooted tree T, let $C(v)$ and $D(v)$ denote the set of children and descendants of v, respectively and let $D[v] = D(v) \cup \{v\}$. Moreover, the depth of v, $\text{depth}(v)$, is the largest distance from v to a vertex in $D(v)$. The *maximal subtree rooted at* v, denoted by T_v, consists of v and all its descendants. We write P_n for the *path* of order n. A tree T is a *double star* if it contains exactly two vertices that are not leaves. A double star with, respectively p and q leaves attached at each support vertex is denoted $DS_{p,q}$. For a real-valued function $f : V \longrightarrow \mathbb{R}$, the weight of f is $w(f) = \sum_{v \in V} f(v)$, and for $S \subseteq V$ we define $f(S) = \sum_{v \in S} f(v)$. So $w(f) = f(V)$.

A *dominating set* (DS) in a graph G is a set of vertices $S \subseteq V(G)$ such that any vertex of $V - S$ is adjacent to at least one vertex of S. A *dominating set* S of G is said to be a *perfect dominating set* (PDS) if each vertex in $V - S$ is adjacent to exactly one vertex in S. The minimum cardinality of a *(perfect) dominating set* of a graph G is the *(perfect) domination number* $\gamma(G)$ $(\gamma^p(G))$. Perfect domination was introduced by Livingston and Stout in [1] and has been studied by several authors [2–6].

A function $f : V(\Gamma) \to \{0, 1, 2\}$ is a *Roman dominating function* (RDF) on G if every vertex $u \in V$ for which $f(u) = 0$ is adjacent to at least one vertex v for which $f(v) = 2$. A *perfect Roman dominating function* (PRDF) on a graph G is an RDF f such that every vertex assigned a 0 is adjacent to exactly one vertex assigned a 2 under f. The minimum weight of a (perfect) RDF on a graph G is the *(perfect) Roman domination number* $\gamma_R(G)$ $(\gamma_R^p(G))$. A (perfect) RDF on G with weight $\gamma_R(G)$ $(\gamma_R^p(G))$ is called a $\gamma_R(G)$-function ($\gamma_R^p(G)$-function). An RDF f on a graph $G = (V, E)$ can be represented by the ordered partition (V_0, V_1, V_2) of V, where $V_i = \{v \in V | f(v) = i\}$ for $i = 0, 1, 2$. The concept of Roman domination was introduced by Cockayne et al. in [7] and was inspired by the manuscript of the authors of [8], and Stewart [9] about the defensive strategy of the Roman Empire decreed by Constantine I The Great, while perfect Roman domination was introduced by Henning, Klostermeyer and MacGillivray in [10] and has been studied in [11–13]. For more on Roman domination, we refer the reader to the book chapters [14,15] and surveys [16–18].

It was shown in [10] that for any tree G of order $n \geq 3$, $\gamma_R^p(G) \leq \frac{4n}{5}$. Moreover, the authors have characterized all trees attaining this upper bound. Note that the previous upper bound have been improved by Henning and Klostermeyer [13] for cubic graphs of order n by showing that $\gamma_R^p(G) \leq \frac{3n}{4}$.

It is worth mentioning that if S is a minimum *(perfect) dominating set* of a graph G, then clearly $(V - S, \emptyset, S)$ is a (perfect) RDF and thus

$$\gamma_R(G) \leq 2\gamma(G) \quad \text{and} \quad \gamma_R^p(G) \leq 2\gamma^p(G). \tag{1}$$

On the other hand, if $f = (V_0, V_1, V_2)$ is a $\gamma_R(G)$-function, then $V_1 \cup V_2$ is a *dominating set* of G yielding

$$\gamma(G) \leq \gamma_R(G). \tag{2}$$

It is natural to ask whether the inequality (2) remains valid between $\gamma^p(G)$ and $\gamma_R^p(G)$ for any graph G. The answer is negative as it can be seen by considering the graph H obtained from a double star $DS_{p,p}$, $(p \geq 3)$ with central vertices u, v by subdividing the edge uv with vertex w, and adding $2k$ $(k \geq 3)$ new vertices, where k vertices are attached to both u and w and the remaining k vertices are attached to both v and w (see Figure 1). Clearly, $\gamma^p(H) = 2k + 3$ while $\gamma_R^p(H) = 5$ and so the difference $\gamma^p(H) - \gamma_R^p(H)$ can be even very large.

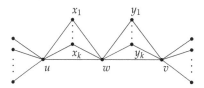

Figure 1. The graph H.

Motivated by the above example, we shall show in this paper that $\gamma_R^p(T) \geq \gamma^p(T) + 1$ for every nontrivial tree T, and we characterize all trees attaining this bound.

2. Preliminaries

We start by providing some useful definitions and observations throughout the paper.

Definition 1. *For any graph G, let*

$$
\begin{aligned}
W_G^{R,1} &= \{u \in V \mid \text{there exists a } \gamma_R^p(G)\text{-function } f \text{ such that } f(u) = 2\},\\
W_G^{R,\leq 1} &= \{u \in V \mid f(u) \leq 1 \text{ for some } \gamma_R^p(G)\text{-function } f\},\\
W_G^{R,\geq 1} &= \{u \in V \mid \text{for each } v \in N_G(u),\, f(v) \leq 1 \text{ for every } \gamma_R^p(G)\text{-function } f\},\\
W_G^{P,A} &= \{u \in V \mid u \text{ belongs to every } \gamma^p(G)\text{-set}\}.
\end{aligned}
$$

Definition 2. *Let u be a vertex of a graph G. A set S is said to be an almost perfect dominating set (almost PDS) with respect to u, (i) if each vertex $x \in V \setminus (S \cup \{u\})$ has exactly one neighbor in S, and (ii) if $u \in V \setminus S$, then u has at most one neighbor in S. Let*

$$
\gamma^p(G; u) = \min\{|S| : S \text{ is an almost PDS with respect to } u\}.
$$

Trivially, every PDS of G is an almost PDS with respect to any vertex of G and thus $\gamma^p(G; u)$ is well defined. Hence $\gamma^p(G; u) \leq \gamma^p(G)$ for each vertex $u \in V$. Let

$$
W_G^{APD} = \{u \in V \mid \gamma^p(G; u) = \gamma^p(G)\}.
$$

The proof of the following two results are given in [12].

Observation 1. *Let G be a graph.*

1. *Any strong support vertex belongs to $W_G^{P,A}$.*
2. *Any support vertex adjacent to a strong support vertex, belongs to $W_G^{P,A}$.*
3. *For any leaf u of G, there is a $\gamma_R^p(G)$-function f such that $f(u) \leq 1$.*

Proposition 1. *Let G be a graph. G has a $\gamma_R^p(G)$-function that assigns 2 to every end strong support vertex. Thus every end strong support vertex of a graph G belongs to $W_G^{R,1}$.*

The next result is a consequence of Observation 1 and Proposition 1.

Corollary 1. *Let u be an end strong support vertex of a graph H. If G is the graph obtained from H by adding a vertex x and an edge ux, then $\gamma^p(G) = \gamma^p(H)$ and $\gamma_R^p(G) = \gamma_R^p(H)$.*

Proposition 2. *Let H be a graph and $u \in V(H)$. If G is a graph obtained from H by adding a path $P_2 : x_1 x_2$ attached at u by an edge ux_1, then:*

1. *$\gamma^p(G) \leq \gamma^p(H) + 1$ and $\gamma_R^p(G) \geq \gamma_R^p(H) + 1$.*
2. *If $u \in W_H^{R,1} \cup W_H^{R,\geq 1}$, then $\gamma_R^p(G) = \gamma_R^p(H) + 1$.*
3. *If $u \in W_H^{APD}$, then $\gamma^p(G) = \gamma^p(H) + 1$.*

Proof.

1. For a $\gamma^p(H)$-set S, let $S' = S \cup \{x_1\}$ if $u \in S$, and $S' = S \cup \{x_2\}$ if $u \notin S$. Clearly, S' is a PDS of G and thus $\gamma^p(G) \leq \gamma^p(H) + 1$.

   Now let f be a $\gamma_R^p(G)$-function. Obviously, $f(x_1) + f(x_2) \geq 1$. If $f(u) \geq 1$, then the function f restricted to H is a PRDF on H yielding $\gamma_R^p(G) \geq \gamma_R^p(H) + 1$. Thus assume that $f(u) = 0$. Then $f(x_1) + f(x_2) = 2$ and the function $g : V(H) \to \{0,1,2\}$ defined by $g(u) = 1$ and $g(x) = f(x)$ for $x \in V(H) \setminus \{u\}$ is a PRDF on H of weight $\gamma_R^p(G) - 1$. Hence in any case, $\gamma_R^p(G) \geq \gamma_R^p(H) + 1$.

2. Assume first that $u \in W_H^{R,1}$ and let f be a $\gamma_R^p(H)$-function with $f(u) = 2$. Then f can be extended to a PRDF of G by assigning a 1 to x_2 and a 0 to x_1 and thus $\gamma_R^p(G) \leq \gamma_R^p(H) + 1$. The equality follows by item 1. Assume now that $u \in W_{G'}^{R,\geq 1}$ and let f be a $\gamma_R^p(H)$-function. By the definition of $W_H^{R,\geq 1}$, we must have $f(u) \geq 1$ to Roman dominate u. Now, if $f(u) = 2$, then using the same argument as above we obtain $\gamma_R^p(G) = \gamma_R^p(H) + 1$. Hence assume that $f(u) = 1$. Then the function $g : V(G) \to \{0, 1, 2\}$ defined by $g(x_1) = 2$, $g(u) = g(x_2) = 0$ and $g(x) = f(x)$ for all $x \in V(H) \setminus \{u\}$ is a PRDF of G of weight $\gamma_R^p(H) + 1$. Therefore $\gamma_R^p(G) \leq \gamma_R^p(H) + 1$, and the equality follows by item 1.

3. Let S be a $\gamma^p(G)$-set. Clearly, $|S \cap \{x_1, x_2\}| \geq 1$ and $S - \{x_1, x_2\}$ is an almost PDS of H with respect to u. Since $u \in W_H^{APD}$, we have $|S - \{x_1, x_2\}| \geq \gamma^p(G'; u) = \gamma^p(H)$. Therefore $\gamma^p(G) = |S| \geq \gamma^p(H) + 1$, and the equality follows from item 1. □

For a graph G and a vertex u of G, we denote by $G_{K_{1,3}}^u$ the graph obtained from G by adding a star $K_{1,3}$ and joining one of its leaf to u.

Proposition 3. *Let G be a graph and u a vertex of G.*

1. $\gamma^p(G_{K_{1,3}}^u) \leq \gamma^p(G) + 2$ *and* $\gamma_R^p(G) + 2 \leq \gamma_R^p(G_{K_{1,3}}^u)$.
2. *If* $u \in W_G^{P,A} \cap W_G^{APD}$, *then* $\gamma^p(G_{K_{1,3}}^u) = \gamma^p(G) + 2$.
3. *If* $u \in W_G^{R,\leq 1}$, *then* $\gamma_R^p(G_{K_{1,3}}^u) = \gamma_R^p(G) + 2$.

Proof. Let x be the center of the star $K_{1,3}$ and x_1 a leaf of $K_{1,3}$ attached at u by an edge ux_1.

1. For a $\gamma^p(G)$-set S, let $S' = S \cup \{x, x_1\}$ if $u \in S$, and $S' = S \cup \{x\}$ for otherwise. Clearly, S' is a PDS of $G_{K_{1,3}}^u$ and thus $\gamma^p(G_{K_{1,3}}^u) \leq \gamma^p(G) + 2$.

   Now, let f be a $\gamma_R^p(G_{K_{1,3}}^u)$-function. By Proposition 1, we may assume that $f(x) = 2$. If $f(x_1) \leq 1$, then the function f restricted to G is a PRDF on G of weight at most $\gamma_R^p(G_{K_{1,3}}^u) - 2$. Thus, we assume that $f(x_1) = 2$. Then the function $g : V(G) \to \{0, 1, 2\}$ defined by $g(u) = 1$ and $g(x) = f(x)$ for all $x \in V(G) \setminus \{u\}$ is a PRDF on G of weight $\gamma_R^p(G_{K_{1,3}}^u) - 3$. In any case, $\gamma_R^p(G) \leq \gamma_R^p(G_{K_{1,3}}^u) - 2$.

2. Let S be a $\gamma^p(G_{K_{1,3}}^u)$-set. By Observation 1-(1), we have $x \in S$. Now, if $u \in S$, then $x_1 \in S$ and clearly $S - \{x, x_1\}$ is a PDS of G, implying that $\gamma^p(G_{K_{1,3}}^u) \geq \gamma^p(G) + 2$. Thus, assume that $u \notin S$. If $x_1 \notin S$, then $S - \{x\}$ is a PDS of G that does not contain u and since $u \in W_G^{P,A}$ we deduce that $|S - \{x\}| \geq \gamma^p(G) + 1$. Hence $\gamma^p(G_{K_{1,3}}^u) \geq \gamma^p(G) + 2$. If $x_1 \in S$, then $S - \{x, x_1\}$ is an almost PDS of G and since $u \in W_G^{APD}$ we conclude that $|S - \{x, x_1\}| \geq \gamma^p(G)$. Hence $\gamma^p(G_{K_{1,3}}^u) \geq \gamma^p(G) + 2$. Whatever the case, the equality follows from item 1.

3. Assume that $u \in W_G^{R,\leq 1}$ and let f be a $\gamma_R^p(G)$-function such that $f(u) \leq 1$. Then f can be extended to a PRDF on $G_{K_{1,3}}^u$ by assigning a 2 to x and a 0 to every neighbor of x and thus $\gamma_R^p(G_{K_{1,3}}^u) \leq \gamma_R^p(G) + 2$. The equality follows from item 1. □

Proposition 4. *Let G' be a graph and let u be an end support vertex of G' which is adjacent to a strong support vertex v. If G is a graph obtained from G' by adding a vertex x and an edge ux, then $\gamma^p(G) = \gamma^p(G')$ and $\gamma_R^p(G) \geq \gamma_R^p(G')$. Moreover, if $u \in W_{G'}^{R,1}$, then $\gamma_R^p(G) = \gamma_R^p(G')$.*

Proof. Let S be a $\gamma^p(G')$-set. By Observation 1, $v \in S$. Thus $u \in S$ for otherwise u would have two neighbors in S. Hence S is a PDS of G and so $\gamma^p(G) \leq \gamma^p(G')$. On the other hand, by Observation 1, any $\gamma^p(G)$-set contains both u and v, and thus remains a PDS of G'. It follows that $\gamma^p(G) \geq \gamma^p(G')$, and the desired equality is obtained.

Since u is an end strong support vertex in G, $u \in W_G^{R,1}$. By Proposition 1, there is a $\gamma_R^p(G)$-function f such that $f(u) = 2$, and clearly f restricted to G' is a PRDF on G' yielding $\gamma_R^p(G) \geq \gamma_R^p(G')$.

Now, assume that $u \in W_{G'}^{R,1}$ and let g be a $\gamma_R^p(G')$-function with $g(u) = 2$. Then g can be extended to a PRDF on G by assigning a 0 to x. Thus $\gamma_R^p(G) \leq \gamma_R^p(G')$, and the desired equality follows. □

Proposition 5. *Let G' be a graph and u a vertex of G'. If G is a graph obtained from G' by adding a double star $DS_{2,2}$ attached at u by one of its leaves, then:*

1. $\gamma^p(G) \leq \gamma^p(G') + 3$ *and* $\gamma_R^p(G) \geq \gamma_R^p(G') + 3$.
2. *If $u \in W_{G'}^{R,1}$, then* $\gamma_R^p(G) = \gamma_R^p(G') + 3$.
3. *If $u \in W_{G'}^{P,A} \cap W_{G'}^{APD}$, then* $\gamma^p(G) = \gamma^p(G') + 3$.

Proof. Let x, y be the non-leaf vertices of the double star $DS_{2,2}$, and let $L_x = \{x_1, x_2\}$ and $L_y = \{y_1, y_2\}$. We assume that $x_1 u \in E(G)$.

1. For a $\gamma^p(G')$-set S, let $S' = S \cup \{x, y\}$ if $u \notin S$, and $S' = S \cup \{x_1, x, y\}$ if $u \in S$. Clearly, S' is a PDS of G and thus $\gamma^p(G) \leq \gamma^p(G') + 3$.

   Consider now a $\gamma_R^p(G)$-function f such that $f(y) = 2$ (according to Proposition 1). Clearly, $f(x) + f(x_2) \geq 1$. If $f(x_1) \leq 1$, then f restricted to G' is a PRDF on G' of weight at most $\gamma_R^p(G) - 3$ and thus $\gamma_R^p(G) \geq \gamma_R^p(G') + 3$. If $f(x_1) = 2$, then $f(u) = 0$ and the function $g : V(G') \to \{0, 1, 2\}$ defined by $g(u) = 1$ and $g(w) = f(w)$ otherwise, is a PRDF onG' of weight at most $\gamma_R^p(G) - 4$ yielding $\gamma_R^p(G) \geq \gamma_R^p(G') + 4$. In any case we have $\gamma_R^p(G) \geq \gamma_R^p(G') + 3$.

2. Assume that $u \in W_{G'}^{R,1}$ and let f be a $\gamma_R^p(G')$-function such that $f(u) = 2$. Then f can be extended to a PRDF on G by assigning a 2 to y, a 1 to x_2 and a 0 to x, x_1, y_1, y_2. Hence $\gamma_R^p(G) \leq \gamma_R^p(G') + 3$, and the desired equality follows from item 1.

3. Assume that $u \in W_{G'}^{P,A} \cap W_{G'}^{APD}$, and let S be a $\gamma^p(G)$-set. By items 1 and 2 of Observation 1, $x, y \in S$. If $u \in S$, then $x_1 \in S$ and thus $S - \{x, y, x_1\}$ is a PDS of G', implying that $\gamma^p(G) \geq \gamma^p(G') + 3$. Hence, assume that $u \notin S$. If $x_1 \notin S$, then $S - \{x, y\}$ is a PDS of G' that does not contain u. But since $u \in W_{G'}^3$, we deduce that $|S - \{x, y\}| \geq \gamma^p(G') + 1$ which yields $\gamma^p(G) \geq \gamma^p(G') + 3$. Thus suppose that $x_1 \in S$. Then $S - \{x, y, x_1\}$ is an almost PDS of G', and since $u \in W_{G'}^{APD}$ we conclude that $|S - \{x, y, x_1\}| \geq \gamma^p(G'; u) = \gamma^p(G')$. Hence $\gamma^p(G) \geq \gamma^p(G') + 3$, and the desired equality is obtained by item 1.

□

Proposition 6. *Let G' be a graph and let u be an end strong support vertex of degree 3 whose non-leaf neighbor is a support vertex, say v, of degree 3, where $|L_v| = 1$. Let G be a graph obtained from G' by adding four vertices, where two are attached to a leaf of u and the other two are attached to the leaf of v. Then $\gamma^p(G) = \gamma^p(G') + 2$ and $\gamma_R^p(G) = \gamma_R^p(G') + 2$.*

Proof. Let $L_u = \{x, x'\}$ and $L_v = \{y\}$. Let x_1, x_2, y_1 and y_2 be the four added vertices, where $xx_1, xx_2, yy_1, yy_2 \in E(G)$. By items 1 and 2 of Observation 1, any $\gamma^p(G')$-set contains u and v. Clearly such a set can be extended to a PDS of G by adding x, y which yields $\gamma^p(G) \leq \gamma^p(G') + 2$. On the other hand, let D be a $\gamma^p(G)$-set. Then by items 1 and 2 of Observation 1, we have $x, u, y, v \in D$, and thus $D \setminus \{x, y\}$ is a PDS of G', implying that $\gamma^p(G) \geq \gamma^p(G') + 2$. Therefore $\gamma^p(G) = \gamma^p(G') + 2$.

Next we shall show that $\gamma_R^p(G) = \gamma_R^p(G') + 2$. First we show that $\gamma_R^p(G) \leq \gamma_R^p(G') + 2$. Since u is an end strong support vertex of G', let f be a $\gamma_R^p(G')$-function with $f(u) = 2$ (by Proposition 1) such that $f(v)$ is as small as possible. If $f(v) \leq 1$, then $f(y) = 1$, and thus the function $g : V(G) \to \{0, 1, 2\}$ defined by $g(x) = g(y) = 2$, $g(x') = 1$, $g(u) = g(x_1) = g(x_2) = g(y_1) = g(y_2) = 0$ and $g(w) = f(w)$ otherwise, is a PRDF on G. Hence $\gamma_R^p(G) \leq \gamma_R^p(G') + 2$. If $f(v) = 2$, then by our choice of f, we have $f(z) = 0$ for any $z \in N(v) \setminus \{u\}$ and thus the function $h : V(G) \to \{0, 1, 2\}$ defined by $h(z) = 1$ for $z \in N(v) \setminus \{u, y\}$ and $h(x') = 1$, $h(x) = h(y) = 2$, $h(u) = h(v) = h(x_1) = h(x_2) = h(y_1) = h(y_2) = 0$ and $h(w) = f(w)$ otherwise, is a PRDF on G yielding $\gamma_R^p(G) \leq \gamma_R^p(G') + 2$. Hence $\gamma_R^p(G) \leq \gamma_R^p(G') + 2$. Now we show that $\gamma_R^p(G) \geq \gamma_R^p(G') + 2$. By Proposition 1, let g be a $\gamma_R^p(G)$-function such that

$g(x) = g(y) = 2$. It can be seen that $g(x') = 1$. If $f(v) = 0$, then the function $h : V(G') \rightarrow \{0,1,2\}$ defined by $h(u) = 2, h(y) = 1, h(x) = h(x') = 0$ and $h(w) = g(w)$ otherwise, is a PRDF on G' of weight at most $\gamma_R^p(G) - 2$. If $f(v) \geq 1$, then the function $h : V(G') \rightarrow \{0,1,2\}$ defined by $h(u) = h(v) = 2$, $h(x) = h(x') = h(y) = 0$ and $h(w) = g(w)$ otherwise, is a PRDF on G' of weight at most $\gamma_R^p(G) - 2$. In any case, $\gamma_R^p(G) \geq \gamma_R^p(G') + 2$, and the equality follows. $\square$

3. The Family $\mathcal{T}$

In this section, we define the family $\mathcal{T}$ of unlabeled trees T that can be obtained from a sequence $T_1, T_2, \ldots, T_k$ $(k \geq 1)$ of trees such that $T_1 \in \{P_2, P_3\}$ and $T = T_k$. If $k \geq 2$, then T_{i+1} is obtained recursively from T_i by one of the following operations.

Operation $\mathcal{O}_1$: If $u \in V(T_i)$ is an end strong support vertex, then $\mathcal{O}_1$ adds a vertex x attached at u by an edge ux to obtain T_{i+1}.

Operation $\mathcal{O}_2$: If $u \in (W_{T_i}^{R,1} \cup W_{T_i}^{R, \geq 1}) \cap W_{T_i}^{APD}$, then $\mathcal{O}_2$ adds a path $P_2 = x_1 x_2$ attached at u by an edge ux_1 to obtain T_{i+1}.

Operation $\mathcal{O}_3$: If $u \in W_{T_i}^{R, \leq 1} \cap W_{T_i}^{P,A} \cap W_{T_i}^{APD}$, then $\mathcal{O}_3$ adds a star $K_{1,3}$ centered at x by attaching one of its leaves, say x_1, to u to obtain T_{i+1}.

Operation $\mathcal{O}_4$: If $u \in W_{T_i}^{R,1}$ is an end support vertex which is adjacent to a strong support vertex, then $\mathcal{O}_4$ adds a vertex x attached at u by an edge ux to obtain T_{i+1}.

Operation $\mathcal{O}_5$: If $u \in W_{T_i}^{R,1} \cap W_{T_i}^{P,A} \cap W_{T_i}^{APD}$, then $\mathcal{O}_5$ adds a double star $DS_{2,2}$ by attaching one of its leaves, say x_1, to u to obtain T_{i+1}.

Operation $\mathcal{O}_6$: If $u \in V(T_i)$ is an end strong support vertex of degree 3 with $x \in L_u$ such that u is adjacent to a support vertex v of degree 3 with $L_v = \{y\}$, then $\mathcal{O}_6$ adds four vertices x_1, x_2, y_1, y_2 attached at x and y by edges xx_1, xx_2, yy_1, yy_2 to obtain T_{i+1}.

Lemma 1. *If T_i is a tree with $\gamma_R^p(T_i) = \gamma^p(T_i) + 1$ and T_{i+1} is a tree obtained from T_i by one of the Operations $\mathcal{O}_1, \ldots, \mathcal{O}_6$, then $\gamma_R^p(T_{i+1}) = \gamma^p(T_{i+1}) + 1$.*

Proof. If T_{i+1} is obtained from T_i by Operation $\mathcal{O}_1$, then by Corollary 1 and the assumption $\gamma_R^p(T_i) = \gamma^p(T_i) + 1$, we have $\gamma_R^p(T_{i+1}) = \gamma_R^p(T_i) = \gamma^p(T_i) + 1 = \gamma^p(T_{i+1}) + 1$. If T_{i+1} is obtained from T_i by Operation $\mathcal{O}_2$, then as above the result follows from Proposition 2 (items 2, 3 and 4). If T_{i+1} is obtained from T_i by Operation $\mathcal{O}_3$, then the result follows from Proposition 3 (items 2 and 3). If T_{i+1} is obtained from T_i by Operation $\mathcal{O}_4$, then the result follows from Proposition 4. If T_{i+1} is obtained from T_i by Operation $\mathcal{O}_5$, then the result follows from Proposition 5. Finally, if T_{i+1} is obtained from T_i by Operation $\mathcal{O}_6$, then the result follows from Proposition 6. $\square$

In the rest of the paper, we shall prove our main result:

Theorem 1. *For any tree T of order $n \geq 2$,*

$$\gamma_R^p(T) \geq \gamma^p(T) + 1,$$

with equality if and only if $T \in \mathcal{T}$.

4. Proof of Theorem 1

Lemma 2. *If $T \in \mathcal{T}$, then $\gamma_R^p(T) = \gamma^p(T) + 1$.*

Proof. Let T be a tree of $\mathcal{T}$. Then there exists a sequence of trees $T_1, T_2, \ldots, T_k$ $(k \geq 1)$ such that $T_1 \in \{P_2, P_3\}$, and if $k \geq 2$, then T_{i+1} can be obtained from T_i by one of the aforementioned operations. We proceed by induction on the number of operations used to construct T. If $k = 1$, then $T \in \{P_2, P_3\}$ and clearly $\gamma_R^p(T) = \gamma^p(T) + 1$. This establishes our basis case. Let $k \geq 2$ and assume that the result holds for each tree $T \in \mathcal{T}$ which can be obtained from a sequence of operations of length $k - 1$ and let $T' = T_{k-1}$. By the induction hypothesis, $\gamma_R^p(T') = \gamma^p(T') + 1$. Since $T = T_k$ is obtained from T' by one of the Operations $\mathcal{O}_i$ $(i \in \{1, 2, \ldots, 6\})$, we conclude from Lemma 1 that $\gamma_R^p(T) = \gamma^p(T) + 1$. $\square$

Theorem 2. *For any tree T of order $n \geq 2$,*

$$\gamma_R^p(T) \geq \gamma^p(T) + 1,$$

with equality only if $T \in \mathcal{T}$.

Proof. We use an induction on n. If $n \in \{2, 3\}$, then $T \in \{P_2, P_3\}$, where $\gamma_R^p(T) = 2 = \gamma^p(T) + 1$ and $T \in \mathcal{T}$. If $n = 4$ and $\mathrm{diam}(T) = 2$, then $T = K_{1,3}$, where $\gamma_R^p(T) = 2 = \gamma^p(T) + 1$ and $T \in \mathcal{T}$ because it can be obtained from P_3 by applying Operation $\mathcal{O}_1$. If $n = 4$ and $\mathrm{diam}(T) = 3$, then $T = P_4$, where $\gamma_R^p(T) = 3 = \gamma^p(T) + 1$ and clearly $T \in \mathcal{T}$ since it can be obtained from P_2 by Operation $\mathcal{O}_2$. Let $n \geq 5$ and assume that every tree T' of order n' with $2 \leq n' < n$ satisfies $\gamma_R^p(T') \geq \gamma^p(T') + 1$ with equality only if $T' \in \mathcal{T}$.

Let T be a tree of order n. If $\mathrm{diam}(T) = 2$, then T is a star, where $\gamma_R^p(T) = 2 = \gamma^p(T) + 1$ and $T \in \mathcal{T}$ because T it can be obtained from P_3 by frequently use of Operation $\mathcal{O}_1$. Hence assume that $\mathrm{diam}(T) = 3$, and thus T is a double star $DS_{p,q}$, $(q \geq p \geq 1)$. If $T = DS_{1,q}$ $(q \geq 2)$, then $\gamma_R^p(T) = 3 = \gamma^p(T) + 1$ and $T \in \mathcal{T}$ since it is obtained from P_3 by applying Operation $\mathcal{O}_2$. If $T = DS_{p,q}$, $(q \geq p \geq 2)$, then $\gamma^p(T) = 2$, $\gamma_R^p(T) = 4$ and so $\gamma_R^p(T) > \gamma^p(T) + 1$. Henceforth, we assume that $\mathrm{diam}(T) \geq 4$. Let $v_1 v_2 \ldots v_k$ $(k \geq 5)$ be a diametrical path in T such that $\deg_T(v_2)$ is as large as possible. Root T at v_k and consider the following cases.

Case 1. $\deg_T(v_2) \geq 4$.
Let $T' = T - v_1$. By Corollary 1 and the induction hypothesis on T', we obtain

$$\gamma_R^p(T) = \gamma_R^p(T') \geq \gamma^p(T') + 1 = \gamma^p(T) + 1.$$

Further if $\gamma_R^p(T) = \gamma^p(T) + 1$, then we have equality throughout this inequality chain. In particular, $\gamma_R^p(T') = \gamma^p(T') + 1$. By induction on T', we have $T' \in \mathcal{T}$. It follows that $T \in \mathcal{T}$ since it can be obtained from T' by applying operation $\mathcal{O}_1$.

Case 2. $\deg_T(v_2) = \deg_T(v_3) = 2$.
Let $T' = T - T_{v_3}$. For a $\gamma^p(T')$-set S, let $S' = S \cup \{v_1\}$ if $v_4 \in S$ and $S' = S \cup \{v_2\}$ for otherwise. Clearly S' is a PDS of T and thus $\gamma^p(T) \leq \gamma^p(T') + 1$. Consider now a $\gamma_R^p(T)$-function f. If $f(v_3) \in \{0, 1\}$, then $f(v_1) + f(v_2) = 2$ and the function f, restricted to T' is a PRDF on T' of weight at most $\gamma_R^p(T) - 2$. If $f(v_3) = 2$, then $f(v_4) = 0$ and the function $g : V(T') \to \{0, 1, 2\}$ defined by $g(v_4) = 1$ and $g(z) = f(z)$ otherwise, is a PRDF on T'. In any case, $\gamma_R^p(T) \geq \gamma_R^p(T') + 2$. By the induction hypothesis on T', we obtain

$$\gamma_R^p(T) \geq \gamma_R^p(T') + 2 \geq \gamma^p(T') + 1 + 2 \geq \gamma^p(T) - 1 + 3 > \gamma^p(T) + 1.$$

Case 3. $\deg_T(v_2) = 2$ and $\deg_T(v_3) \geq 3$.
Let $T' = T - T_{v_2}$. By Proposition 2, we have $\gamma^p(T) \leq \gamma^p(T') + 1$ and $\gamma_R^p(T) \geq \gamma_R^p(T') + 1$. It follows from the induction hypothesis that

$$\gamma_R^p(T) \geq \gamma_R^p(T') + 1 \geq \gamma^p(T') + 1 + 1 \geq \gamma^p(T) + 1.$$

Further if $\gamma_R^p(T) = \gamma^p(T) + 1$, then we have equality throughout this inequality chain. In particular, $\gamma^p(T) = \gamma^p(T') + 1$, $\gamma_R^p(T) = \gamma_R^p(T') + 1$ and $\gamma_R^p(T') = \gamma^p(T') + 1$. By induction on T', we deduce that $T' \in \mathcal{T}$. Next, we shall show that $v_3 \in (W_{T'}^{R,1} \cup W_{T'}^{R, \geq 1}) \cap W_{T'}^{APD}$. Let f be a $\gamma_R^p(T)$-function. If $f(v_3) = 2$, then $f(v_1) = 1$ and $f(v_2) = 0$ and the function $f|_{V(T')}$ is a $\gamma_R^p(T')$-function with $f(v_3) = 2$

and hence $v_3 \in W_{T'}^{R,1}$. Hence, assume that $f(v_3) \leq 1$. Then $f(v_1) + f(v_2) = 2$. If $f(v_2) \leq 1$ or $f(v_2) = 2$ and $f(v_3) = 1$, then the function f restricted to T' is a PRDF on T' of weight $\gamma_R^p(T) - 2$, contradicting the fact $\gamma_R^p(T) = \gamma_R^p(T') + 1$. Hence we assume $f(v_2) = 2$ and $f(v_3) = 0$. Then the function $g : V(T') \to \{0, 1, 2\}$ defined by $g(v_3) = 1$ and $g(x) = f(x)$ otherwise, is a $\gamma_R^p(T')$-function and so $v_3 \in W_{T'}^{R,\geq 1}$. Hence $v_3 \in W_{T'}^{R,1} \cup W_{T'}^{R,\geq 1}$. It remains to show that $v_3 \in W_{T'}^{APD}$. Suppose that $v_3 \notin W_{T'}^{S}$ and let S be an almost PDS of T' of size less that $\gamma^p(T')$. Clearly, $v_3 \notin S$ and v_3 has no neighbor in S. Therefore, $S \cup \{v_2\}$ is a PDS of T of size at most $\gamma^p(T') = \gamma^p(T) - 1$, a contradiction. Hence $v_3 \in W_{T'}^{APD}$. It follows that $T \in \mathcal{T}$ since it can be obtained from T' by Operation $\mathcal{O}_2$.

Case 4. $\deg_T(v_2) = 3$.

Let $L_{v_2} = \{v_1, w\}$. According to Cases 1, 2 and 3, we may assume that any end support vertex on a diametrical path has degree 3. Consider the following subcases.

Subcase 4.1. $\deg_T(v_3) = 2$.

Let $T' = T - T_{v_3}$. By Proposition 3-(1) and the induction hypothesis we have:

$$\gamma_R^p(T) \geq \gamma_R^p(T') + 2 \geq \gamma^p(T') + 1 + 2 \geq \gamma^p(T) + 1.$$

Further if $\gamma_R^p(T) = \gamma^p(T) + 1$, then we have equality throughout this inequality chain. In particular, $\gamma_R^p(T) = \gamma_R^p(T') + 2$, $\gamma^p(T) = \gamma^p(T') + 2$ and $\gamma_R^p(T') = \gamma^p(T') + 1$. It follows from the induction hypothesis that $T' \in \mathcal{T}$. In the next, we shall show that $v_4 \in W_{T'}^{R,\leq 1} \cap W_{T'}^{P,A} \cap W_{T'}^{APD}$.

Suppose that $v_4 \notin W_{T'}^{P,A}$ and let S be a $\gamma^p(T')$-set that does not contain v_4. Then $S \cup \{v_2\}$ is a PDS of T, contradicting the fact $\gamma^p(T) = \gamma^p(T') + 2$. Hence $v_4 \in W_{T'}^{P,A}$. Suppose now that $v_4 \notin W_{T'}^{APD}$ and let D be an almost PDS of T' with respect to v_4 such that $|D| < \gamma^p(T')$. Then $v_4 \notin D$ and v_4 has no neighbor in D, and thus $D \cup \{v_2, v_3\}$ is a PDS of T of cardinality less $\gamma^p(T') + 2$, a contradiction. Hence $v_4 \in W_{T'}^{APD}$. It remains to show that $v_4 \in W_{T'}^{R,\leq 1}$. By Proposition 1, let f be a $\gamma_R^p(T)$-function such that $f(v_2) = 2$. If $f(v_4) = 2$, then we must have $f(v_3) \geq 1$. But f restricted to T' is a PRDF on T' of weight at most $\gamma_R^p(T) - 3$, contradicting $\gamma_R^p(T) = \gamma_R^p(T') + 2$. Hence $f(v_4) \leq 1$. If $f(v_4) = 0$ and $f(v_3) = 2$, then the function $g : V(T') \to \{0, 1, 2\}$ defined by $g(v_4) = 1$ and $g(x) = f(x)$ otherwise, is a PRDF of T' of weight at most $\gamma_R^p(T) - 3$, a contradiction as above. Thus $f(v_4) = 1$ or $f(v_4) = 0$ and $f(v_3) \leq 1$. Then f restricted to T' is a $\gamma_R^p(T')$-function showing that $v_4 \in W_{T'}^{R,\leq 1}$. Hence $v_4 \in W_{T'}^{R,\leq 1} \cap W_{T'}^{P,A} \cap W_{T'}^{APD}$. Therefore, $T \in \mathcal{T}$ because it can be obtained from T' by Operation $\mathcal{O}_3$.

Subcase 4.2. $\deg_T(v_3) \geq 3$.

We distinguish between some situations.

(a) v_3 is a strong support vertex.

Let $T' = T - v_1$. By Proposition 4 and the induction hypothesis we have:

$$\gamma_R^p(T) \geq \gamma_R^p(T') \geq \gamma^p(T') + 1 = \gamma^p(T) + 1.$$

Further if $\gamma_R^p(T) = \gamma^p(T) + 1$, then we have equality throughout this inequality chain. In particular, $\gamma_R^p(T) = \gamma_R^p(T')$, $\gamma^p(T) = \gamma^p(T')$ and $\gamma_R^p(T') = \gamma^p(T') + 1$. By the induction hypothesis, $T' \in \mathcal{T}$. To show $v_2 \in W_{T'}^{R,1}$, let f be a $\gamma_R^p(T)$-function such that $f(v_2) = 2$ (by Proposition 1). Since $\gamma_R^p(T) = \gamma_R^p(T')$, f is also a $\gamma_R^p(T')$-function with $f(v_2) = 2$, implying that $v_2 \in W_{T'}^{R,1}$. Therefore $T \in \mathcal{T}$ because it can be obtained from T' by Operation $\mathcal{O}_4$.

(b) v_3 has two children x, y with depth one, different from v_2.

Then u and w are both strong support vertices of degree 3. Let $T' = T - T_{v_2}$. By Observation 1, any $\gamma^p(T')$-set S contains x and y and thus $v_3 \in S$. Hence $S \cup \{v_2\}$ is a PDS of T yielding $\gamma^p(T) \leq \gamma^p(T') + 1$. Now, let f be a $\gamma_R^p(T)$ function such that $f(v_2) = 2$ and $f(x) = 2$

(by Proposition 1). Then $f(v_3) \geq 1$. It follows that the function f restricted to T' is a PRDF on T' of weight $\gamma_R^p(T) - 2$, and hence $\gamma_R^p(T) \geq \gamma_R^p(T') + 2$. By the induction hypothesis we have

$$\gamma_R^p(T) \geq \gamma_R^p(T') + 2 \geq \gamma^p(T') + 3 \geq \gamma^p(T) + 2 > \gamma^p(T) + 1.$$

(c) v_3 is a support vertex and has a child u with depth one different from v_2.

Let w_1 be the unique leaf adjacent to v_3. Note that u is a strong support vertices of degree 3. Let $T' = T - T_{v_2}$. If S is a $\gamma^p(T')$-set, then by Observation 1-(2), $v_3 \in S$ and thus $S \cup \{v_2\}$ is a PDS of T yielding $\gamma^p(T) \leq \gamma^p(T') + 1$. By Proposition 1, let f be a $\gamma_R^p(T)$-function such that $f(v_2) = 2$ and $f(u) = 2$. By the definition of perfect Roman dominating functions, we have $f(v_3) \geq 1$. Then, the function f restricted to T' is a PRDF on T' of weight $\gamma_R^p(T) - 2$ and thus $\gamma_R^p(T) \geq \gamma_R^p(T') + 2$. It follows from the induction hypothesis that

$$\gamma_R^p(T) \geq \gamma_R^p(T') + 2 \geq \gamma^p(T') + 3 \geq \gamma^p(T) + 2 > \gamma^p(T) + 1.$$

According to (a), (b) and (c), we can assume for the next that $\deg_T(v_3) = 3$.

(d) $\deg_T(v_3) = 3$ and v_3 has a child x with depth one different from v_2.

Note that x is a strong support vertices of degree 3. Let $L_x = \{x_1, x_2\}$ and let T' be the tree obtained from T by removing the set of vertices $\{v_1, v_2, w, x, x_1, x_2\}$. For a $\gamma^p(T')$-set S, let $S' = S \cup \{v_2, x\}$ if $v_3 \in S$ and $S' = S \cup \{v_2, v_3, x\}$ when $v_3 \notin S$. Clearly, S' is a PDS of T and so $\gamma^p(T) \leq \gamma^p(T') + 3$. Now let f be a $\gamma_R^p(T)$-function such that $f(v_2) = f(x) = 2$. Then $f(v_3) \geq 1$ and the function f restricted to T' is a PRDF on T' of weight at most $\gamma_R^p(T) - 4$. By the induction hypothesis we have:

$$\gamma_R^p(T) \geq \gamma_R^p(T') + 4 \geq \gamma^p(T') + 1 + 4 \geq \gamma^p(T) - 3 + 5 > \gamma^p(T) + 1.$$

(e) $\deg_T(v_3) = 3$ and v_3 is adjacent to exactly one leaf w'.

If v_4 has a child s with depth one and degree two, then let T' be the tree obtained from T by removing s and its unique leaf. This case can be treated in the same way as in Case 3. Moreover, if v_4 has a child s with depth one and degree at least four, then let T' be the tree obtained from T by removing a leaf neighbor of s. This case can be treated in the same way as in Case 1. Hence, we may assume that each child of v_4 is a leaf or a vertex with depth one and degree 3 or a vertex with depth two whose maximal subtree is isomorphic to T_{v_3}. First assume that $\deg_T(v_4) \geq 4$, and let $T = T - T_{v_3}$. Clearly, any $\gamma^p(T')$-set contains v_4 and such a set can be extended to a PDS of T by adding v_2, v_3. Hence $\gamma^p(T) \leq \gamma^p(T') + 2$. Now let f be a $\gamma_R^p(T)$-function such that $f(v_2) = 2$. Clearly, $f(v_3) + f(w') \geq 1$. If $f(v_3) \leq 1$ or $f(v_3) = 2$ and $f(v_4) \geq 1$, then the function f restricted to T' is a PRDF on T' and thus $\gamma_R^p(T) \geq \gamma_R^p(T') + 3$. Hence assume that $f(v_3) = 2$ and $f(v_4) = 0$. Then the function $g : V(T') \to \{0, 1, 2\}$ defined by $g(v_4) = 1$ and $g(u) = f(u)$ otherwise, is a PRDF of T' of weight $\gamma_R^p(T) - 3$ and thus $\gamma_R^p(T) \geq \gamma_R^p(T') + 3$. By the induction hypothesis we have:

$$\gamma_R^p(T) \geq \gamma_R^p(T') + 3 \geq \gamma^p(T') + 1 + 3 \geq \gamma^p(T) - 2 + 4 > \gamma^p(T) + 1.$$

From now on, we can assume that $\deg_T(v_4) \leq 3$. We examine different cases.

(e.1.) v_4 has a child x of degree 3 and depth 1.

Let $L_x = \{z_1, z_2\}$ and let T' be the tree obtained from T by removing the set $\{v_1, w, z_1, z_2\}$. By Proposition 6, we have $\gamma^p(T) = \gamma^p(T') + 2$ and $\gamma_R^p(T) = \gamma_R^p(T') + 2$. We deduce from the induction hypothesis that

$$\gamma_R^p(T) = \gamma_R^p(T') + 2 \geq \gamma^p(T') + 1 + 2 = \gamma^p(T) - 2 + 3 = \gamma^p(T) + 1.$$

Further if $\gamma_R^p(T) = \gamma^p(T) + 1$, then we have equality throughout this inequality chain. In particular, $\gamma_R^p(T') = \gamma^p(T') + 1$. By induction on T', we have $T' \in \mathcal{T}$. Therefore $T \in \mathcal{T}$ since it can be obtained from T' by Operation $\mathcal{O}_6$.

(e.2.) v_4 has a child v_3' with depth two.

Note that $T_{v_3'}$ and T_{v_3} are isomorphic. Let $T' = T - (T_{v_3} \cup T_{v_3'})$, and observe that v_4 is a leaf in T'. Since any $\gamma^p(T')$-set can be extended to a PDS of T by adding v_4 and the support vertices of $T_{v_3} \cup T_{v_3'}$ we obtain $\gamma^p(T) \leq \gamma^p(T') + 5$. Moreover, as above we can see that $\gamma_R^p(T) \geq \gamma_R^p(T') + 6$. Now, by induction hypothesis we obtain:

$$\gamma_R^p(T) \geq \gamma_R^p(T') + 6 \geq \gamma^p(T') + 1 + 6 \geq \gamma^p(T) - 5 + 7 > \gamma^p(T) + 1.$$

(e.3.) $\deg_T(v_4) = 2$.

Let $T' = T - T_{v_4}$. If $V(T') = \{v_5\}$, then it can be seen that T is tree with $\gamma_R^p(T) = 5$ and $\gamma^p(T) = 3$, implying that $\gamma_R^p(T) > \gamma^p(T) + 1$. Hence we assume that T' is nontrivial. By Proposition 5 and by the inductive hypothesis we have:

$$\gamma_R^p(T) \geq \gamma_R^p(T') + 3 \geq \gamma^p(T') + 1 + 3 \geq \gamma^p(T) - 3 + 4 = \gamma^p(T) + 1.$$

Further if $\gamma_R^p(T) = \gamma^p(T) + 1$, then we have equality throughout this inequality chain. In particular, $\gamma_R^p(T) = \gamma_R^p(T') + 3$, $\gamma^p(T) = \gamma^p(T') + 3$ and $\gamma_R^p(T') = \gamma^p(T') + 1$. By induction on T', we have $T' \in \mathcal{T}$. Next, we shall show that $v_5 \in W_{T'}^{R,1} \cap W_{T'}^{P,A} \cap W_{T'}^{APD}$. Suppose that $v_5 \notin W_{T'}^{P,A}$ and let S be a $\gamma^p(T')$-set that does not contain v_5. Then $S \cup \{v_2, v_3\}$ is a PDS of T contradicting $\gamma^p(T') = \gamma^p(T') + 3$. Hence $v_5 \in W_{T'}^{P,A}$. Suppose that $v_5 \notin W_{T'}^{APD}$ and let S be an almost PDS of T' such that $|S| \leq \gamma^p(T') - 1$. Clearly, $v_5 \notin S$ and v_5 has no neighbor in S. It follows that $S \cup \{v_4, v_3, v_2\}$ is a PDS of T of size $|S| + 3 \leq \gamma^p(T) - 1$, a contradiction. Thus $v_5 \in W_{T'}^{APD}$. Next we show that $v_5 \in W_{T'}^{R,1}$. Let f be a $\gamma_R^p(T)$-function such that $f(v_2) = 2$. To Roman dominate w', we must have either $f(w') = 1$ or $f(v_3) = 2$. We claim that $f(v_4) \leq 1$. Suppose, to the contrary, that $f(v_4) = 2$. By definition of perfect Roman dominating functions, we may assume that $f(v_3) = 2$. But then the function $g : V(T') \to \{0,1,2\}$ defined by $g(v_5) = 1$ and $g(x) = f(x)$ otherwise, is a PRDF of T' of weight $\gamma_R^p(T') - 5$ contradicting $\gamma_R^p(T) = \gamma_R^p(T') + 3$. Hence $f(v_4) \leq 1$. It follows that the function f restricted to T' is a PRDF of T' of weight at most $\gamma_R^p(T) - 3$ for which we conclude from $\gamma_R^p(T) = \gamma_R^p(T') + 3$ that $f(v_3) = f(v_4) = 0$ and $f(w') = 1$. Hence to Roman dominate v_4, we must have $f(v_5) = 2$ and thus function f restricted to T' is a $\gamma_R^p(T')$-function that assigns a a 2 to v_5. Hence $v_5 \in W_{T'}^{R,1}$, and thus $v_5 \in W_{T'}^{R,1} \cap W_{T'}^{P,A} \cap W_{T'}^{APD}$. Therefore, $T \in \mathcal{T}$ since it can be obtained from T' by Operation $\mathcal{O}_5$.

(e.4.) $\deg_T(v_4) = 3$ and v_4 has a child z with depth 0.

Seeing the above Cases and Subcases as we did in the beginning of Case (e), we may assume that any child of v_5 is a leaf, or an end strong support vertex of degree 3, or a vertex with depth 2 whose maximal subtree is isomorphic to T_{v_3}, or a vertex with depth 3 whose maximal subtree is isomorphic to T_{v_4}. Assume first that $\deg_T(v_5) \geq 4$, and let $T' = T - T_{v_4}$. Clearly, v_5 belongs to any $\gamma^p(T')$-set and such a set $\gamma^p(T')$-set can be extended to a PDS of T by adding v_2, v_3, v_4, implying that $\gamma^p(T) \leq \gamma^p(T') + 3$. Next we show that $\gamma_R^p(T) \geq \gamma_R^p(T') + 4$. Let f be a $\gamma_R^p(T)$-function such that $f(v_2) = 2$. Clearly $f(v_3) + f(w') \geq 1$ and $f(v_4) + f(z) \geq 1$. If $f(v_4) \leq 1$ or $f(v_5) \geq 1$, then the function f restricted to T' is a PRDF on T' yielding $\gamma_R^p(T) \geq \gamma_R^p(T') + 4$. Hence assume that $f(v_4) = 2$ and $f(v_5) = 0$. Then the function

$g : V(T') \rightarrow \{0,1,2\}$ defined by $g(v_5) = 1$ and $g(u) = f(u)$ otherwise, is a PRDF of T' yielding $\gamma_R^p(T) \geq \gamma_R^p(T') + 4$. By induction on T', it follows that

$$\gamma_R^p(T) \geq \gamma_R^p(T') + 4 \geq \gamma^p(T') + 5 \geq \gamma^p(T) + 2 > \gamma^p(T) + 1.$$

For the next, we assume that $\deg_T(v_5) \leq 3$. If $\deg_T(v_5) = 1$, then it can be seen that T is a tree with $\gamma_R^p(T) = 6$, $\gamma^p(T)$ and so $\gamma_R^p(T) > \gamma^p(T) + 1$. Hence we assume that $\deg_T(v_5) \in \{2,3\}$. Consider the following situations.

(e.4.1.) $\deg_T(v_5) = 2$.
Let $T' = T - T_{v_5}$. If $V(T') = \{v_6\}$, then T is a tree with $\gamma_R^p(T) = 6$ and $\gamma^p(T) = 4$, yielding $\gamma_R^p(T) > \gamma^p(T) + 1$. Hence, assume that T' is nontrivial. For a $\gamma^p(T')$-set S, let $S' = S \cup \{v_2, v_3, v_4, v_5\}$ if $v_6 \in S$, and $S' = S \cup \{v_2, v_3, v_4\}$ if $v_6 \notin S$. Then S' is a PDS of T, implying that $\gamma^p(T) \leq \gamma^p(T') + 4$. Moreover, it is easy to see that $\gamma_R^p(T) \geq \gamma_R^p(T') + 5$. By induction on T', we obtain $\gamma_R^p(T) > \gamma^p(T) + 1$.

(e.4.3.) $\deg_T(v_5) = 3$ and v_5 has a child v_4' with depth 3.
Then T_{v_4} and $T_{v_4'}$ are isomorphic. If u is a vertex in T_{v_4}, then let u' be the vertex of $T_{v_4'}$ corresponding to u in T_{v_4}. Let $T = T - (T_{v_4} \cup T_{v_4'})$. Clearly, any $\gamma^p(T')$-set can be extended to a PDS of T by adding $v_5, v_2, v_3, v_4, v_2', v_3', v_4'$ and thus $\gamma^p(T) \leq \gamma^p(T') + 7$. Moreover, it is not hard to see that $\gamma_R^p(T) \geq \gamma_R^p(T') + 8$. By induction on T', we obtain $\gamma_R^p(T) > \gamma^p(T) + 1$.

(e.4.4.) $\deg_T(v_5) = 3$ and v_5 has a children y with depth 1 and degree 3.
Let $T' = T - (T_{v_4} \cup T_y)$. Clearly, any $\gamma^p(T')$-set can be extended to a PDS of T by adding v_5, v_2, v_3, v_4, y and thus $\gamma^p(T) \leq \gamma^p(T') + 5$. Next, we show that $\gamma_R^p(T) \geq \gamma_R^p(T') + 6$. Let f be a $\gamma_R^p(T)$-function such that $f(v_2) = 2$ and $f(y) = 2$ (by Proposition 1). Clearly $f(v_3) + f(w') \geq 1$ and $f(v_4) + f(z) \geq 1$. If $f(v_5) \geq 1$, then the function f restricted to T' is a PRDF on T' yielding $\gamma_R^p(T) \geq \gamma_R^p(T') + 6$. Thus, let $f(v_5) = 0$. Then to Roman dominate z, v_4, w', we must have $f(z) + f(v_4) + f(v_3) + f(w') \geq 4$. Then the function $g : V(T') \rightarrow \{0,1,2\}$ defined by $g(v_5) = 1$ and $g(u) = f(u)$ otherwise, is a PRDF on T' yielding $\gamma_R^p(T) \geq \gamma_R^p(T') + 6$. It follows from the induction hypothesis that

$$\gamma_R^p(T) \geq \gamma_R^p(T') + 6 \geq \gamma^p(T') + 7 \geq \gamma^p(T) + 2 > \gamma^p(T) + 1.$$

(e.4.5.) $\deg_T(v_5) = 3$ and v_5 has a child v_3' with depth 2 such that $T_{v_3'} \cong T_{v_3}$.
If u is a vertex in T_{v_3}, then let u' be the vertex of $T_{v_3'}$ corresponding to u in T_{v_3}. Let $T = T - (T_{v_4} \cup T_{v_3'})$. Clearly, any $\gamma^p(T')$-set can be extended to a PDS of T by adding $v_5, v_2, v_3, v_4, v_2', v_3'$ and so $\gamma^p(T) \leq \gamma^p(T') + 6$. Moreover, it is not hard to see that $\gamma_R^p(T) \geq \gamma_R^p(T') + 7$. By the induction hypothesis we obtain $\gamma_R^p(T) > \gamma^p(T) + 1$.

(e.4.6.) $\deg_T(v_5) = 3$ and v_5 has a children z' with depth 0.
If $V(T') = \{v_6\}$, then T is a tree with $\gamma_R^p(T) = 6$ and $\gamma^p(T) = 4$, yielding $\gamma_R^p(T) > \gamma^p(T) + 1$. Hence we assume that $\deg_T(v_6) \geq 2$. Suppose first that $\deg_T(v_6) = 2$ and let $T' = T - T_{v_6}$. If $V(T') = \{v_7\}$, then T is a tree with $\gamma_R^p(T) \geq 7$ and $\gamma^p(T) = 5$, yielding $\gamma_R^p(T) > \gamma^p(T) + 1$. Hence assume that T' is nontrivial. Clearly, any $\gamma^p(T')$-set can be extended to a PDS of T by adding v_2, v_3, v_4, v_5, v_6 and thus $\gamma^p(T) \leq \gamma^p(T') + 5$. On the other hand, it is not hard to see that $\gamma_R^p(T) \geq \gamma_R^p(T') + 7$. By the induction hypothesis we obtain $\gamma_R^p(T) > \gamma^p(T) + 1$.

Assume now that $\deg_T(v_6) \geq 3$. By above Cases and Subcases, we may assume that any child of v_6 is a leaf, or a vertex with depth j whose maximal subtree is isomorphic to $T_{v_{j+1}}$ for $j = 2, 3, 4$. Let T' be a tree obtained from T by removing v_3, w', v_4, z, v_5, z' and joining v_2 to v_6. Clearly, any $\gamma^p(T')$-set contains v_2, v_6 and such a set can be extended to a PDS of T by v_3, v_4, v_5 yielding $\gamma^p(T) \leq \gamma^p(T') + 3$. Now, let f be a $\gamma_R^p(T)$-function, and let $r = f(v_3) + f(w') + f(v_4) + f(z) + f(v_5) + f(z')$. To Roman dominate the vertices v_3, w', v_4, z, v_5, z', we must have $r \geq 5$ when $f(v_5) \leq 1$ or $r = 4$ when $f(v_5) = 2$. If $r = 4$ or $r \geq 5$ and $f(v_6) \geq 1$, then the function f restricted to T' is a PRDF on T' implying that $\gamma_R^p(T) \geq \gamma_R^p(T') + 4$. Hence assume that $r \geq 5$ and $f(v_6) = 0$. Then the function $h : V(T') \to \{0, 1, 2\}$ defined by $h(v_6) = 1$ and $h(x) = f(x)$ otherwise, is a PRDF on T' yielding $\gamma_R^p(T) \geq \gamma_R^p(T') + 4$. By the induction hypothesis we obtain

$$\gamma_R^p(T) \geq \gamma_R^p(T') + 4 \geq \gamma^p(T') + 1 + 4 \geq \gamma^p(T) - 3 + 5 > \gamma^p(T) + 1,$$

and the proof is complete.

□

According to Lemma 2 and Theorem 2, we have proven Theorem 1.

Author Contributions: Z.S. and S.M.S. contribute for supervision, methodology, validation, project administration and formal analyzing. S.K., M.C., M.S. contribute for investigation, resources, some computations and wrote the initial draft of the paper which were investigated and approved by Z.S. and M.C. wrote the final draft. All authors have read and agreed to the published version of the manuscript.

Funding: This work was supported by the National Key R & D Program of China (Grant No. 2019YFA0706402) and the Natural Science Foundation of Guangdong Province under grant 2018A0303130115.

Conflicts of Interest: The authors declare no conflict of interest.

References

1. Livingston, M.; Stout, Q.F. Perfect dominating set. *Congr. Numer.* **1990**, *79*, 187–203.
2. Chaluvaraju, B.; Chellali, M.; Vidya, K.A. Perfect *k*-domination in graphs. *Australas. J. Comb.* **2010**, *48*, 175–184.
3. Cockayne, E.J.; Hartnell, B.L.; Hedetniemi, S.T.; Laskar, R. Perfect domination in graphs. *J. Comb. Inform. System Sci.* **1993**, *18*, 136–148.
4. Dejter, I.J.; Pujol, J. Perfect Domination and Symmetry. *Congr. Numer.* **1995**, *111*, 18–32.
5. Fellows, M.R.; Hoover, M.N. Perfect domination. *Australas. J. Comb.* **1991**, *3*, 141–150.
6. Li, Z.; Shao, Z.; Rao, Y.; Wu, P.; Wang, S. The characterization of perfect Roman domination stable trees. *arXiv* **2018**, arXiv:1806.03164.
7. Cockayne, E.J.; Dreyer, P.A., Jr.; Hedetniemic, S.M.; Hedetniemic, S.T. Roman domination in graphs. *Discrete Math.* **2004**, *278*, 11–22. [CrossRef]
8. Revelle, C.S.; Rosing, K.E. Defendens imperium romanum: A classical problem in military strategy. *Am. Math. Monthly* **2000**, *107*, 585–594. [CrossRef]
9. Stewart, I. Defend the Roman Empire. *Sci. Am.* **1999**, *281*, 136–139. [CrossRef]
10. Henning, M.A.; Klostermeyer, W.F.; MacGillivray, G. Perfect Roman domination in trees. *Discrete Appl. Math.* **2018**, *236*, 235–245. [CrossRef]
11. Alhevaz, A.; Darkooti, M.; Rahbani, H.; Shang, Y. Strong equality of perfect Roman and weak Roman domination in trees. *Mathematics* **2019**, *7*, 997. [CrossRef]
12. Chellali, M.; Sheikholeslami, S.M.; Soroudi, M. A characterization of perfect Roman trees. *Discrete Appl. Math.* **2020**, submitted.
13. Henning, M.A.; Klostermeyer, W.F. Perfect Roman domination in regular graphs. *Appl. Anal. Discrete Math.* **2018**, *12*, 143–152. [CrossRef]
14. Chellali, M.; Jafari Rad, N.; Sheikholeslami, S.M.; Volkmann, L. Roman domination in graphs. In *Topics in Domination in Graphs*; Haynes, T.W., Hedetniemi, S.T., Henning, M.A., Eds.; Springer: Basel, Switzerland, 2020.
15. Chellali, M.; Jafari Rad, N.; Sheikholeslami, S.M.; Volkmann, L. Varieties of Roman domination. In *Structures of Domination in Graphs*; Haynes, T.W., Hedetniemi, S.T., Henning, M.A., Eds.; 2020, to appear.

16. Chellali, M.; Jafari Rad, N.; Sheikholeslami, S.M.; Volkmann, L. Varieties of Roman domination II. *AKCE J. Graphs Comb.* **2020**, to appear.

17. Chellali, M.; Jafari Rad, N.; Sheikholeslami, S.M.; Volkmann, L. A survey on Roman domination parameters in directed graphs. *J. Combin. Math. Comb. Comput.* **2020**, to appear.

18. Chellali, M.; Jafari Rad, N.; Sheikholeslami, S.M.; Volkmann, L. The Roman domatic problem in graphs and digraphs: A survey. *Discuss. Math. Graph Theory* **2020**. [CrossRef]

Article

Secure Total Domination in Rooted Product Graphs

Abel Cabrera Martínez, Alejandro Estrada-Moreno and Juan A. Rodríguez-Velázquez *

Departament d'Enginyeria Informàtica i Matemàtiques, Universitat Rovira i Virgili, Av. Països Catalans 26, 43007 Tarragona, Spain; abel.cabrera@urv.cat (A.C.M.); alejandro.estrada@urv.cat (A.E.-M.)
* Correspondence: juanalberto.rodriguez@urv.cat

Received: 16 March 2020; Accepted: 14 April 2020; Published: 15 April 2020

Abstract: In this article, we obtain general bounds and closed formulas for the secure total domination number of rooted product graphs. The results are expressed in terms of parameters of the factor graphs involved in the rooted product.

Keywords: secure total domination; total domination; domination; rooted product graph

---

1. Introduction

Recently, many authors have considered the following approach to the problem of protecting a graph [1–7]: suppose that one "entity" is stationed at some of the vertices of a (simple) graph G and that an entity at a vertex can deal with a problem at any vertex in its closed neighbourhood. In general, an entity could consist of a robot, an observer, a legion, a guard, and so on. Informally, we say that a graph G is protected under a given placement of entities if there exists at least one entity available to handle a problem at any vertex. Various strategies (or rules for entities placements) have been considered, under each of which the graph is deemed protected. As we can expect, the minimum number of entities required for protection under each strategy is of interest. Among these strategies we cite, for instance, domination [8,9], total domination [10], secure domination [1], secure total domination [2], Roman domination [6,7], Italian domination, [11] and weak Roman domination [5]. The first four strategies are described below.

The simplest strategies of graph protection are the strategy of domination and the strategy of total domination. In such cases, the sets of vertices containing the entities are dominating sets and total dominating sets, respectively. Typically, a vertex in a graph $G = (V(G), E(G))$ dominates itself and its neighbouring vertices. A set $S \subseteq V(G)$ is said to be a dominating set of G if every vertex in $V(G) \setminus S$ is dominated by at least one vertex in S, while S is said to be a total dominating set if every vertex $v \in V(G)$ is dominated by at least one vertex in $S \setminus \{v\}$.

The minimum cardinality among all dominating sets of G is the domination number of G, denoted by $\gamma(G)$. The total domination number, denoted by $\gamma_t(G)$, is defined by analogy. These two parameters have been extensively studied. For instance, we cite the following books, [8–10].

Let $N(v)$ be the open neighbourhood of $v \in V(G)$ and let $S \subseteq V(G)$. In the case of the secure (total) domination strategy, a vertex $v \in V(G) \setminus S$ is deemed (totally) protected under $S \subseteq V(G)$ if S is a (total) dominating set and there exists $u \in N(v) \cap S$ such that $(S \cup \{v\}) \setminus \{u\}$ is a (total) dominating set. In such a case, in order to emphasise the role of vertex u, we say that v is (totally) protected by u under S. A set $S \subseteq V(G)$ is said to be a secure (total) dominating set if every vertex in $v \in V(G) \setminus S$ is (totally) protected under S.

For instance, let G be the graph shown in Figure 1, and suppose that an observer is stationed at vertex a and another one is stationed at b. In such a case, the graph is under the control of the observers, as its vertices are (i.e., $\{a, b\}$ is a dominating set). Now, if the observer stationed at vertex a moves to any vertex in $\{c, d, e\}$, then the graph is under the control of the observers as well. In this case, $\{a, b\}$ is a secure dominating set. Furthermore, if there are three observers and they are stationed at a, b, and c, then every vertex of the graph (including a, b, and c) is under the control of the observers, and this property is preserved if the observer stationed at c moves to d or e. Hence, $\{a,b,c\}$ is a secure total dominating set.

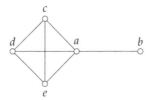

Figure 1. In this case, $\{a\}$ is a dominating set, $\{a,b\}$ is a total dominating set and also a secure dominating set, while $\{a,b,c\}$ is a secure total dominating set.

The minimum cardinality among all secure dominating sets of G is the secure domination number of G, denoted by $\gamma_s(G)$. This domination parameter was introduced by Cockayne et al. in [1] and studied further in a number of works including [12–17]. Now, the minimum cardinality among all secure total dominating sets of G is the secure total domination number of G, which is denoted by $\gamma_{st}(G)$. This parameter was introduced by Benecke et al. in [2] and studied further in [3,4,16,18,19].

A secure total dominating set of cardinality $\gamma_{st}(G)$ will be called a $\gamma_{st}(G)$-*set*. A similar agreement will be assumed when referring to optimal sets associated to other parameters used in the article.

The problem of computing $\gamma_{st}(G)$ is NP-hard [18], even when restricted to chordal bipartite graphs, planar bipartite graphs with arbitrary large girth and maximum degree three, split graphs and graphs of separability at most two. This suggests finding the secure total domination number for special classes of graphs or obtaining tight bounds on this invariant. This is precisely the aim of this article in which we study the case of rooted product graphs.

2. Some Notation and Tools

All graphs considered in this paper are finite and undirected, without loops or multiple edges. The minimum degree of a graph G will be denoted by $\delta(G)$, i.e., $\delta(G) = \min_{v \in V(G)} |N(v)|$. As usual, the closed neighbourhood of a vertex $v \in V(G)$ is denoted by $N[v] = N(v) \cup \{v\}$. We say that a vertex $v \in V(G)$ is a universal vertex if $N[v] = V(G)$. By analogy with the notation used for vertices, the open neighbourhood of $S \subseteq V(G)$ is the set $N(S) = \cup_{v \in S} N(v)$, while the closed neighbourhood is the set $N[S] = N(S) \cup S$.

A set $S \subseteq V(G)$ is a double dominating set of G if $|N[u] \cap S| \geq 2$ for every $u \in V(G)$. The double domination number of G, denoted by $\gamma_{\times 2}(G)$, is the minimum cardinality among all double dominating sets of G. The k-domination number of a graph G, denoted by $\gamma_k(G)$, is the cardinality of a smallest set of vertices such that every vertex not in the set is adjacent to at least k vertices of the set. Such sets are called k-dominating sets.

Remark 1. *Every secure total dominating set is a double dominating set and every double dominating set is a 2-dominating set. Therefore, for any graph G with no isolated vertex, $\gamma_{st}(G) \geq \gamma_{\times 2}(G) \geq \gamma_2(G)$.*

By Remark 1, for every secure total dominating set S and every vertex $v \in S$, the set $S \setminus \{v\}$ is a dominating set. Therefore, the following remark holds.

Remark 2. *For every graph G with no isolated vertex, $\gamma_{st}(G) \geq \gamma(G) + 1$.*

A *leaf* of G is a vertex of degree one. A support vertex of G is a vertex which is adjacent to a leaf and a strong support vertex is a support vertex which is adjacent to at least two leaves. A leaf is said to be a strong leaf if it is adjacent to a strong support vertex, otherwise it is called a weak leaf. The set of leaves, support vertices, strong leaves and weak leaves are denoted by $\mathcal{L}(G)$, $\mathcal{S}(G)$, $\mathcal{L}_s(G)$, and $\mathcal{L}_w(G)$, respectively.

Remark 3. *If D is a secure total dominating set of a graph G, then* $(\mathcal{S}(G) \cup \mathcal{L}(G)) \subseteq D$ *and no vertex of G is totally protected under D by vertices in* $\mathcal{S}(G) \cup \mathcal{L}(G)$.

If v is a vertex of a graph H, then the vertex-deletion subgraph $H - \{v\}$ is the subgraph of H induced by $V(H) \setminus \{v\}$. In Section 3 we will show the importance of $\gamma_{st}(H - \{v\})$ in the study of the secure total domination number of rooted product graphs. Now we proceed to state some basic tools.

Lemma 1. *Let H be a graph with no isolated vertex. If* $v \in V(H) \setminus (\mathcal{L}_w(H) \cup \mathcal{S}(H))$, *then*

$$\gamma_{st}(H - \{v\}) \geq \gamma_{st}(H) - 2.$$

Furthermore, if $\gamma_{st}(H - \{v\}) > \gamma_{st}(H)$, *then v belongs to every* $\gamma_{st}(H)$-*set.*

Proof. Assume that $v \in V(H) \setminus (\mathcal{L}_w(H) \cup \mathcal{S}(H))$ and let D be a $\gamma_{st}(H - \{v\})$-set. Suppose that $|D| \leq \gamma_{st}(H) - 3$. If $|N(v) \cap D| \geq 2$, then $D \cup \{v\}$ is a secure total dominating set of H of cardinality $|D \cup \{v\}| \leq \gamma_{st}(H) - 2$, which is a contradiction. Suppose that $|N(v) \cap D| \leq 1$. If $v \notin \mathcal{L}(H)$, then for every $y \in N(v) \setminus D$ we have that $D \cup \{v, y\}$ is a secure total dominating set of H of cardinality $|D \cup \{v, y\}| \leq \gamma_{st}(H) - 1$, which is a contradiction. Now, if $v \in \mathcal{L}_s(H)$, then by Remark 3 we can conclude that $D \cup \{v\}$ is a secure total dominating set of H of cardinality $|D \cup \{v\}| \leq \gamma_{st}(H) - 2$, which is a contradiction again. Hence, $\gamma_{st}(H - \{v\}) = |D| \geq \gamma_{st}(H) - 2$.

On the other hand, if there exists a $\gamma_{st}(H)$-set S such that $v \notin S$, then S is a secure total dominating set of $H - \{v\}$, and so $\gamma_{st}(H - \{v\}) \leq |S| = \gamma_{st}(H)$. Therefore, if $\gamma_{st}(H - \{v\}) > \gamma_{st}(H)$, then $v \in S$ for every $\gamma_{st}(H)$-set S. $\square$

If v is a weak leaf of H, then it could be that $\gamma_{st}(H) \geq \gamma_{st}(H - \{v\}) + 2$. For instance, Figure 2 shows the existence of cases in which the gap $\gamma_{st}(H) - \gamma_{st}(H - \{v\})$ is arbitrarily large. In Remark 4 we highlight this fact.

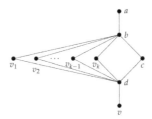

Figure 2. A graph H where $V(H)$ is the $\gamma_{st}(H)$-set. Since $\{a, b, c, d\}$ forms a $\gamma_{st}(H - \{v\})$-set, we have that $\gamma_{st}(H) - \gamma_{st}(H - \{v\}) = k + 1$ for every integer $k \geq 1$.

Remark 4. *For any integer* $k \geq 1$ *there exists a graph H having a weak leaf vertex v such that* $\gamma_{st}(H) - \gamma_{st}(H - \{v\}) = k + 1$.

In contrast to Remark 4, the following result shows the case where v is a strong leaf.

Lemma 2. *Let H be a graph with no isolated vertex. If* $v \in \mathcal{L}_s(H)$, *then*

$$\gamma_{st}(H - \{v\}) = \gamma_{st}(H) - 1.$$

Proof. Let D be a $\gamma_{st}(H)$-set, $v \in \mathcal{L}_s(H)$ and $N(v) = \{s_v\}$. By Remark 3 we deduce that $D \setminus \{v\}$ is a secure total dominating set of $H - \{v\}$ and so $\gamma_{st}(H - \{v\}) \leq |D \setminus \{v\}| \leq \gamma_{st}(H) - 1$. Now, let D' be a $\gamma_{st}(H - \{v\})$-set. Since $s_v \in S(H - \{v\})$, by Remark 3 we have that $s_v \in D'$ and no vertex of $H - \{v\}$ is totally protected by s_v under D', which implies that $D' \cup \{v\}$ is a secure total dominating set of H and, as a result, $\gamma_{st}(H) - 1 \leq |D' \cup \{v\}| - 1 = |D'| = \gamma_{st}(H - \{v\})$. Therefore, $\gamma_{st}(H - \{v\}) = \gamma_{st}(H) - 1$. $\square$

Lemma 3. *For any graph H having a universal vertex v,*

$$\gamma_{st}(H) = \gamma(H - \{v\}) + 1.$$

Proof. Let D be a $\gamma(H - \{v\})$-set. Since v is a universal vertex of H, it is straightforward that $D \cup \{v\}$ is a secure total dominating set of H. Thus, $\gamma_{st}(H) \leq |D \cup \{v\}| = \gamma(H - \{v\}) + 1$.

From now on, suppose that $\gamma_{st}(H) \leq \gamma(H - \{v\})$ and let S be a $\gamma_{st}(H)$-set. We differentiate the following two cases.

Case 1. $v \in S$. In this case, as $|S| \leq \gamma(H - \{v\})$, we deduce that $S \setminus \{v\}$ is not a dominating set of $H - \{v\}$. Hence, there exists a vertex $y \in V(H - \{v\})$ such that $N(y) \cap S = \{v\}$, which is a contradiction, as S is a 2-dominating set, by Remark 1.

Case 2. $v \notin S$. In this case, S is a secure total dominating set of $H - \{v\}$ and so $\gamma_{st}(H - \{v\}) \leq |S| \leq \gamma(H - \{v\})$, which is a contradiction with Remark 2.

Therefore, the result follows. $\square$

3. The Case of Rooted Product Graphs

Given a graph G of order $n(G)$ and a graph H with root vertex v, the rooted product graph $G \circ_v H$ is defined as the graph obtained from G and H by taking one copy of G and $n(G)$ copies of H and identifying the ith vertex of G with the root vertex v in the ith copy of H for every $i \in \{1, 2, \ldots, n(G)\}$.

If H or G is a trivial graph, then $G \circ_v H$ is equal to G or H, respectively. In this sense, hereafter we will only consider graphs G and H of order greater than or equal to two.

For every $x \in V(G)$, $H_x \cong H$ will denote the copy of H in $G \circ_v H$ containing x. The restriction of any set $S \subseteq V(G \circ_v H)$ to $V(H_x)$ will be denoted by S_x, and the restriction to $V(H_x - \{x\})$ will be denoted by S_x^-. Hence, $V(G \circ_v H) = \bigcup_{x \in V(G)} V(H_x)$ and for every $\gamma_{st}(G \circ_v H)$-set S we have that

$$\gamma_{st}(G \circ_v H) = |S| = \sum_{x \in V(G)} |S_x| = \sum_{x \in V(G)} |S_x^-| + |S \cap V(G)|.$$

Theorem 1. *For any graphs G and H with no isolated vertex and any $v \in V(H)$,*

$$\gamma_{st}(G \circ_v H) \leq n(G)\gamma_{st}(H).$$

Furthermore, if $v \notin S(H)$, then

$$\gamma_{st}(G \circ_v H) \leq \gamma_{st}(G) + n(G)\gamma_{st}(H - \{v\}).$$

Proof. Let D be a $\gamma_{st}(H)$-set and $S \subseteq V(G \circ_v H)$ such that S_x is the subset of $V(H_x)$ induced by D for every $x \in V(G)$. Since S is a secure total dominating set of $G \circ_v H$, we deduce that $\gamma_{st}(G \circ_v H) \leq \sum_{x \in V(G)} |S_x| = n(G)\gamma_{st}(H)$.

Now, assume that $v \notin S(H)$. Let W be a $\gamma_{st}(H - \{v\})$-set and $S' \subseteq V(G \circ_v H) \setminus V(G)$ such that S_x' is the subset of $V(H_x - \{x\})$ induced by W for every $x \in V(G)$. Since for any $\gamma_{st}(G)$-set X, we have that $X \cup S'$ is a secure total dominating set of $G \circ_v H$, we deduce that $\gamma_{st}(G \circ_v H) \leq |X \cup S'| = \gamma_{st}(G) + n(G)\gamma_{st}(H - \{v\})$. $\square$

We now proceed to analyse three cases in which it is not difficult to give closed formulas for $\gamma_{st}(G \circ_v H)$. Specifically, we consider the cases in which the root vertex v is a support vertex, a strong leaf, or a universal vertex.

Theorem 2. *The following statements hold for any graphs G and H with no isolated vertex.*

(i)   *If $v \in S(H)$, then $\gamma_{st}(G \circ_v H) = n(G)\gamma_{st}(H)$. Furthermore, $|D_x| = \gamma_{st}(H)$ for every $\gamma_{st}(G \circ_v H)$-set D and every $x \in V(G)$.*

(ii) *If $v \in V(H)$ is a universal vertex, then $\gamma_{st}(G \circ_v H) = n(G)\gamma_{st}(H)$.*

(iii) *If $v \in \mathcal{L}_s(H)$, then $\gamma_{st}(G \circ_v H) = \gamma(G) + n(G)(\gamma_{st}(H) - 1)$.*

Proof. Let D be a $\gamma_{st}(G \circ_v H)$-set. Let us first consider the case where $v \in S(H)$. Since $x \in S(G \circ_v H)$ for every $x \in V(G)$, by Remark 3 we deduce that D_x is a secure total dominating set of H_x, and as a consequence $|D_x| \geq \gamma_{st}(H_x)$ for every $x \in V(G)$. Hence, $\gamma_{st}(G \circ_v H) = \sum_{x \in V(G)} |D_x| \geq n(G)\gamma_{st}(H)$. Now, if $|D_x| \geq \gamma_{st}(H_x) + 1$ for some $x \in V(G)$, then $\gamma_{st}(G \circ_v H) > n(G)\gamma_{st}(H)$, which contradicts Theorem 1. Therefore, (i) follows.

Let us now consider the case where $v \notin S(H)$ is a universal vertex. Let $x \in V(G)$. If $x \in D_x$, then D_x is a secure total dominating set of H_x and, as a result, $|D_x| \geq \gamma_{st}(H_x)$. Now, if $x \notin D_x$, then D_x^- is a secure total dominating set of $H_x - \{x\}$, and so Remark 2 and Lemma 3 lead to $|D_x| \geq \gamma_{st}(H_x - \{x\}) \geq \gamma(H_x - \{x\}) + 1 = \gamma_{st}(H_x)$. Hence, $\gamma_{st}(G \circ_v H) = \sum_{x \in V(G)} |D_x| \geq n(G)\gamma_{st}(H)$ and (ii) follows by Theorem 1.

From now on we assume that $v \in \mathcal{L}_s(H)$. Let $s_x \in V(H_x)$ be the support of x in H_x for every $x \in V(G)$. Since $x \in \mathcal{L}_s(H_x)$, we have that $s_x \in S(H_x - \{x\}) \cap D$. Hence, by Remark 3 we deduce that D_x^- is a secure total dominating set of $H_x - \{x\}$, and by Lemma 2 we have that $|D_x^-| \geq \gamma_{st}(H_x - \{x\}) = \gamma_{st}(H) - 1$. Moreover, since $N(x) \cap D_x = \{s_x\}$ for every $x \in V(G)$, by Remark 1 it follows that every vertex in $V(G) \setminus D$ has to have a neighbour in $V(G) \cap D$, which implies that $V(G) \cap D$ is a dominating set of G. Therefore, $\gamma_{st}(G \circ_v H) = |D| = |D \cap V(G)| + \left| \bigcup_{x \in V(G)} D_x^- \right| \geq \gamma(G) + n(G)(\gamma_{st}(H) - 1)$.

It remains to show that $\gamma_{st}(G \circ_v H) \leq \gamma(G) + n(G)(\gamma_{st}(H) - 1)$. To this end, let X be a $\gamma(G)$-set, Y a $\gamma_{st}(H - \{v\})$-set, and $W \subseteq V(G \circ_v H) \setminus V(G)$ such that W_x is the subset of $V(H_x - \{x\})$ induced by Y for every $x \in V(G)$. Notice that $s_x \in W_x$. In order to show that $S = X \cup W$ is a secure total dominating set of $G \circ_v H$, we only need to observe that every vertex in $V(G) \setminus S$ is totally protected under S by any neighbour in X, while every $w \in V(H_x) \setminus W_x$ is totally protected under S by some neighbour in W_x. Thus, $\gamma_{st}(G \circ_v H) \leq |S| = \gamma(G) + n(G)\gamma_{st}(H - \{v\})$, and by Lemma 2 we deduce that $\gamma_{st}(G \circ_v H) \leq \gamma(G) + n(G)(\gamma_{st}(H) - 1)$. Therefore, (iii) follows. $\square$

Given two graphs G and G', the corona graph $G \odot G'$ can be seen as a rooted product graph $G \circ_v H$ where H is the join (The join graph $G' + G''$ is the graph obtained from G' and G'' by joining each vertex of G' to all vertices of G'') graph $K_1 + H$ and v is the vertex of K_1. Therefore, Lemma 3 and Theorem 2 (ii) lead to the following result on corona graphs.

Theorem 3. *If G is a graph with no isolated vertex, then for every nontrivial graph G',*

$$\gamma_{st}(G \odot G') = n(G)(\gamma(G') + 1).$$

As we will see later, the behaviour of $\gamma_{st}(G \circ_v H)$ changes depending on whether the root vertex v is a weak leaf or not. First we proceed to consider the cases where the root vertex is not a weak leaf.

Lemma 4. *Let S be a $\gamma_{st}(G \circ_v H)$-set and $x \in V(G)$. If $v \notin \mathcal{L}_w(H)$, then the following statements hold.*

- $|S_x| \geq \gamma_{st}(H) - 2$.
- *If $|S_x| = \gamma_{st}(H) - 2$, then $N[x] \cap S_x = \emptyset$.*

Proof. Let $x \in V(G)$. Notice that every vertex in $V(H_x) \setminus (S \cup \{x\})$ is totally protected under S by some vertex in S_x. Now, suppose that $|S_x| \leq \gamma_{st}(H) - 3$ and let $y \in N(x) \cap V(H_x)$. If $y \notin S_x$, then $S_x \cup \{x, y\}$ is a secure total dominating set of H_x of cardinality at most $\gamma_{st}(H) - 1$, which is a contradiction. Assume that $N(x) \cap V(H_x) \subseteq S_x$. If $N(x) \cap V(H_x) = \{y\}$, then $x \in \mathcal{L}_s(H_x)$ and $y \in \mathcal{S}(G \circ_v H)$. Thus, by Remark 3 no vertex in $V(H_x)$ is totally protected by y under S, and so $S_x \cup \{x\}$ is a secure total dominating set of H_x of cardinality at most $\gamma_{st}(H) - 2$, which is a contradiction. Finally, if $|N(x) \cap V(H_x)| \geq 2$, then $S_x \cup \{x\}$ is a secure total dominating set of H_x and, as above, we arrive to a contradiction. Therefore, $|S_x| \geq \gamma_{st}(H) - 2$.

Now, assume that $|S_x| = \gamma_{st}(H) - 2$. First, suppose that $x \in S$. Notice that if $N(x) \cap V(H_x) \subseteq S_x$, then S_x is a secure total dominating set of H_x, which is a contradiction. Hence, there exists $y \in (N(x) \cap V(H_x)) \setminus S_x$, and so $S_x \cup \{y\}$ is a secure total dominating set of H_x and $|S_x \cup \{y\}| = \gamma_{st}(H) - 1$, which is a contradiction. Thus, $x \notin S$. Now, suppose that $N(x) \cap S_x \neq \emptyset$. If there exists $z \in (N(x) \cap V(H_x)) \setminus S_x$, then $S_x \cup \{z\}$ is a secure total dominating set of H_x and $|S_x \cup \{z\}| = \gamma_{st}(H) - 1$, which is a contradiction. Now, if $N(x) \cap V(H_x) \subseteq S_x$, then one can easily check that $S_x \cup \{x\}$ is a secure total dominating set of H_x, which is a contradiction again, as $|S_x \cup \{x\}| = \gamma_{st}(H) - 1$. Therefore, $N(x) \cap V(H_x) \cap S = \emptyset$. $\square$

From Lemma 4 we deduce that if $v \notin \mathcal{L}_w(H)$, then any $\gamma_{st}(G \circ_v H)$-set S induces a partition $\{\mathcal{A}_S, \mathcal{B}_S, \mathcal{C}_S\}$ of $V(G)$ as follows.

$$\mathcal{A}_S = \{x \in V(G) : |S_x| \geq \gamma_{st}(H)\},$$

$$\mathcal{B}_S = \{x \in V(G) : |S_x| = \gamma_{st}(H) - 1\},$$

$$\mathcal{C}_S = \{x \in V(G) : |S_x| = \gamma_{st}(H) - 2\}.$$

The following corollary is a direct consequence of Theorem 2 (i).

Corollary 1. *Let S be a $\gamma_{st}(G \circ_v H)$-set. If $\mathcal{B}_S \cup \mathcal{C}_S \neq \emptyset$, then $v \notin \mathcal{S}(H)$.*

Lemma 5. *Let S be a $\gamma_{st}(G \circ_v H)$-set, where $v \notin \mathcal{L}_w(H)$. If $\mathcal{C}_S \neq \emptyset$, then $\gamma_{st}(H - \{v\}) = \gamma_{st}(H) - 2$.*

Proof. By Lemma 4, if $x \in \mathcal{C}_S$, then $N[x] \cap S_x = \emptyset$, which implies that S_x^- is a secure total dominating set of $H_x - \{x\}$ of cardinality $|S_x^-| = |S_x| = \gamma_{st}(H_x) - 2$. Hence, $x \notin \mathcal{S}(H_x)$ and $\gamma_{st}(H_x - \{x\}) \leq |S_x^-| = \gamma_{st}(H_x) - 2$. Notice that Lemma 2 leads to $x \notin \mathcal{L}_s(H_x)$. Thus, by Lemma 1 we conclude that $\gamma_{st}(H_x - \{x\}) = \gamma_{st}(H_x) - 2$. Therefore, the result follows. $\square$

The following result states the intervals in which the secure total domination number of a rooted product graph can be found.

Theorem 4. *Let G and H be two graphs with no isolated vertex. At least one of the following statements holds for every $v \in V(H) \setminus \mathcal{L}_w(H)$.*

(i) $\gamma_{st}(G \circ_v H) = n(G)\gamma_{st}(H)$.
(ii) $n(G)(\gamma_{st}(H) - 1) \leq \gamma_{st}(G \circ_v H) \leq \gamma_{st}(G) + n(G)(\gamma_{st}(H) - 1)$.
(iii) $\gamma_{\times 2}(G) + n(G)(\gamma_{st}(H) - 2) \leq \gamma_{st}(G \circ_v H) \leq \gamma_{st}(G) + n(G)(\gamma_{st}(H) - 2)$.

Proof. Let S be a $\gamma_{st}(G \circ_v H)$-set and consider the partition $\{\mathcal{A}_S, \mathcal{B}_S, \mathcal{C}_S\}$ of $V(G)$ defined above. We differentiate the following four cases.

Case 1. $\mathcal{B}_S \cup \mathcal{C}_S = \emptyset$. In this case, for any $x \in V(G)$ we have that $|S_x| \geq \gamma_{st}(H)$ and, as a consequence, $\gamma_{st}(G \circ_v H) \geq n(G)\gamma_{st}(H)$. Thus, Theorem 1 leads to (i).

Case 2. $\mathcal{B}_S \neq \emptyset$ and $\mathcal{C}_S = \emptyset$. In this case, for any $x \in V(G)$ we have that $|S_x| \geq \gamma_{st}(H) - 1$ and, as a result, $\gamma_{st}(G \circ_v H) \geq n(G)(\gamma_{st}(H) - 1)$.

In order to conclude the proof of (ii), we proceed to show that $\gamma_{st}(G \circ_v H) \leq \gamma_{st}(G) + n(G)(\gamma_{st}(H) - 1)$. To this end, we fix $x' \in \mathcal{B}_S$, $y_{x'} \in V(H_{x'}) \cap N(x')$, a $\gamma_{st}(G)$-set D and define a subset W of vertices of $G \circ_v H$ as follows.

(a) If $x' \notin S$, then for any $x \in V(G)$ we set $W \cap V(G) = D$ and W_x^- is induced by $S_x^- = S_{x'}$. It is readily seen that the set W constructed in this manner is a secure total dominating set of $G \circ_v H$ and so $\gamma_{st}(G \circ_v H) \leq |W| = |D| + n(G)|S_{x'}| = \gamma_{st}(G) + n(G)(\gamma_{st}(H) - 1)$.

(b) Assume that $x' \in S$. If $x \in V(G) \setminus \mathcal{L}(G)$, then W_x is induced by $S_{x'}$, while if $x \in \mathcal{L}(G)$, then W_x is induced by $S_{x'} \cup \{y_{x'}\}$. It is readily seen that the set W constructed in this manner is a secure total dominating set of $G \circ_v H$ and, as a result, $\gamma_{st}(G \circ_v H) \leq |W| = |\mathcal{L}(G)| + n(G)|S_{x'}| \leq \gamma_{st}(G) + n(G)(\gamma_{st}(H) - 1)$.

Case 3. $\mathcal{B}_S = \emptyset$ and $\mathcal{C}_S \neq \emptyset$. By Corollary 1, $v \notin S(H)$, and by Lemma 5 we have that $\gamma_{st}(H - \{v\}) = \gamma_{st}(H) - 2$. Hence, by Theorem 1 we conclude that $\gamma_{st}(G \circ_v H) \leq \gamma_{st}(G) + n(G)(\gamma_{st}(H) - 2)$.

From Lemma 4 we deduce that $\mathcal{A}_S$ is a 2-dominating set of G. Hence, $\gamma_{st}(G \circ_v H) \geq |\mathcal{A}_S|\gamma_{st}(H) + |\mathcal{C}_S|(\gamma_{st}(H) - 2) = 2|\mathcal{A}_S| + n(G)(\gamma_{st}(H) - 2) \geq 2\gamma_2(G) + n(G)(\gamma_{st}(H) - 2) \geq \gamma_{\times 2}(G) + n(G)(\gamma_{st}(H) - 2)$. Therefore, in this case (iii) holds.

Case 4. $\mathcal{B}_S \neq \emptyset$ and $\mathcal{C}_S \neq \emptyset$. By Corollary 1, $v \notin S(H)$, and by Lemma 5, $\gamma_{st}(H - \{v\}) = \gamma_{st}(H) - 2$. Thus, by Theorem 1 we conclude that $\gamma_{st}(G \circ_v H) \leq \gamma_{st}(G) + n(G)(\gamma_{st}(H) - 2)$.

In order to conclude that in this case (iii) holds, let us define a double dominating set D of G such that $|D| \leq 2|\mathcal{A}_S| + |\mathcal{B}_S|$. Set D has minimum cardinality among the sets satisfying that $\mathcal{A}_S \cup \mathcal{B}_S \subseteq D$ and for any $x \in \mathcal{A}_S$, if $N(x) \cap \mathcal{C}_S \neq \emptyset$, then there exists $x' \in N(x) \cap \mathcal{C}_S \cap D$. Notice that every vertex in $\mathcal{A}_S$ is dominated by at least one vertex in D and, by Lemma 4, every vertex in $\mathcal{C}_S$ is dominated by at least two vertices in $\mathcal{A}_S \cup \mathcal{B}_S \subseteq D$. Furthermore, if there exists one vertex $x \in \mathcal{B}_S$ such that $N(x) \cap \mathcal{A}_S \cap \mathcal{B}_S = \emptyset$, then S_x is a secure total dominating set of H_x, which is a contradiction, as $|S_x| = \gamma_{st}(H_x) - 1$. Hence, D is a double dominating set of G. Therefore, $\gamma_{st}(G \circ_v H) = |S| \geq |\mathcal{A}_S|\gamma_{st}(H) + |\mathcal{B}_S|(\gamma_{st}(H) - 1) + |\mathcal{C}_S|(\gamma_{st}(H) - 2) \geq |D| + n(G)(\gamma_{st}(H) - 2) \geq \gamma_{\times 2}(G) + n(G)(\gamma_{st}(H) - 2)$. $\square$

The bounds given in the previous theorem are tight. To see this, we consider the following examples where H_1 and H_2 are the graphs shown in Figure 3.

- $\gamma_{st}(G \circ_v P_7) = n(G)(\gamma_{st}(P_7) - 1)$, where v is the central vertex of P_7 and G is a graph with $\delta(G) \geq 2$.
- $\gamma_{st}(K_r \circ_v H_1) = 2 + r(3 - 1) = \gamma_{st}(K_r) + n(K_r)(\gamma_{st}(H_1) - 1)$, where $r \geq 2$.
- Theorem 5 gives some conditions to achieve the equalities $\gamma_{st}(G \circ_v H) = \gamma_{st}(G) + n(G)(\gamma_{st}(H) - 2) = \gamma_{\times 2}(G) + n(G)(\gamma_{st}(H) - 2)$. In this case we can take $H \cong H_2$.

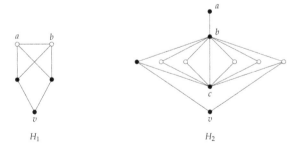

H_1 H_2

Figure 3. The set of black-coloured vertices forms a $\gamma_{st}(H_i)$-set for $i \in \{1, 2\}$. The set $\{a, b\}$ is a $\gamma_{st}(H_1 - \{v\})$-set, while $\{a, b, c\}$ is a $\gamma_{st}(H_2 - \{v\})$-set.

We now consider some particular cases in which we impose some additional restrictions on G and H. We begin with an immediate consequence of Theorem 4.

Theorem 5. *Let G and H be two graphs with no isolated vertex and $v \in V(H) \setminus \mathcal{L}_w(H)$. If $\gamma_{st}(H - \{v\}) = \gamma_{st}(H) - 2$ and $\gamma_{st}(G) = \gamma_{\times 2}(G)$, then*

$$\gamma_{st}(G \circ_v H) = \gamma_{st}(G) + n(G)(\gamma_{st}(H) - 2).$$

Proof. If $\gamma_{st}(H - \{v\}) = \gamma_{st}(H) - 2$, then $v \notin \mathcal{S}(H)$ and Theorem 1 leads to $\gamma_{st}(G \circ_v H) \leq \gamma_{st}(G) + n(G)(\gamma_{st}(H) - 2)$. Thus, by Theorem 4 we conclude that if $\gamma_{st}(G) = \gamma_{\times 2}(G)$, then $\gamma_{st}(G \circ_v H) = \gamma_{st}(G) + n(G)(\gamma_{st}(H) - 2)$. □

The following result considers the case in which $\gamma_{st}(H - \{v\}) \geq \gamma_{st}(H) - 1$.

Theorem 6. *Let G and H be two graphs with no isolated vertex and $v \in V(H) \setminus \mathcal{L}_w(H)$. If $\gamma_{st}(H - \{v\}) \geq \gamma_{st}(H) - 1$, then*

$$n(G)(\gamma_{st}(H) - 1) \leq \gamma_{st}(G \circ_v H) \leq n(G)\gamma_{st}(H).$$

Now, if $\delta(G) \geq 2$ and $\gamma_{st}(H - \{v\}) \geq \gamma_{st}(H)$, then $\gamma_{st}(G \circ_v H) = n(G)(\gamma_{st}(H) - 1)$ or $\gamma_{st}(G \circ_v H) = n(G)\gamma_{st}(H)$.

Proof. Let S be a $\gamma_{st}(G \circ_v H)$-set and assume that $\gamma_{st}(H - \{v\}) \geq \gamma_{st}(H) - 1$. By Lemma 5 we have that $\mathcal{C}_S = \varnothing$, and so Lemma 4 leads to $|S_x| \geq \gamma_{st}(H_x) - 1$ for every $x \in V(G)$. Thus, $\gamma_{st}(G \circ_v H) = \sum_{x \in V(G)} |S_x| \geq n(G)(\gamma_{st}(H) - 1)$. Therefore, Theorem 1 leads to $n(G)(\gamma_{st}(H) - 1) \leq \gamma_{st}(G \circ_v H) \leq n(G)\gamma_{st}(H)$.

From now on we assume that $\delta(G) \geq 2$ and $\gamma_{st}(H - \{v\}) \geq \gamma_{st}(H)$. Let us distinguish between two cases, according to whether or not $\gamma_{st}(H - \{v\}) > \gamma_{st}(H)$.

Case 1. $\gamma_{st}(H - \{v\}) > \gamma_{st}(H)$. We define a set $D \subseteq V(G \circ_v H)$ as follows. For any $x \in V(G) \setminus S$ we take $D \cap V(H_x)$ as a $\gamma_{st}(H_x)$-set, while for any $x \in V(G) \cap S$ we set $D \cap V(H_x) = S_x$. Notice that D is a secure total dominating set of $G \circ_v H$. Now, if there exists a vertex $x \in V(G) \setminus S$, then the set S_x^- is a secure total dominating set of $H_x - \{x\}$. Hence, $|S_x| = |S_x^-| \geq \gamma_{st}(H - \{x\}) > \gamma_{st}(H_x) = |D_x|$, and so $|D| < |S|$, which is a contradiction. Thus, $V(G) \subseteq S$.

If $|S_x| \geq \gamma_{st}(H)$ for every $x \in V(G)$, then Theorem 1 leads to $\gamma_{st}(G \circ_v H) = n(G)\gamma_{st}(H)$. Suppose that there exists a vertex $x \in V(G)$ such that $|S_x| \leq \gamma_{st}(H) - 1$. We define a set $D' \subseteq V(G \circ_v H)$ as follows. For every $z \in V(G)$, the restriction of D' to $V(H_z)$ is induced by S_x. Notice that $V(G) \subseteq D'$ and, if $\delta(G) \geq 2$, then every vertex in $V(H_z) \setminus D'$ is totally protected under D' by some vertex in D'_z, which implies that D' is a secure total dominating set of $G \circ_v H$. Therefore, $\gamma_{st}(G \circ_v H) \leq |D'| \leq n(G)(\gamma_{st}(H) - 1)$, concluding that $\gamma_{st}(G \circ_v H) = n(G)(\gamma_{st}(H) - 1)$.

Case 2. $\gamma_{st}(H - \{v\}) = \gamma_{st}(H)$. First, assume that $V(G) \cap S = \varnothing$. Since S_x^- is a secure total dominating set of $H_x - \{x\}$ for every $x \in V(G)$, we have that $\gamma_{st}(G \circ_v H) = \sum_{x \in V(G)} |S_x^-| \geq \sum_{x \in V(G)} \gamma_{st}(H - \{x\}) = n(G)\gamma_{st}(H - \{v\}) = n(G)\gamma_{st}(H)$, and so Theorem 1 leads to $\gamma_{st}(G \circ_v H) = n(G)\gamma_{st}(H)$.

Now, assume that there exists $y \in V(G) \cap S$. Notice that Lemma 5 leads to $\mathcal{C}_S = \varnothing$. Hence, $y \in \mathcal{A}_S \cup \mathcal{B}_S$. If $y \in \mathcal{B}_S$, we define a set $D' \subseteq V(G \circ_v H)$ as follows. For every $z \in V(G)$, the restriction of D' to $V(H_z)$ is induced by S_y. As in Case 1, we deduce that D' is a secure total dominating set of $G \circ_v H$ and so we can conclude that $\gamma_{st}(G \circ_v H) = |D'| = n(G)(\gamma_{st}(H) - 1)$. Finally, if $\mathcal{B}_S = \varnothing$, then $V(G) = \mathcal{A}_S$ and by Theorem 1 we conclude that $\gamma_{st}(G \circ_v H) = |S| = n(G)\gamma_{st}(H)$. □

Now, we consider a particular case in which $\gamma_{st}(H - \{v\}) = \gamma_{st}(H)$.

Theorem 7. *Let G be a graph with no isolated vertex. Let H be a graph and $v \in V(H)$ such that $\gamma_{st}(H - \{v\}) = \gamma_{st}(H)$. If $v \notin S$ for every $\gamma_{st}(H)$-set S, then*

$$\gamma_{st}(G \circ_v H) = n(G)\gamma_{st}(H).$$

Proof. Assume that $v \notin S$ for every $\gamma_{st}(H)$-set S. Notice that $v \notin \mathcal{L}(H) \cup \mathcal{S}(H)$. Let D be a $\gamma_{st}(G \circ_v H)$-set. By Lemma 5 we conclude that $\mathcal{C}_D = \emptyset$. Now, if $\mathcal{B}_D = \emptyset$, then by analogy to Case 1 in the proof of Theorem 4 it follows that $\gamma_{st}(G \circ_v H) = n(G)\gamma_{st}(H)$.

Suppose that there exists a vertex $x \in \mathcal{B}_D$. If $x \notin D$, then D_x^- is a secure total dominating set of $H_x - \{x\}$, which implies that $\gamma_{st}(H - \{v\}) = \gamma_{st}(H_x - \{x\}) \le |D_x^-| = |D_x| = \gamma_{st}(H) - 1$, which is a contradiction. Hence, $x \in D$. Now, if $N(x) \cap V(H_x) \subseteq D$, then D_x is a secure total dominating set of H_x and so $\gamma_{st}(H_x) \le |D_x| = \gamma_{st}(H_x) - 1$, which is a contradiction. Finally, if there exists $x' \in N(x) \cap V(H_x) \setminus D$, then $D_x' = D_x \cup \{x'\}$ is a secure total dominating set of H_x of cardinality $\gamma_{st}(H_x)$ and $x \in D_x'$, which is a contradiction again. Therefore, $\mathcal{B}_D = \emptyset$, and we are done. $\square$

The Case in Which the Root Vertex Is a Weak Leaf

The first part of this section is devoted to the case in which the support vertex of the root v has degree greater than or equal to three. From Remark 4 we learned that if $v \in \mathcal{L}_w(H)$, $N(v) = \{s\}$ and $|N(s)| \ge 3$, then the gap $\gamma_{st}(H) - \gamma_{st}(H - \{v\})$ could be arbitrarily large.

Remark 5. *Let H be a graph with no isolated vertex, $v \in \mathcal{L}_w(H)$ and $N(v) = \{s\}$. If $|N(s)| \ge 3$, then*

$$\gamma_{st}(H) \ge \gamma_{st}(H - \{v\}).$$

Proof. Let S be a $\gamma_{st}(H)$-set. By Remark 3, we have that $v, s \in S$. If $N(s) \subseteq S$, then since $|N(s)| \ge 3$, we deduce $S \setminus \{v\}$ is a secure total dominating set of $H - \{v\}$. Hence, $\gamma_{st}(H - \{v\}) \le |S \setminus \{v\}| < \gamma_{st}(H)$. Now, if there exists $u \in N(s) \setminus S$, then $(S \setminus \{v\}) \cup \{u\}$ is also a secure total dominating set of $H - \{v\}$. Thus, $\gamma_{st}(H - \{v\}) \le |(S \setminus \{v\}) \cup \{u\}| = \gamma_{st}(H)$. Therefore, the result follows. $\square$

By Remarks 4 and 5, it seems reasonable to express $\gamma_{st}(G \circ_v H)$ in terms of $\gamma_{st}(H - \{v\})$ rather than $\gamma_{st}(H)$. To this end, we consider the following lemma.

Lemma 6. *Let S be a $\gamma_{st}(G \circ_v H)$-set. If $v \in \mathcal{L}_w(H)$, $N(v) = \{s\}$ and $|N(s)| \ge 3$, then $|S_x| \ge \gamma_{st}(H - \{v\})$ for every $x \in V(G)$*

Proof. Let $x \in V(G)$. Notice that every vertex in $V(H_x) \setminus (S \cup \{x\})$ is totally protected under S by some vertex in S_x. Now, suppose that $|S_x| < \gamma_{st}(H - \{v\})$ and let $N(x) \cap V(H_x) = \{s_x\}$. If $x \notin S$, then S_x^- is a secure total dominating set of $H_x - \{x\}$, which is a contradiction as $|S_x^-| = |S_x| < \gamma_{st}(H - \{v\}) = \gamma_{st}(H_x - \{x\})$. Hence, $x \in S$. Now, if $N(s_x) \subseteq S$, then we set $S' = (S_x \setminus \{x\}) \cup \{s_x\}$ and otherwise we set $S' = (S_x \setminus \{x\}) \cup \{w\}$ for any $w \in N(s_x) \setminus S$. In both cases, S' is a secure total dominating set of $H_x - \{x\}$ and $\gamma_{st}(H_x - \{x\}) - 1 > |S_x| - 1 \ge |S'| \ge \gamma_{st}(H_x - \{x\})$, which is a contradiction. Therefore, $|S_x| \ge \gamma_{st}(H - \{v\})$. $\square$

By Theorem 1 and Lemma 6, we deduce the next result.

Theorem 8. *Let G and H be two graphs with no isolated vertex. If $v \in \mathcal{L}_w(H)$, $N(v) = \{s\}$ and $|N(s)| \ge 3$, then*

$$n(G)\gamma_{st}(H - \{v\}) \le \gamma_{st}(G \circ_v H) \le \min\{n(G)\gamma_{st}(H), \gamma_{st}(G) + n(G)\gamma_{st}(H - \{v\})\}.$$

The following result is an immediate consequence of the theorem above.

Corollary 2. *Let G and H be two graphs with no isolated vertex. Let $v \in \mathcal{L}_w(H)$ and $N(v) = \{s\}$. If $|N(s)| \ge 3$ and $\gamma_{st}(H - \{v\}) = \gamma_{st}(H)$, then*

$$\gamma_{st}(G \circ_v H) = n(G)\gamma_{st}(H).$$

Theorem 9. *Let G be a graph with $\delta(G) \geq 2$ and H a graph with no isolated vertex. Let $v \in \mathcal{L}_w(H)$ and $N(v) = \{s\}$. If $|N(s)| \geq 3$ and $N(s) \cap S(H) \neq \varnothing$, then the following statements hold.*

(i) *If $s \notin D$ for every $\gamma_{st}(H - \{v\})$-set D, then*

$$\gamma_{st}(G \circ_v H) = \gamma_{st}(G) + n(G)\gamma_{st}(H - \{v\}).$$

(ii) *If there exists a $\gamma_{st}(H - \{v\})$-set D such that $s \in D$, then*

$$\gamma_{st}(G \circ_v H) \in \{n(G)\gamma_{st}(H - \{v\}), \gamma(G) + n(G)\gamma_{st}(H - \{v\}), \gamma_t(G) + n(G)\gamma_{st}(H - \{v\})\}.$$

Proof. Let S be a $\gamma_{st}(G \circ_v H)$-set such that $|S \cap N[V(G)]|$ is maximum. For any vertex $x \in V(G)$, let $\{s_x\} = N(x) \cap V(H_x)$. Let $\{\mathcal{M}_0, \mathcal{M}_1, \mathcal{N}_0, \mathcal{N}_1\}$ be the partition of $V(G)$ defined as follows.

$$\mathcal{M}_0 = \{x \in V(G) \setminus S : s_x \in S\}, \quad \mathcal{M}_1 = \{x \in V(G) \cap S : s_x \in S\},$$

$$\mathcal{N}_0 = \{x \in V(G) \setminus S : s_x \notin S\}, \quad \mathcal{N}_1 = \{x \in V(G) \cap S : s_x \notin S\}.$$

By Theorem 1 we have that $\gamma_{st}(G \circ_v H) \leq \gamma_{st}(G) + n(G)\gamma_{st}(H - \{v\})$. Hence, in order to prove (i) we proceed to show that $\gamma_{st}(G \circ_v H) \geq \gamma_{st}(G) + n(G)\gamma_{st}(H - \{v\})$. To this end, we need to estimate the gap $|S_x| - \gamma_{st}(H - \{v\})$. Obviously, if $x \in \mathcal{N}_0$, then $|S_x| = \gamma_{st}(H - \{v\})$. Now, since $N(s_x) \cap S(H_x) \neq \varnothing$, if $x \in \mathcal{M}_0 \cup \mathcal{M}_1$, then S_x^- is a secure total dominating set of $H_x - \{x\}$, and so $|S_x^-| \geq \gamma_{st}(H_x - \{x\}) = \gamma_{st}(H - \{v\})$. By hypothesis of (i) we deduce that, if $x \in \mathcal{M}_0$, then $|S_x| \geq |S_x^-| > \gamma_{st}(H - \{v\})$, while if $x \in \mathcal{M}_1$, then $|S_x| > |S_x^-| > \gamma_{st}(H - \{v\})$. We now consider the case $x \in \mathcal{N}_1$. By Lemma 6 we have that $|S_x| \geq \gamma_{st}(H - \{v\})$. If $|S_x| = \gamma_{st}(H - \{v\})$, then $S_x^- \cup \{s_x\}$ is a secure total dominating set of $H_x - \{x\}$ and $|S_x^- \cup \{s_x\}| = |S_x| = \gamma_{st}(H - \{v\}) = \gamma_{st}(H_x - \{x\})$, which contradicts the hypothesis of (i). Hence, $x \in \mathcal{N}_1$ leads to $|S_x| > \gamma_{st}(H - \{v\})$.

In summary, we can conclude that if $x \in \mathcal{N}_0$, then $|S_x| = \gamma_{st}(H - \{v\})$, if $x \in \mathcal{M}_0 \cup \mathcal{N}_1$, then $|S_x| \geq \gamma_{st}(H - \{v\}) + 1$, while if $x \in \mathcal{M}_1$, then $|S_x| \geq \gamma_{st}(H - \{v\}) + 2$. We claim that there exists a secure total dominating set Z of G such that $|Z| \leq |\mathcal{N}_1| + |\mathcal{M}_0| + 2|\mathcal{M}_1|$.

We define Z as a set of minimum cardinality satisfying that $\mathcal{N}_1 \cup \mathcal{M}_0 \cup \mathcal{M}_1 \subseteq Z$ and for any $x \in \mathcal{M}_1$ with $N(x) \cap \mathcal{N}_0 \neq \varnothing$ there exists $w_x \in N(x) \cap \mathcal{N}_0 \cap Z$. Notice that, by definition, Z is a double dominating set of G and, since $\delta(G) \geq 2$, every vertex in $\mathcal{M}_1$ has at least two neighbours in $Z \setminus \mathcal{N}_0$ or one neighbour in $Z \cap \mathcal{N}_0$. Let $x \in V(G) \setminus Z$. Since $x \in \mathcal{N}_0$, there exists $y \in S \cap V(G) = \mathcal{M}_1 \cap \mathcal{N}_1 \subseteq Z$ such that x is totally protected under S by y. We claim that $Z' = (Z \setminus \{y\}) \cup \{x\}$ is a total dominating set of G. Since Z is a total dominating set of G, we have that every vertex in $V(G) \setminus N(y)$ is dominated by some vertex in Z'. Now, if there exists $u \in N(y) \cap V(G)$ such that $N(u) \cap S \cap V(G) = \{y\}$, then $u \in \mathcal{M}_1$, and so $N(u) \cap Z \cap \mathcal{N}_0 \neq \varnothing$, concluding that Z' is a total dominating set of G. Hence, Z is a secure total dominating set of G, and as a consequence,

$$
\begin{aligned}
\gamma_{st}(G \circ_v H) &= \textstyle\sum_{x \in V(G)} |S_x| \\
&= \textstyle\sum_{x \in \mathcal{M}_1} |S_x| + \sum_{x \in \mathcal{M}_0} |S_x| + \sum_{x \in \mathcal{N}_1} |S_x| + \sum_{x \in \mathcal{N}_0} |S_x| \\
&\geq \textstyle\sum_{x \in \mathcal{M}_1} (\gamma_{st}(H - \{v\}) + 2) + \sum_{x \in \mathcal{M}_0 \cup \mathcal{N}_1} (\gamma_{st}(H - \{v\}) + 1) + \sum_{x \in \mathcal{N}_0} \gamma_{st}(H - \{v\}) \\
&= \textstyle\sum_{x \in V(G)} \gamma_{st}(H - \{v\}) + (2|\mathcal{M}_1| + |\mathcal{M}_0| + |\mathcal{N}_1|) \\
&\geq \textstyle\sum_{x \in V(G)} \gamma_{st}(H - \{v\}) + |Z| \\
&\geq \textstyle n(G)\gamma_{st}(H - \{v\}) + \gamma_{st}(G).
\end{aligned}
$$

Therefore, proof of (i) is complete.

We now proceed to prove (ii). From Lemma 6 we can consider the partition $\{R_0, R_1\}$ of $V(G)$ defined as follows.

$$R_0 = \{x \in V(G) : |S_x| = \gamma_{st}(H - \{v\})\}, \quad R_1 = \{x \in V(G) : |S_x| > \gamma_{st}(H - \{v\})\}.$$

By assumptions, there exists a $\gamma_{st}(H - \{v\})$-set D such that $s \in D$. Let $W \subseteq V(G \circ_v H) \setminus V(G)$ such that W_x is induced by D for every vertex $x \in V(G)$.

If $x \in \mathcal{N}_0$, then $S' = (S \setminus S_x) \cup W_x$ is a $\gamma_{st}(G \circ_v H)$-set with $|S' \cap N[V(G)]| > |S \cap N[V(G)]|$, which is a contradiction. Hence, $\mathcal{N}_0 = \varnothing$. If $x \in R_1 \cap \mathcal{N}_1$, then $S' = (S \setminus S_x) \cup (W_x \cup \{x\})$ is a $\gamma_{st}(G \circ_v H)$-set with $|S' \cap N[V(G)]| > |S \cap N[V(G)]|$, which is a contradiction. Hence, $R_1 \cap \mathcal{N}_1 = \varnothing$, and so $\mathcal{N}_1 \subseteq R_0$. Now, by hypothesis of (ii), $\mathcal{M}_0 \subseteq R_0$. Moreover, if $x \in \mathcal{M}_1$, then S_x^- is a secure total dominating set of $H_x - \{x\}$, and so $x \in R_1$. Therefore, $R_1 = \mathcal{M}_1$ and $R_0 = \mathcal{M}_0 \cup \mathcal{N}_1$.

Now, we suppose that there exists a vertex $x' \in \mathcal{N}_1$. Let $W' \subseteq V(G \circ_v H)$ such that W'_x is induced by $S_{x'}$ for every vertex $x \in V(G)$. Since $\delta(G) \geq 2$ we have that W' is a secure total dominating set of $G \circ_v H$ of cardinality $n(G)\gamma_{st}(H - \{v\})$. Therefore, $\gamma_{st}(G \circ_v H) \leq n(G)\gamma_{st}(H - \{v\})$ and by Theorem 8, we deduce that $\gamma_{st}(G \circ_v H) = n(G)\gamma_{st}(H - \{v\})$.

From now on, we assume that $\mathcal{N}_1 = \varnothing$. Hence, $R_1 = \mathcal{M}_1$ and $R_0 = \mathcal{M}_0$. Let $x \in \mathcal{M}_1$. As $N(s_x) \cap S(H_x) \neq \varnothing$, we have that S_x^- is a secure total dominating set of $H_x - \{x\}$, and by hypothesis of (ii) we deduce that $|S_x^-| = \gamma_{st}(H - \{v\})$, which implies that $|S_x| = \gamma_{st}(H - \{v\}) + 1$. Hence, $\gamma_{st}(G \circ_v H) = |\mathcal{M}_1| + n(G)\gamma_{st}(H - \{v\})$.

Since $V(G) = \mathcal{M}_0 \cup \mathcal{M}_1$ and $\mathcal{M}_0 \cap \mathcal{M}_1 = \varnothing$, by Remark 1, any vertex in $\mathcal{M}_0$ is dominated by at least one vertex in $\mathcal{M}_1$. Hence, $\mathcal{M}_1$ is a dominating set of G and we differentiate the following two cases.

Case 1. There exists a $\gamma_{st}(H - \{v\})$-set D containing s, such that no vertex in $N(s) \setminus D$ is necessarily totally protected by s under D. Let $W'' \subseteq V(G \circ_v H) \setminus V(G)$ such that W''_x is induced by D for every vertex $x \in V(G)$. In this case, for every $\gamma(G)$-set X we have that $X \cup W''$ is a secure total dominating set of $G \circ_v H$. Hence $|\mathcal{M}_1| = \gamma(G)$, and as a consequence, $\gamma_{st}(G \circ_v H) = \gamma(G) + n(G)\gamma_{st}(H - \{v\})$.

Case 2. For every $\gamma_{st}(H - \{v\})$-set D containing s, there exists a vertex in $V(H) \setminus D$ that is totally protected uniquely by s under D. In this case, any vertex in $\mathcal{M}_1$ is dominated by another vertex in $\mathcal{M}_1$, which implies that $\mathcal{M}_1$ is a total dominating set of G. As in Case 1, let $W'' \subseteq V(G \circ_v H) \setminus V(G)$ such that W''_x is induced by D for every vertex $x \in V(G)$. In this case, for every $\gamma_t(G)$-set X we have that $X \cup W''$ is a secure total dominating set of $G \circ_v H$. Hence $|\mathcal{M}_1| = \gamma_t(G)$. Therefore, $\gamma_{st}(G \circ_v H) = \gamma_t(G) + n(G)\gamma_{st}(H - \{v\})$. $\square$

From now on we consider the case in which the support vertex of the root v has degree two.

Lemma 7. *Let H be a graph with no isolated vertex. If $v \in \mathcal{L}_w(H)$, $N(v) = \{s\}$ and $|N(s)| = 2$, then $\gamma_{st}(H - \{v\}) \geq \gamma_{st}(H) - 1$.*

Proof. Suppose that $\gamma_{st}(H - \{v\}) \leq \gamma_{st}(H) - 2$ and let D be a $\gamma_{st}(H - \{v\})$-set. Since both s and its support vertex in $H - \{v\}$ are included in D, we have that $D \cup \{v\}$ is a secure total dominating set of H. Hence, $\gamma_{st}(H) \leq |D \cup \{v\}| = \gamma_{st}(H - \{v\}) + 1 \leq \gamma_{st}(H) - 1$, which is a contradiction. Therefore, $\gamma_{st}(H - \{v\}) \geq \gamma_{st}(H) - 1$, which completes the proof. $\square$

Theorem 10. *Let S be a $\gamma_{st}(G \circ_v H)$-set. If $v \in \mathcal{L}_w(H)$, $N(v) = \{s\}$ and $|N(s)| = 2$, then for any $x \in V(G)$,*

$$\gamma_{st}(H) - 1 \leq |S_x| \leq \gamma_{st}(H).$$

Therefore, with the assumptions above,

$$n(G)(\gamma_{st}(H) - 1) \leq \gamma_{st}(G \circ_v H) \leq n(G)\gamma_{st}(H).$$

Proof. We first consider the case in which S_x is a secure total dominating set of H_x. Since $x \in \mathcal{L}(H_x)$ we have that x belongs to every $\gamma_{st}(H_x)$-set. So, $|S_x| = \gamma_{st}(H_x) = \gamma_{st}(H)$.

Now, assume that S_x is not a secure total dominating set of H_x. Notice that every vertex in $V(H_x) \setminus (S \cup \{x\})$ is totally protected under S by some vertex in S_x. Since $\{x, s_x\} \cap S_x \neq \varnothing$, we have that $S_x \cup \{x, s_x\}$ is a secure total dominating set of H_x. Hence, $\gamma_{st}(H) - 1 = \gamma_{st}(H_x) - 1 \leq |S_x \cup$

$\{x, s_x\}| - 1 \leq |S_x|$. Now, if there exists $x' \in V(G)$ such that $|S_{x'}| > \gamma_{st}(H)$, then for any $\gamma_{st}(H_{x'})$-set D, we have that $S' = (S \setminus S_{x'}) \cup D$ is a secure total dominating set of $G \circ_v H$ and $|S'| < |S|$, which is a contradiction. Therefore, $\gamma_{st}(H) - 1 \leq |S_x| \leq \gamma_{st}(H)$ for every $x \in V(G)$, and since $\gamma_{st}(G \circ_v H) = \sum_{x \in V(G)} |S_x|$, the result follows. $\square$

We now consider the particular case where $\delta(G) \geq 2$. By Lemma 7 we only need to consider two cases according to whether $\gamma_{st}(H - \{v\}) \geq \gamma_{st}(H)$ or $\gamma_{st}(H - \{v\}) = \gamma_{st}(H) - 1$. These two cases are discussed in Theorems 11 and 12, respectively.

Theorem 11. *Let G be a graph with $\delta(G) \geq 2$ and H a graph with no isolated vertex. Let $v \in \mathcal{L}_w(H)$, $N(v) = \{s\}$ and $|N(s)| = 2$. If $\gamma_{st}(H - \{v\}) \geq \gamma_{st}(H)$, then*

$$\gamma_{st}(G \circ_v H) \in \{n(G)\gamma_{st}(H), n(G)(\gamma_{st}(H) - 1)\}.$$

Proof. Let S be a $\gamma_{st}(G \circ_v H)$-set such that $|S| < n(G)\gamma_{st}(H)$. For any vertex $x \in V(G)$, let $\{s_x\} = N(x) \cap V(H_x)$ and $\{s'_x\} = N(s_x) \setminus \{x\}$. By Theorem 10 there exists a vertex $y \in V(G)$ such that $|S_y| = \gamma_{st}(H) - 1$. If $y \notin S_y$, then S_y^- is a secure total dominating set of $H_y - \{y\}$ and so $|S_y^-| = |S_y| = \gamma_{st}(H) - 1 < \gamma_{st}(H - \{v\}) = \gamma_{st}(H_y - \{y\})$, which is a contradiction. Hence, $y \in S_y$.

We suppose that $s_y \in S_y$. Since $|S_y| = \gamma_{st}(H) - 1$, we deduce that $s'_y \notin S_y$. So, the set $D = (S_y \setminus \{y\}) \cup \{s'_y\}$ is a secure total dominating set of $H_y - \{y\}$ of cardinality $|D| = |S_y| = \gamma_{st}(H) - 1 < \gamma_{st}(H - \{v\}) = \gamma_{st}(H_y - \{y\})$, which is a contradiction. Hence, $s_y \notin S_y$, and so $s'_y \in S_y$.

Let $W \subseteq V(G \circ_v H)$ such that W_x is induced by S_y, for any $x \in V(G)$. Since $\delta(G) \geq 2$, we deduce that W is a secure total dominating set of $G \circ_v H$, and, as a result, $\gamma_{st}(G \circ_v H) \leq |W| = n(G)|S_y| = n(G)(\gamma_{st}(H) - 1)$. By Theorem 10 we obtain that $\gamma_{st}(G \circ_v H) = n(G)(\gamma_{st}(H) - 1)$, which completes the proof. $\square$

Theorem 12. *Let G be a graph with $\delta(G) \geq 2$ and H a graph with no isolated vertex. Let $v \in \mathcal{L}_w(H)$, $N(v) = \{s\}$ and $|N(s)| = 2$. If $\gamma_{st}(H - \{v\}) = \gamma_{st}(H) - 1$, then*

$$\gamma_{st}(G \circ_v H) \in \{n(G)(\gamma_{st}(H) - 1), \gamma(G) + n(G)(\gamma_{st}(H) - 1)\}.$$

Proof. By Theorem 10 we have that $\gamma_{st}(G \circ_v H) \geq n(G)(\gamma_{st}(H) - 1)$. Since $s \in \mathcal{L}(H - \{v\})$, any $\gamma_{st}(H - \{v\})$-set D contains $N[s] \setminus \{v\}$ as a subset. Let $W \subseteq V(G \circ_v H) \setminus V(G)$ such that W_x is induced by D for every vertex $x \in V(G)$. As for any $\gamma(G)$-set X, the set $X \cup W$ is a secure total dominating set of $G \circ_v H$, we deduce that $\gamma_{st}(G \circ_v H) \leq |X \cup W| = \gamma(G) + n(G)\gamma_{st}(H - \{v\}) = \gamma(G) + n(G)(\gamma_{st}(H) - 1)$.

Let S be a $\gamma_{st}(G \circ_v H)$-set such that $|S| > n(G)(\gamma_{st}(H) - 1)$. For any vertex $x \in V(G)$, let $\{s_x\} = N(x) \cap V(H_x)$. By Theorem 10, we can conclude that the set $Z = \{z \in V(G) : |S_z| = \gamma_{st}(H)\}$ is not empty. Since there exists a $\gamma_{st}(H)$-set containing $N[s]$, we can assume, without loss of generality, that $N[s_z] \subseteq S_z$ for every vertex $z \in Z$. We claim that Z is a dominating set of G. Let $x' \in V(G) \setminus Z$ and suppose that $x' \in S$. In such a case, $|S_{x'}| = \gamma_{st}(H) - 1$ and we can define a set $W' \subseteq V(G \circ_v H)$ such that W'_x is induced by $S_{x'}$ for every vertex $x \in V(G)$. Notice that W is a secure total dominating set of $G \circ_v H$ and $|W| = n(G)(\gamma_{st}(H) - 1)$, which is a contradiction. Thus, $(V(G) \setminus Z) \cap S = \emptyset$, which implies that Z is a dominating set of G and so $\gamma_{st}(G \circ_v H) = |S| \geq |\bigcup_{x \in V(G)} S_x| = |Z| + n(G)(\gamma_{st}(H) - 1) \geq \gamma(G) + n(G)(\gamma_{st}(H) - 1)$, which completes the proof. $\square$

Theorem 13. *Let G be a graph such that $\delta(G) \geq 2$ and H a graph with no isolated vertex. If $v \in \mathcal{L}_w(H)$, $N(v) = \{s\}$, $|N(s)| = 2$ and $N(s) \cap \mathcal{S}(H) \neq \emptyset$, then*

$$\gamma_{st}(G \circ_v H) = n(G)(\gamma_{st}(H) - 1).$$

Proof. For any vertex $x \in V(G)$, let $\{s_x\} = N(x) \cap V(H_x)$ and notice that any $\gamma_{st}(H_x)$-set D_x satisfies that $N[s_x] \subseteq D_x$ and $D_x \setminus \{x, s_x\}$ is a secure total dominating set of $H_x - \{x, s_x\}$. Since $\delta(G) \geq 2$, we have that $D = \bigcup_{x \in V(G)}(D_x \setminus \{s_x\})$ is a secure total dominating set of $G \circ_v H$. Hence, $\gamma_{st}(G \circ_v H) \leq |D| = n(G)(\gamma_{st}(H) - 1)$. By Theorem 10 we obtain that $\gamma_{st}(G \circ_v H) = n(G)(\gamma_{st}(H) - 1)$, which completes the proof. $\square$

4. Concluding Remarks

It is well-known that the problem of finding the secure total domination number of a graph is NP-hard. This suggests the challenge of finding closed formulas or giving tight bounds for this parameter. In this paper we develop the theory for the class of rooted product graph. The study shows that if the root vertex is strong leaf, a support, or a universal vertex, then there exists a formula for the secure total domination number of the rooted product graph. In the remaining cases, two different behaviours are observed depending on whether the root vertex is a weak leaf or not. Although in a different way, in both cases we were able to give the intervals to which the parameter belongs. The endpoints of these intervals are expressed in terms of other domination parameters of the graphs G and H involved in the product, which allows us to obtain closed formulas when certain conditions are imposed on G or H.

Author Contributions: All authors contributed equally to this work. All authors have read and agreed to the published version of the manuscript.

Funding: This research received no external funding.

Conflicts of Interest: The authors declare no conflict of interest.

References

1. Cockayne, E.J.; Grobler, P.J.P.; Gründlingh, W.R.; Munganga, J.; Van Vuuren, J.H. Protection of a graph. *Util.Math.* **2005**, *67*, 19–32.
2. Benecke, S.; Cockayne,E.J.; Mynhardt, C.M. Secure total domination in graphs. *Util. Math.* **2007**, *74*, 247–259.
3. Cabrera Martínez, A.; Montejano, L.P.; Rodríguez-Velázquez, J.A. On the secure total domination number of graphs. *Symmetry* **2019**, *11*, 1165. [CrossRef]
4. Cabrera Martínez, A.; Montejano, L.P.; Rodríguez-Velázquez, J.A. Total weak Roman domination in graphs. *Symmetry* **2019**, *11*, 831. [CrossRef]
5. Henning, M.A.; Hedetniemi, S.T. Defending the Roman Empire—A new strategy. *Discrete Math.* **2003**, *266*, 239–251. [CrossRef]
6. Cockayne, E.J.; Dreyer, P.A., Jr.; Hedetniemi, S.M.; Hedetniemi, S.T. Roman domination in graphs. *Discrete Math.* **2004**, *278*, 11–22. [CrossRef]
7. Stewart, I. *Defend the Roman Empire!*. Scientific American: New York, NY, USA, 1999; Volume 281, pp. 136–138.
8. Haynes, T.W.; Hedetniemi, S.T.; Slater, P.J. *Domination in Graphs: Advanced Topics.*; Chapman and Hall/CRC Pure and Applied Mathematics Series; Marcel Dekker, Inc.: New York, NY, USA, 1998.
9. Haynes, T.W.; Hedetniemi, S.T.; Slater, P.J. *Fundamentals of Domination in Graphs*; Chapman and Hall/CRC Pure and Applied Mathematics Series; Marcel Dekker, Inc.: New York, NY, USA, 1998.
10. Henning, M.; Yeo, A. *Total Domination in Graphs. Springer Monographs in Mathematics*; Springer: New York, NY, USA, 2013.
11. Chellali, M.; Haynes, T.W.; Hedetniemi, S.T.; McRae, A.A. Roman 2-domination. *Discrete Appl. Math.* **2016**, *204*, 22–28. [CrossRef]
12. Boumediene Merouane, H.; Chellali, M. On secure domination in graphs. *Inform. Process. Lett.* **2015**, *115*, 786–790. [CrossRef]
13. Burger, A.P.; Henning, M.A.; Van Vuuren, J.H. Vertex covers and secure domination in graphs. *Quaest. Math.* **2008**, *31*, 163–171. [CrossRef]
14. Chellali, M.; Haynes, T.W.; Hedetniemi, S.T. Bounds on weak Roman and 2-rainbow domination numbers. *Discrete Appl. Math.* **2014**, *178*, 27–32. [CrossRef]
15. Cockayne, E.J.; Favaron, O.; Mynhardt, C.M. Secure domination, weak Roman domination and forbidden subgraphs, *Bull. Inst. Combin. Appl.* **2003**, *39*, 87–100.

16. Klostermeyer, W.F.; Mynhardt, C.M. Secure domination and secure total domination in graphs. *Discuss. Math. Graph Theory.* **2008**, *28*, 267–284. [CrossRef]
17. Valveny, M.; Rodríguez-Velázquez, J.A. Protection of graphs with emphasis on Cartesian product graphs. *Filomat* **2019**, *33*, 319–333. [CrossRef]
18. Duginov, O. Secure total domination in graphs: Bounds and complexity. *Discrete Appl. Math.* **2017**, *222*, 97–108. [CrossRef]
19. Kulli, V.R.; Chaluvaraju, B.; Kumara, M. Graphs with equal secure total domination and inverse secure total domination numbers. *J. Inf. Optim. Sci.* **2018**, *39*, 467–473. [CrossRef]

Article

Efficient Open Domination in Digraph Products

Dragana Božović [1,2] **and Iztok Peterin** [1,2,*]

[1] Faculty of Electrical Engineering and Computer Science, University of Maribor, Koroška cesta 46, 2000 Maribor, Slovenia; dragana.bozovic@um.si

[2] Institute of Mathematics, Physics and Mechanics, Jadranska 19, 1000 Ljubljana, Slovenia

* Correspondence: iztok.peterin@um.si

Received: 6 February 2020; Accepted: 27 March 2020; Published: 2 April 2020

Abstract: A digraph D is an efficient open domination digraph if there exists a subset S of $V(D)$ for which the open out-neighborhoods centered in the vertices of S form a partition of $V(D)$. In this work we deal with the efficient open domination digraphs among four standard products of digraphs. We present a method for constructing the efficient open domination Cartesian product of digraphs with one fixed factor. In particular, we characterize those for which the first factor has an underlying graph that is a path, a cycle or a star. We also characterize the efficient open domination strong product of digraphs that have factors whose underlying graphs are uni-cyclic graphs. The full characterizations of the efficient open domination direct and lexicographic product of digraphs are also given.

Keywords: efficient open domination; digraphs; products of digraphs

1. Introduction

In this work we join two natural concepts. The first one is operations on digraphs (under some rules) that result in a bigger digraph than the starting ones. The second one is partitions of sets. There exist many digraph products for which the vertex set is the Cartesian product of vertex sets of its factors (there are also several operations which have (di)graph product in their name, but the vertex set is defined in a different manner). They differ by the definitions of the edge sets. Among them, four are called standard products. These are the Cartesian product, the strong product, the direct product and the lexicographic product. One can find a rich bibliography about them (see [1]). One standard approach of studying the digraph products is to study their structure and how to recognize them. Another approach is to deduce the properties of (di)graph products with respect to some properties of their factors. The later is also the topic of this work.

Partitions of objects are always interesting and useful as a mathematical concept, as every partition yields an equivalence relation. This further enables a factor structure of starting objects, which often brings simplification and deeper insight. Therefore, it is natural to study different kinds of partitions and the existence of them. Unfortunately, we are often not in the position to describe the mentioned relation with the properties of the investigated objects. This often disables further studies.

Graph theory offers a wide range of possibilities for partitions, one of them being the partitions of vertices. Open neighborhoods are a natural example for partitioning the set of vertices. Among graphs this was initiated in 1993 by Cockayne et al. in [2], where such partitions were named total perfect codes. The terminology efficient open domination graphs was introduced by Gavlas and Schultz in 2002 (see [3]). The study of efficient open domination of Cayley graphs can be found in [4]. Grid graphs, that is Cartesian products of two paths, were investigated in [5–7] and direct products of graphs with such a partition were characterized in [8]. Characterizations of efficient open domination graphs among lexicographic, strong and disjunctive product of two graphs can be found in [9]. In the same paper [9] the Cartesian products of some known families of graphs with respect to efficient open domination were also investigated. Later, in [10], one factor of a Cartesian product was fixed while the other factor was characterized in such a way that its Cartesian product is an efficient open domination graph.

Existence of a partition of vertices of a graph into closed neighborhoods was initiated even earlier by Biggs in 1976 (see [11]) under the name 1-perfect graphs. The name efficient (closed) domination graphs was proposed later by Bange et al. in [12]. This subject became quite popular and throughout the years several combinatorial and computational results were presented. One of the latest results of this type is that the problem of efficient closed domination is solvable in polynomial time for the class of P_6-free graphs, as shown in [13] and independently in [14]. This was further investigated in [15] for some subclasses of P_6-free graphs. The authors use the maximum weight independent set problem of a square graph G^2 to which the efficient closed domination of G can be reduced. Among products the strong product was treated in [16] and the direct product of (an arbitrary number of) cycles was covered in a series of papers [17–19]. For the lexicographic product the topic was covered in [20], while Mollard deals with the efficient closed domination Cartesian product in [21]. Recently, graphs that are both efficient open and efficient closed domination at the same time were considered in [22].

In the case of digraphs one can also distinguish between in- and out-neighborhoods besides open and closed neighborhoods. However, this dilemma is artificial because if we reverse the orientation of the digraph, then in-neighborhoods become out-neighborhoods and vice versa. Hence, we can deal with efficient open and efficient closed domination digraphs. Efficient open domination digraphs were introduced in [23] and studied further in [24–27]. In [28] Schaudt presented a useful characterization under the name of efficient total domination digraphs. See also [29] for more recent results. As in the case of graphs, there is more literature concerning efficient closed domination digraphs than that of efficient open domination digraphs. Here we mention only [30], a recent work that brings the results on the efficient closed domination among standard products of digraphs.

The paper is organized as follows. In the coming section we first settle the terminology. A section with several results on efficient open domination Cartesian products of digraphs follows. There we present a method for constructing an efficient open domination Cartesian product of digraphs with one fixed factor. Section four is devoted to the efficient open domination strong products of digraphs. We characterize those for which the factors have uni-cyclic graphs as their underlying graphs. Moreover, we conjecture that these are the only efficient open domination digraphs among strong products. The last section brings characterizations of the efficient open domination direct and lexicographic products of digraphs.

2. Preliminaries

The terminology and basic definitions in this section are summarized from [30] where the authors present the results on the efficient closed domination among standard products of digraphs.

Let D be a digraph with the vertex set $V(D)$ and the arc set $A(D)$. For any two vertices $u, v \in V(D)$, we write (u, v) as the *arc* with *direction* or *orientation* from u to v, and say u is *adjacent* to v, or v is *adjacent* from u. For an arc (u, v) we also say that u is the *in-neighbor* of v and that v is the *out-neighbor* of u. For a vertex $v \in V(D)$, the *open out-neighborhood* of v (*open in-neighborhood* of v) is $N_D^+(v) = \{u \in V(D) : (v, u) \in A(D)\}$ ($N_D^-(v) = \{u \in V(D) : (u, v) \in A(D)\}$). The *in-degree* of v is $\delta_D^-(v) = |N_D^-(v)|$, the *out-degree* of v is $\delta_D^+(v) = |N_D^+(v)|$ and the degree of v is $\delta_D(v) = \delta_D^-(v) + \delta_D^+(v)$. Moreover, $N_D^-[v] = N_D^-(v) \cup \{v\}$ is the *closed in-neighborhood* of v ($N_D^+[v] = N_D^+(v) \cup \{v\}$ is the *closed out-neighborhood* of v). In the above notation we omit D if there is no ambiguity with respect to the digraph D. We similarly proceed with any other notation which uses such a style of subscripts. Throughout the paper we use $[k] = \{1, \ldots, k\}$.

A vertex v of D with $\delta^+(v) = |V(D)| - 1$ is called an *out-universal vertex*, and if $\delta^-(v) = |V(D)| - 1$, then v is called an *in-universal vertex*. A vertex v of D with $\delta^+(v) = 0$ is called a *sink*, and if $\delta^-(v) = 0$, then v is called a *source*. If $\delta(v) = 0$, then v is an *isolated vertex* or a *singleton*. An arc of the form (v, v) is called a *loop* and can be considered as a directed cycle of length one. A vertex v with $\delta(v) = 1$ is called a *leaf* and is either a sink (if $\delta^+(v) = 0$) or a source (if $\delta^-(v) = 0$). Clearly, any vertex u with $\delta(u) = 2$ is either a sink, or a source, or $\delta^-(u) = 1 = \delta^+(u)$.

The *underlying graph* of a digraph D is a graph G_D with $V(G_D) = V(D)$ and for every arc (u, v) from D we have an edge uv in $E(G_D)$. If (u, v) and (v, u) are both arcs, then we have two edges between u and v in the underlying graph. A *directed path* is a digraph $D \cong P_n$ with one source and one sink where its underlying graph is isomorphic to a path P_n. Similarly, a *directed cycle* is a digraph $D \cong C_n$ without sinks and sources with a cycle C_n as its underlying graph. We also consider a loop as a directed cycle C_1 of length one and double arc with different orientation as a directed cycle C_2 of length two. The distance $d_D(u, v)$ between two vertices u and v is the minimum number of arcs on a directed path from u to v or ∞ if such a directed path does not exist. For $A \subseteq V(D)$ we denote by $D - A$ a digraph obtained from D by deleting all vertices from A. By $D[A]$ we denote the subdigraph of D that is induced on the vertices from A.

Let D be a digraph and let $S \subseteq V(D)$. The set S is called a *total dominating set* of D if the open out-neighborhoods centered in vertices of S cover $V(D)$, that is $V(D) = \bigcup_{v \in S} N_D^+(v)$. Let S be a total dominating set of D. If $N_D^+(v) \cap N_D^+(u) = \emptyset$ for every two different vertices $u, v \in S$, then the set $\{N_D^+(v) : v \in S\}$ not only covers $V(D)$ but also partitions $V(D)$. In this case we say that S is an *efficient open dominating set* (or an *EOD set* for short) of D. If there exists an EOD set S for the digraph D, then D is called an *efficient open domination digraph* (or an *EOD digraph* for short). For $A \subseteq V(D)$ we say that $S_A \subseteq V(D)$ is *efficient open domination set only* (or *an EOD set only* for short) for a digraph $D - A$ if every vertex from $V(D) - A$ has exactly one in-neighbor in S_A and in addition $A \cap N_D^+(S_A) = \emptyset$.

Let D and F be digraphs. Different products of digraphs D and F have, similarly as in graphs, their set of vertices equal to $V(D) \times V(F)$. We roughly and briefly discuss the four standard products of digraphs: the *Cartesian product* $D \square F$, the *direct product* $D \times F$, the *strong product* $D \boxtimes F$ and the *lexicographic product* $D \circ F$ (sometimes also denoted $D[F]$). Adjacency in different products is defined as follows.

- In the Cartesian product $D \square F$ there exists an arc from vertex (d, f) to vertex (d', f') if there exists an arc from d to d' in D and $f = f'$ or $d = d'$ and there exists an arc from f to f' in F.
- If there is an arc from d to d' in D and an arc from f to f' in F, then there exists an arc from (d, f) to (f', d') in the direct product $D \times F$.
- In the strong product we have $((d, f), (d', f')) \in A(D \boxtimes F)$ if $((d, d') \in A(D)$ and $f = f')$ or $(d = d'$ and $(f, f') \in A(F))$ or $((d, d') \in A(D)$ and $(f, f') \in A(F))$.
- There is an arc in the lexicographic product $D \circ F$ from a vertex (d, f) to a vertex (d', f'), whenever $(d, d') \in A(D)$ or $(d = d'$ and $(f, f') \in A(F))$.

Some examples of the above mentioned products appear in Figure 1.

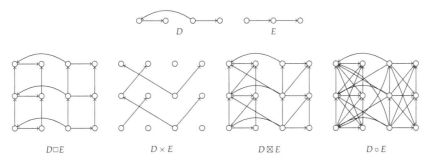

Figure 1. The digraphs D and E, and their Cartesian, direct, strong and lexicographic products.

Let $* \in \{\square, \times, \boxtimes, \circ\}$. The map $p_D : V(D * F) \to V(D)$ defined by $p_D((d, f)) = d$ is called the *projection map onto D*. Similarly, we define p_F as the *projection map onto F*. Projections are defined as maps between vertices, but frequently it is more convenient to see them as maps between digraphs. In this case we observe the subdigraphs induced by $B \subseteq V(D \circ F)$ and $p_X(B)$ for $X \in \{D, F\}$. Notice that in the Cartesian and in the strong product the arcs project either to arcs (with the same orientation) or to a vertex. In the case of the direct product arcs always project to arcs (with the same orientation). In the lexicographic product $D \circ F$ the projection p_D maps arcs into arcs (with the same orientation) or into vertices. In the same product the projection p_F maps arcs into vertices, into arcs with the same orientation, into arcs with different orientation or into two vertices without an arc between them.

For a fixed $f \in V(F)$ we call set $D^f = \{(d, f) \in V(D * F) : d \in V(D)\}$ a *D-layer through f* in $D * F$, where $* \in \{\Box, \times, \boxtimes, \circ\}$. Symmetrically, an *F-layer F^d through d* is defined for a fixed $d \in V(D)$. Notice that for the Cartesian product, for the strong product and for the lexicographic product, $(D * F)[D^f]$ is isomorphic to D and $(D * F)[F^d]$ is isomorphic to F, respectively. In the case of the direct product loops play an important role. If there are no loops in f and in d, then the subdigraphs $(D * F)[F^d]$ and $(D * F)[D^f]$ are isomorphic to an empty digraph on $|V(F)|$ and $|V(D)|$ vertices, respectively. If we have $(d, d) \in A(D)$ and $(f, f) \in A(F)$, then $(D * F)[F^d]$ and $(D * F)[D^f]$ are isomorphic to F and D, respectively.

It is easy to see that open out-neighborhoods in the direct product of digraphs satisfy

$$N_{D \times F}^+((d, f)) = N_D^+(d) \times N_F^+(f) \tag{1}$$

and for the lexicographic product of digraphs it holds that

$$N_{D \circ F}^+((d, f)) = \left(N_D^+(d) \times V(F)\right) \cup \left(\{d\} \times N_F^+(f)\right). \tag{2}$$

Using these two equalities a complete characterization of the EOD digraphs among the direct and the lexicographic product is presented in the last section.

3. The Cartesian Product

Definition 1. *Let F be a digraph and let $S_1, \ldots, S_k \subseteq V(F)$. If S_i is an EOD set only for $F - S_{i-1}$, $i \in [k]$, where $S_0 = \emptyset$, then we say that F is a k-EOD path divisible. Similarly, if S_i is an EOD set only for $F - S_{i-1}$, $i \in [k]$, where $S_0 = S_k$, then we say that F is a k-EOD cycle divisible. We say that sets $S_1, \ldots, S_k$ are k-EOD path or k-EOD cycle divisible sets of F.*

Notice that every k-EOD path divisible digraph is also an EOD digraph, because S_1 is an EOD set only for $F - S_0 = F$. Therefore, an EOD digraph F with an EOD set S_1 is 1-EOD path divisible. Also if F is n-EOD path divisible, then it is also m-EOD path divisible for every $m \leq n$. In particular, let F be a directed cycle, that is F is an EOD digraph with the EOD set $S = V(F)$. If we set $S_{2i-1} = V(F)$ and $S_{2i} = \emptyset$, then F is k-EOD path divisible for every positive integer k. If F is k-EOD path divisible, then it can happen that $S_i \cap S_j \neq \emptyset$. See an example of this on Figure 2.

With the following example we underline the rich structure of n-EOD path (or cycle) divisible digraphs. We will show that every digraph can be an induced digraph of an n-EOD path (or cycle) divisible digraph. A complete digraph K_n contains an arc in both directions between all different vertices of K_n. Let $V(K_n) = \{v_1, \ldots, v_n\}$. Digraph K_n^- is obtained from K_n by deleting all arcs (v_{i+1}, v_i), $i \in [n-1]$. For a digraph F we construct an n-EOD path divisible digraph F^+ in the folowing way. We take one copy of F and two copies of K_n^-, the first copy containing the vertices $V_1 = \{v_1, \ldots, v_n\}$ and the second copy containing the vertices $V_2 = \{v_1', \ldots, v_n'\}$. The arc set of F^+ contains $A(F)$, all arcs from both copies of K_n^-, the set $\{(v_i, v_i'), (v_i', v_i) : i \in [n]\}$, all arcs from the set $\{(v_i, f) : v_i \in V_1, f \in V(F)\}$ and an arbitrary subset of $\{(f, v_i), (f, v_i') : f \in V(F), v_i \in V_1, v_i' \in V_2\}$. It is not hard to see that F^+ is an n-EOD path divisible digraph with n-EOD path divisible sets $S_i = \{v_i, v_i'\}$ for every $i \in [n]$.

Similar construction can be done to get an n-EOD cycle divisible digraph. We only need to delete arcs (v_1, v_n) and (v_1', v_n') from F^+. Also if F is an n-EOD cycle divisible digraph, then F is also an kn-EOD cycle divisible digraph, where kn-EOD cycle divisible sets are repeated cyclically k times.

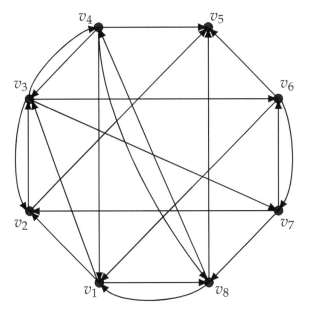

Figure 2. 4-EOD path divisible digraph with $S_1 = \{v_3, v_4\}, S_2 = \{v_6, v_7\}, S_3 = \{v_1, v_8\}, S_4 = \{v_2, v_3\}$ and with $S_1 \cap S_4 = \{v_3\}$.

Next we show that n-EOD path divisibility of F is essential for the Cartesian product $P_n \square F$ to be an EOD digraph, where P_n is a directed path.

Theorem 1. *Let P_n be a directed path and let F be a digraph. The Cartesian product $P_n \square F$ is an EOD digraph if and only if F is an n-EOD path divisible digraph.*

Proof. Let $P_n = v_1 \ldots v_n$ be a directed path where v_1 is the source and v_n is the sink and let F be an arbitrary digraph.

First assume that F is an n-EOD path divisible digraph. Denote by $S_1, \ldots, S_n$ the subsets of $V(F)$ that correspond with n-EOD path divisibility. We will show that $S = \cup_{i=1}^{n} \{v_i\} \times S_i$ is an EOD set of $P_n \square F$, meaning that $|N^-(v_i, u) \cap S| = 1$ for every $i \in [n]$ and $u \in V(F)$. For every (v_1, u) it holds that $|N^-(v_1, u) \cap S| \geq 1$ because S_1 is an EOD set of F and therefore $\{v_1\} \times S_1$ is an EOD set for $(P_n \square F)[F^{v_1}] \cong F$. Since v_1 is a source of P_n, there do not exist any other in-neighbors of vertices in F^{v_1} except those already in F^{v_1}, so $|N^-(v_1, u) \cap S| = 1$. Next we observe (v_i, u) for $2 \leq i \leq n$ and $u \in V(F)$. If $u \in S_{i-1}$, then (v_i, u) has an in-neighbor in $\{v_{i-1}\} \times S_{i-1} \subset S$ and if $u \in V(F) - S_{i-1}$, then (v_i, u) has an in-neighbor in $\{v_i\} \times S_i \subset S$. On the other hand these neighbors are unique in S, because $N_F^+(S_i) \cap S_{i-1} = \varnothing$ and S_i is an EOD set only for $F - S_{i-1}$. Hence, S is an EOD set of $P_n \square F$, which is therefore an EOD digraph.

Now assume that $P_n \square F$ is an EOD digraph and let S be its EOD set. Let $S_i = p_F(S \cap F^{v_i})$ for $i \in [n]$ and let $S_0 = \varnothing$. Clearly, every vertex from F^{v_1} must have exactly one in-neighbor in $\{v_1\} \times S_1$ because v_1 is a source of P_n. Therefore, S_1 is an EOD set of $F - S_0 = F$ and $N_F^+(S_1) \cap S_0 = \varnothing$. Now let $i > 1$. Vertices from $\{v_i\} \times S_{i-1}$ have in-neighbors in $\{v_{i-1}\} \times S_{i-1}$ and therefore do not have in-neighbors in $\{v_i\} \times S_i$, meaning that $N_F^+(S_i) \cap S_{i-1} = \varnothing$. On the other hand all other vertices in F^{v_i} must have an in-neighbor in $\{v_i\} \times S_i$, because S is an EOD set of $P_n \square F$. Thus, S_i is an EOD set only for $F - S_{i-1}$. Therefore, $S_1, \ldots, S_n$ yield that F is an n-EOD path divisible digraph. $\square$

With n-EOD cycle divisibility one can describe all EOD digraphs among $C_n \Box F$ where C_n is a directed cycle. The proof is very similar to the proof of Theorem 1 and is therefore omitted. The main difference is that we do not need to treat layer F^{v_1} separately since everything follows from the general step.

Theorem 2. *Let C_n be a directed cycle and let F be a digraph. The Cartesian product $C_n \Box F$ is an EOD digraph if and only if F is an n-EOD cycle divisible digraph.*

We continue with a path that is oriented in such a way, that it has exactly one source of degree two.

Theorem 3. *Let D be a digraph with an underlying graph $P_n = v_1 \ldots v_n$ with such an orientation that v_k, $1 < k < n$, is the only source, let $m = \max\{k, n - k + 1\}$ and let F be a digraph. The Cartesian product $D \Box F$ is an EOD digraph if and only if F is an m-EOD path divisible digraph.*

Proof. Let v_k be the only source of D. Thus $P' = v_k v_{k-1} \ldots v_1$ is a directed path on k vertices, where v_k is the source and v_1 is the sink, and $P'' = v_k v_{k+1} \ldots v_n$ is a directed path on $n - k + 1$ vertices, where v_k is the source and v_n is the sink. Let $m = \max\{k, n - k + 1\}$. If F is m-EOD path divisible with sets S_i, $i \in [m]$, then F is k-EOD path divisible with sets S_i, $i \in [k]$ and also $(n - k + 1)$-EOD path divisible with sets S_i, $i \in [n - k + 1]$. As shown in the proof of Theorem 1, sets $S(k) = (\cup_{i=1}^{k} \{v_i\} \times S_{k-i+1})$ and $S(n - k + 1) = (\cup_{i=k}^{n} \{v_i\} \times S_i)$ are EOD sets for $P' \Box F$ and $P'' \Box F$, respectively. Clearly, $S = S(k) \cup S(n - k + 1)$ is an EOD set of $D \Box F$ because $F^{v_k} \cap S(k) = F^{v_k} \cap S(n - k + 1)$ and $D \Box F$ is an EOD digraph.

Now assume that $D \Box F$ is an EOD digraph and let S be its EOD set. Since v_k is a source, $P' \Box F$ and $P'' \Box F$ are also EOD digraphs. By Theorem 1 F is a k-EOD path divisible digraph and an $(n - k + 1)$-EOD path divisible digraph. Hence, F is also m-EOD path divisible for $m = \max\{k, n - k + 1\}$. $\Box$

Before we deal with a path that is oriented in such a way, that it has exactly one sink of degree two, we need the following definition.

Definition 2. *Let F be a k-EOD and an ℓ-EOD path divisible digraph. We say that F is k, ℓ-sink friendly if there exist k-EOD path divisible sets $S_1, \ldots, S_k$ and ℓ-EOD path divisible sets $S_1', \ldots, S_\ell'$ such that $S_k \cap S_\ell' = \emptyset$ and there exists a set $S_0 \subseteq V(F)$, which is an EOD set only for $F - (S_k \cup S_\ell')$.*

Theorem 4. *Let D be a digraph with an underlying graph $P_n = v_1 \ldots v_n$ with such an orientation that v_k, $1 < k < n$, is the only sink and let F be a digraph. The Cartesian product $D \Box F$ is an EOD digraph if and only if F is $(k - 1), (n - k)$-sink friendly.*

Proof. Let F be digraph and let D be a digraph with an underlying graph $P_n = v_1 \ldots v_n$ where v_k, $1 < k < n$, is the only sink. This means that v_1 and v_n are the only sources of D.

First assume that F is $(k - 1), (n - k)$-sink friendly. This means that there exist sets $S_1, \ldots, S_{k-1}$ that yield $(k - 1)$-EOD path divisibility of F and sets $S_n, S_{n-1} \ldots, S_{k+1}$ that yield $(n - k)$-EOD path divisibility of F. In addition, $S_{k-1} \cap S_{k+1} = \emptyset$ and there exists a set $S_k \subseteq V(F)$ which is an EOD set only for $F - (S_{k-1} \cup S_{k+1})$. Let $A = \cup_{i=1}^{k-1} (\{v_i\} \times S_i)$ and $B = \cup_{j=k+1}^{n} (\{v_j\} \times S_j)$. We will show that $S = A \cup B \cup (\{v_k\} \times S_k)$ is an EOD set of $D \Box F$. Let $Q = v_1 \ldots v_{k-1}$ and $R = v_n v_{n-1} \ldots v_{k+1}$ be directed subpaths of D. By Theorem 1, $Q \Box F$ and $R \Box F$ are EOD digraphs with EOD sets A and B, respectively. No vertex from F^{v_k} is an in-neighbor of vertices from $Q \Box F$ and $R \Box F$, because v_k is a sink. Therefore, there exists exactly one in-neighbor in S for every vertex from $Q \Box F$ and $R \Box F$. So, we only need to check (v_k, f) for every $f \in V(F)$. If $f \in S_{k-1}$, then $(v_{k-1}, f) \in S$ is the in-neighbor of (v_k, f). On the other hand this is the only neighbor of (v_k, f) from S because $(v_{k+1}, f) \notin S$ as $S_{k-1} \cap S_{k+1} = \emptyset$ and because S_k is an EOD set only for $F - (S_{k-1} \cup S_{k+1})$. By symmetry we can see that (v_k, f) has also exactly one in-neighbor in S whenever $f \in S_{k+1}$. So let $f \in V(F) - (S_{k-1} \cap S_{k+1})$. Clearly (v_k, f) has no in-neighbor from S in $F^{v_{k-1}}$ and in $F^{v_{k+1}}$. Since S_k is an EOD set only for $F - (S_{k-1} \cup S_{k+1})$, there exists exactly one in-neighbor x of f in S_k and (v_k, x) is therefore the only neighbor of (v_k, f) from S. Hence, S is an EOD set of $D \Box F$ which is therefore an EOD digraph.

Now assume that $D \Box F$ is an EOD digraph and let S be its EOD set. Again, for directed paths $Q = v_1 \ldots v_{k-1}$ and $R = v_n v_{n-1} \ldots v_{k+1}$, $Q \Box F$ and $R \Box F$ are EOD digraphs with no influence from F^{v_k} in a product $D \Box F$. Sets $S_i = p_F(S \cap F^{v_i})$ for $i \in [k-1]$ are $(k-1)$-EOD path divisible sets by Theorem 1 and sets $S_j = p_F(S \cap F^{v_j})$ for $j \in \{k+1, \ldots, n\}$ (in reversed order) are $(n-k)$-EOD path divisible sets by the same theorem. If $f \in S_{k-1} \cap S_{k+1}$, then (v_k, f) has two in-neighbors (v_{k-1}, f) and (v_{k+1}, f) in S, a contradiction. Therefore, we have $S_{k-1} \cap S_{k+1} = \emptyset$. Let $S_k = p_F(S \cap F^{v_k})$ and let f be an arbitrary vertex from $\in V(F) - (S_{k-1} \cup S_{k+1})$. Clearly, (v_k, f) has exactly one in-neighbor in $\{v_k\} \times S_k$ because S is an EOD set. Also (v_k, f'), $f' \in S_{k-1} \cup S_{k+1}$, has no in-neighbor in $\{v_k\} \times S_k$ as it has its unique in-neighbor either in S, in $\{v_{k-1}\} \times S_{k-1}$ or in $\{v_{k+1}\} \times S_{k+1}$. Hence, S_k is an EOD set only for $V(F) - (S_{k-1} \cup S_{k+1})$ and F is $(k-1), (n-k)$-sink friendly. $\square$

The next challenge considering digraphs with an underlying graph isomorphic to a path or to a cycle is when we have more sinks and sources of degree two. Clearly, after every sink there comes a source and after each source there is a sink. In the case of a sink v of degree two digraph F must be k, ℓ-sink friendly by Theorem 4, where $k+1$ and $\ell+1$ are the distances to the sources that are closest to v. However this is not always enough. Let x and y be two sinks and let u be a source between them. By Theorem 4 digraph F must be k_1, ℓ_1-sink friendly and k_2, ℓ_2-sink friendly where $k_1 + 1$ and $k_2 + 1$ are the distances between u and x and u and y, respectively. We say that F is k_1, k_2-*source friendly* if $S_1 = S_1'$. Here, sets $S_1, \ldots, S_{k_1}$ and $S_1', \ldots, S_{k_2}'$ are appropriate k_1- and k_2-EOD path divisible sets from k_1, ℓ_1-sink friendly and k_2, ℓ_2-sink friendly constellation, respectively. Now, if we can assure sink friendliness for each sink, and also source friendliness for each source of a digraph F, then this is characteristic for $D \Box F$ to be an EOD digraph. Here, the underlying graph of D is either P_k or C_k with more than one source or sink of degree two. Because the proof is very similar and the formal statement is problematic (it depends on the status of vertices of degree one in D), we omit the proof of this.

We end this section with another fixed factor which this time has a star $K_{1,n}$ as its underlying graph. Vertex of degree n is the source and all the others are sinks.

Theorem 5. *Let D be a digraph with an underlying graph $K_{1,n}$ with the set of vertices $\{v_0, v_1, \ldots, v_n\}$, where $\delta_D^+(v_0) = n$ and let F be an arbitrary digraph. The Cartesian product $D \Box F$ is an EOD digraph if and only if F is a 2-EOD path divisible digraph.*

Proof. Let D be a digraph with an underlying graph $K_{1,n}$ with the set of vertices $\{v_0, v_1, \ldots v_n\}$, where $\delta_D^+(v_0) = n$, which means that v_0 is the source. Clearly, $\delta_D^-(v_i) = 1$ and v_i is a sink for every $i \in [n]$. Let F be an arbitrary digraph. Denote by A the set of vertices of $D \Box F$.

First assume that F is 2-EOD path divisible with sets S_1 and S_2. We will show that $S = (\{v_0\} \times S_1) \cup (\cup_{i=1}^n \{v_i\} \times S_2)$ is an EOD set for $D \Box F$, meaning that $|N^-((e, f)) \cap S| = 1$ for every $(e, f) \in A$. For every $(v_0, f) \in A$ it holds that $|N^-((v_0, f)) \cap S| \geq 1$ since S_1 is an EOD set for F and therefore $\{v_0\} \times S_1$ is an EOD set for $(D \Box F)[F^{v_0}] \cong F$. Since v_0 is a source, there do not exist any other in-neighbors of vertices F^{v_0} except those from F^{v_0}, so $|N^-((v_0, f)) \cap S| = 1$. Now let $(v_i, f) \in A$, $i \in [n]$. Vertices from $\{v_0\} \times S_1$ are the in-neighbors of all of the vertices from $\{v_i\} \times S_1$ and, since F is 2-EOD path divisible, vertices from $\{v_i\} \times S_2$ are the in-neighbors of all of the vertices from $\{v_i\} \times (V(F) - S_1)$. So $|N^-((v_i, f)) \cap S| \geq 1$. By the definition of 2-EOD path divisibility it holds that $|N^+(\{v_i\} \times S_2) \cap (\{v_i\} \times S_1)| = 0$, meaning that $|N^-((v_i, f)) \cap S| = 1$.

Now assume that $D \Box F$ is an EOD digraph and let S be its EOD set. Let v_i be an arbitrary vertex of the star D different from v_0. Vertices from $S \cap F^{v_0}$ are in-neighbors of some (or all) of the vertices of F^{v_i}. Denote the set of those vertices by F_{v_i}. Vertices from $F^{v_i} - F_{v_i}$ have to have in-neighbors in $S \cap F^{v_i}$, since they do not have in-neighbors in $S \cap F^{v_0}$. Vertices from $S \cap F^{v_i}$ are not in-neighbors of any of the vertices from F_{v_i}, since that would mean that there exists $(v_i, f) \in F_{v_i}$ for which $|N^-(v_i, f) \cap S| > 1$, a contradiction with S being an EOD set of $D \square F$. Let $S_1 := p_H(S \cap F^{s_0})$ and $S_2 := p_H(S \cap F^{s_1})$. Clearly, S_1 is an EOD set of F and S_2 is an EOD set only for $F - S_1$. Hence, F is a 2-EOD path divisible digraph. $\square$

4. The Strong Product

In this section we first characterize all EOD strong product digraphs $D \boxtimes F$, such that the underlying graphs of D and F are cycles C_m and C_n, respectively. Then we extend this result to a characterization of all EOD digraphs $D \boxtimes F$ where D and F have uni-cyclic graphs as their underlying graphs. We also conjecture that there are no more EOD digraphs among the strong product of digraphs. We start with several lemmas that come in handy later.

Lemma 1. *Let D and F be two digraphs without isolated vertices. If one of them has a source, then $D \boxtimes F$ is not an EOD digraph.*

Proof. Let D and F be two digraphs. If D has a source u and F has a source v, then vertex (u, v) is a source in $D \boxtimes F$ and it has no in-neighbor. Hence, there does not exist an EOD set for $D \boxtimes F$. Without loss of generality let D have a source u and let F be an arbitrary digraph without a source. We will try to construct an EOD set S for $D \boxtimes F$. Since u is a source, vertex $(u, y), y \in V(F)$, has in-neighbors only in D^u, and since F does not have a source at least one in-neighbor of (u, y) exists. Let $(u, y') \in S$ be the in-neighbor of (u, y). Again, since u is a source and F has no source, there exists an in-neighbor $(u, y'') \in S$ of $(u, y') \in D^u$. Denote by u' an out-neighbor of u in D. It exists since D contains no isolated vertices. By the definition of the strong product of two digraphs, both (u, y') and (u, y'') are in-neighbors of (u', y') and since $(u, y'), (u, y'') \in S$ vertex (u', y') has two different in-neighbors in S. Meaning that S is not an EOD-set, so $D \boxtimes F$ is not an EOD digraph. $\square$

In the rest of this section we use the following notation and orientation for directed cycles $C_m = c_1 c_2 \ldots c_m$ and $C_n = d_n d_{n-1} \ldots d_1$ on m and n vertices, respectively, see Figure 3, and with (c_i, d_j) we denote a vertex of a strong product of those two cycles. All operations on the first index i are via (mod m) and on the second index j are via (mod n). We also partition $V(C_m \boxtimes C_n)$ into sets

$$A = \{(c_i, d_j); i + j = 3q + 1, q \in \mathbb{N}\},$$
$$B = \{(c_i, d_j); i + j = 3q + 2, q \in \mathbb{N}\} \quad \text{and} \tag{3}$$
$$C = \{(c_i, d_j); i + j = 3q, q \in \mathbb{N}\}.$$

Lemma 2. *If there exists an EOD set S for $C_m \boxtimes C_n$, $m, n \geq 3$, and $(c_i, d_j) \in S$, then $(c_{i-1}, d_{j+1}) \in S$.*

Proof. Let $C_m \boxtimes C_n$, $m, n \geq 3$, be an EOD digraph, let S be its EOD set and let $(c_i, d_j) \in S$. The vertex (c_i, d_j) is an in-neighbor of $(c_{i+1}, d_j), (c_i, d_{j-1})$ and (c_{i+1}, d_{j-1}). On the other hand (c_i, d_j) must also have an in-neighbor in S. The only in-neighbors of (c_i, d_j) are $(c_{i-1}, d_j), (c_i, d_{j+1})$ and (c_{i-1}, d_{j+1}). If $(c_{i-1}, d_j) \in S$, then (c_i, d_j) and (c_{i-1}, d_j) are both in-neighbors of (c_i, d_{j-1}), a contradiction. Similarly, if $(c_i, d_{j+1}) \in S$, then (c_i, d_j) and (c_i, d_{j+1}) are both in-neighbors of (c_{i+1}, d_j), a contradiction again. Hence, (c_{i-1}, d_{j+1}) must be in S. $\square$

Lemma 3. *If there exists an EOD set S for $C_m \boxtimes C_n$, $m, n \geq 3$, and $(c_i, d_j) \in S$, then $(c_i, d_{j+3}), (c_{i-3}, d_j) \in S$.*

Proof. Let $C_m \boxtimes C_n$, $m, n \geq 3$, be an EOD digraph and let S be its EOD set. With possible change of notation let $(c_m, d_1) \in S$. A vertex (c_m, d_1) is an in-neighbor of the vertices $(c_1, d_1), (c_m, d_n)$ and (c_1, d_n). Vertex (c_{m-1}, d_2) belongs to S by Lemma 2. Clearly, (c_{m-1}, d_2) is also the in-neighbor of vertices (c_{m-1}, d_1) and (c_m, d_2). So $(c_m, d_2) \notin S$ because otherwise (c_m, d_1) has two in-neighbors in S. If $(c_m, d_3) \in S$, then (c_m, d_2) has two in-neighbors in S again. So $(c_m, d_3) \notin S$.

Vertex $(c_{m-2}, d_3) \in S$ by Lemma 2 since $(c_{m-1}, d_2) \in S$ and (c_{m-2}, d_3) is an in-neighbor of (c_{m-2}, d_2) and (c_{m-1}, d_3). One of the in-neighbors (c_{m-1}, d_3), (c_m, d_4) or (c_{m-1}, d_4) of the vertex (c_m, d_3) must be in S. If $(c_{m-1}, d_3) \in S$, then (c_m, d_2) has two in-neighbors in S. Similarly, if $(c_{m-1}, d_4) \in S$, then (c_{m-1}, d_3) has two in-neighbors in S. Hence, $(c_m, d_4) \in S$.

We can exchange the role of factors and by symmetric arguments get that (c_{i-3}, d_j) also belongs to S. □

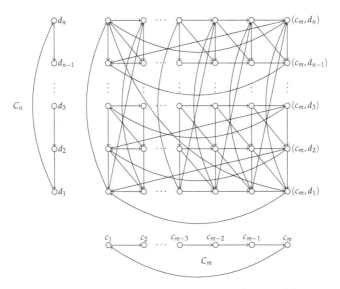

Figure 3. The strong product of two directed cycles C_m and C_n.

Now we can characterize all EOD digraphs among strong product digraphs of two cycles.

Theorem 6. *Let D and F be digraphs with underlying graphs C_m and C_n, respectively. The strong product $D \boxtimes F$ is an EOD digraph if and only if both D and F are directed cycles, $m = 3\ell$ and $n = 3k$ for some $k, \ell \in \mathbb{N}$.*

Proof. First, let $m = 3\ell$ and $n = 3k$, $k, \ell \in \mathbb{N}$, and let $D \cong C_m$ and $F \cong C_n$ be two directed cycles. Recall the sets A, B and C from (3). We will show that A is an EOD set of $C_m \boxtimes C_n$. The in-neighbor of a vertex $(c_i, d_j) \in B$, $i + j = 3q + 2$, that is in A is (c_{i-1}, d_j), since $(i - 1) + j = (i + j) - 1 = (3q + 2) - 1 = 3q + 1$. The in-neighbor of a vertex $(c_i, d_j) \in C$, $i + j = 3q$, that is in A is (c_i, d_{j+1}), since $i + (j + 1) = (i + j) + 1 = 3q + 1$. The in-neighbor of a vertex $(c_i, d_j) \in A$, $i + j = 3q + 1$, that is in A is (c_{i-1}, d_{j+1}), since $(i - 1) + (j + 1) = i + j = 3q + 1$. So every vertex v from $V(C_m \boxtimes C_n)$ is efficiently dominated by A. Moreover v has exactly one in-neighbor in A since exactly one in-neighbor of v has the sum of indices equal to $3q + 1$.

To prove the contrary let D and F be two digraphs with underlying graphs C_m and C_n, respectively, such that $D \boxtimes F$ is an EOD digraph with an EOD set S. If one of the cycles is not directed, then it has a source. By Lemma 1 the strong product $D \boxtimes F$ is not an EOD digraph. So we may assume that both D and F are directed cycles. With possible change of notation we may assume that $(c_m, d_1) \in S$. By consecutive use of Lemma 3 we get that $\{(c_m, d_{3k+1}) : k \in [[n/3]]\} \subseteq S$ and that $\{(c_{m-3\ell}, d_1) : \ell \in [[m/3]]\} \subseteq S$. If $n = 3k$, then $(c_m, d_{n-2}) \in S$ and $(c_m, d_{n+1}) \in S$ by Lemma 3 again where $(c_m, d_{n+1}) = (c_m, d_1)$. If $n = 3k + 1$, then $(c_m, d_n) \in S$ and $(c_m, d_{n+3}) \in S$ by Lemma 3 again where $(c_m, d_{n+3}) = (c_m, d_3)$. Hence, (c_m, d_3), $(c_m, d_4) \in S$ and they are both the in-neighbors of (c_1, d_3), a contradiction. If $n = 3k + 2$, then $(c_m, d_{n-1}) \in S$ and $(c_m, d_{n+2}) \in S$ by Lemma 3 again where $(c_m, d_{n+2}) = (c_m, d_2)$. Hence, (c_m, d_1), $(c_m, d_2) \in S$ and they are both the in-neighbors of (c_1, d_1), a contradiction again. Therefore, $n = 3k$. By symmetric arguments we also get that $m = 3\ell$ and the proof is completed. $\square$

Next we expand Theorem 6 and present a bigger class of EOD strong product digraphs. For this let $T_1, \ldots, T_m$ be arbitrary trees with roots $r_1, \ldots, r_m$, respectively. We define an underlying graph C_m^+ such that we identify root r_i with vertex c_i of a cycle C_m for every $i \in [m]$. Clearly, C_m^+ is exactly a uni-cyclic graph, but we need the before mentioned structure. Notice that $C_m^+ \cong C_m$ if every tree T_i is a one vertex tree. We say that a digraph with the underlying graph C_m^+ is *well oriented* if C_m is a directed cycle and every edge from T_i is oriented away from the root r_i for every $i \in [m]$. We use the same notation C_m^+ for a digraph with the underlying graph C_m^+.

Theorem 7. *Let $m, n \geq 3$ be two positive integers. The strong product $C_m^+ \boxtimes C_n^+$ is an EOD digraph if and only if both C_m^+ and C_n^+ are well oriented, $m = 3\ell$ and $n = 3k$ for some $k, \ell \in \mathbb{N}$.*

Proof. First, let $m = 3\ell$ and $n = 3k$, $k, \ell \in \mathbb{N}$, and let C_m^+ and C_n^+ be well oriented. We show this direction in two steps. First let $C_n^+ \cong C_n$ and we show that $C_m^+ \boxtimes C_n$ is an EOD digraph. By Theorem 6 $C_m \boxtimes C_n$ is an EOD digraph with an EOD set A from (3). We extend set A to set A^+ for which we then show that it is an EOD set of $C_m^+ \boxtimes C_n$. First we choose the notation for all the vertices from $(C_m^+ \boxtimes C_n) - V(C_m \boxtimes C_n)$. With v_i we denote all the vertices from $C_m^+ - V(C_m)$ with $d_{C_m^+}(c_m, v_i) = i$. Notice that different vertices from C_m^+ can have the same notation. Vertices from $(C_m^+ \boxtimes C_n) - V(C_m \boxtimes C_n)$ are then denoted as usual by (v_i, d_j). Furthermore, we denote sets $A' = \{(v_i, d_j) : i + j = 3q + 1, q \in \mathbb{N}\}$, $B' = \{(v_i, d_j) : i + j = 3q + 2, q \in \mathbb{N}\}$ and $C' = \{(v_i, d_j) : i + j = 3q, q \in \mathbb{N}\}$. Now we partition $V(C_m^+ \boxtimes C_n)$ into sets $A^+ = A \cup A'$, $B^+ = B \cup B'$ and $C^+ = C \cup C'$, where A, B and C are from (3). We will show that A^+ is an EOD set of $C_m^+ \boxtimes C_n$.

By Theorem 6 each vertex from A, B and C has exactly one in-neighbor in A. The in-neighbor of a vertex $(v_i, d_j) \in B'$, $i + j = 3q + 2$, that is in A^+ is either (v_{i-1}, d_j) or (c_{i-1}, d_j), since $(i - 1) + j = (i + j) - 1 = (3q + 2) - 1 = 3q + 1$. The in-neighbor of a vertex $(v_i, d_j) \in C'$, $i + j = 3q$, that is in A^+ is (v_i, d_{j+1}), since $i + (j + 1) = (i + j) + 1 = 3q + 1$. The in-neighbor of a vertex $(v_i, d_j) \in A'$, $i + j = 3q + 1$, that is in A^+ is either (v_{i-1}, d_{j+1}) or (c_{i-1}, d_{j+1}), since $(i - 1) + (j + 1) = i + j = 3q + 1$. So every vertex x from $V(C_m^+ \boxtimes C_n)$ has an in-neighbor in A^+. Moreover x has exactly one in-neighbor in A^+ since exactly one in-neighbor of x has the sum of indices equal to $3q + 1$.

By symmetric arguments we can show that $C_m^+ \boxtimes C_n^+$ is an EOD digraph whenever $C_m^+ \cong C_m$. So, we can assume that $C_m^+ \not\cong C_m$ and $C_n^+ \not\cong C_n$. We know by the above arguments that $C_m^+ \boxtimes C_n$ is an EOD digraph with an EOD set A^+. Since there is no arc from vertices of $D = (C_m^+ \boxtimes C_n^+) - V(C_m^+ \boxtimes C_n)$ to vertices of $(C_m^+ \boxtimes C_n)$ we will use the set A^+ for $C_m^+ \boxtimes C_n$ and enlarge it to A^* that will be an EOD set of $C_m^+ \boxtimes C_n^+$. For this we first need to present the following notation for vertices of D. By (c_i, u_k^j) we denote all the vertices from D that belong to layers $(C_m^+)^{d_j}$ and $(C_n^+)^{c_i}$ and are at the distance k from (c_i, d_j). Similarly, we use (v_i, u_k^j) for all the vertices from D that belong to layers $(C_m^+)^{d_j}$ and $(C_n^+)^{v_i}$ and are at the distance k from (v_i, d_j). Notice that different vertices from D can have the same notation. Beside A^+ we put (c_i, u_k^j) and (v_i, u_k^j) in A^* if $(i + j = 3q + 1$ and $k = 3p)$ or $(i + j = 3q + 2$ and $k = 3p - 2)$ or $(i + j = 3q$ and $k = 3p - 1)$ for some $p, q \in \mathbb{N}$.

We will show that A^* is an EOD set of $C_m^+ \boxtimes C_n^+$. We already know that $A^+ \subseteq A^*$ is an EOD set of $C_m^+ \boxtimes C_n$ and we need to show that every vertex from D has exactly one in-neighbor in A^*. Notice that every (x_i, u_k^j), where $x \in \{c, v\}$, has exactly three in-neighbors $(x_{i-1}, u_k^j), (x_{i-1}, u_{k-1}^j)$ and (x_i, u_{k-1}^j). (If $k = 1$, then we put $u_0^j = d_j$.) We need to consider nine cases. They are presented in the following Table 1.

In the first two columns we present all nine options. The middle column contains the in-neighbor of (x_i, u_k^j) from A^* and the last two columns show why this is the in-neighbor of (x_i, u_k^j) in A^*. Finally, we show that only one of the three in-neighbors of (x_i, u_k^j) is in A^*. If $(x_{i-1}, u_{k-1}^j) \in A^*$, then exactly one index of the other two in-neighbors differs by 1 from the same index of (x_{i-1}, u_{k-1}^j) and they are therefore not in A^*. By symmetry (x_{i-1}, u_{k-1}^j) is also not in A^* whenever either (x_{i-1}, u_k^j) or (x_i, u_{k-1}^j) is in A^*. So let $(x_i, u_{k-1}^j) \in A^*$. In this case we can build a similar table as before, only that this table shows that (x_{i-1}, u_k^j) is not in A^*. Similarly, also $(x_i, u_{k-1}^j) \notin A^*$ when $(x_{i-1}, u_k^j) \in A^*$.

Table 1. Nine cases considered that show that every vertex from D has exactly one in-neighbor in A^*.

$i+j$	k	Neighbor in A^*		
$3q$	$3p$	(x_i, u_{k-1}^j)	$i+j=3q$	$k-1=3p-1$
$3q$	$3p-2$	(x_{i-1}, u_k^j)	$i-1+j=3q-1$	$k=3p-2$
$3q$	$3p-1$	(x_{i-1}, u_{k-1}^j)	$i-1+j=3q-1$	$k-1=3p-2$
$3q+1$	$3p$	(x_{i-1}, u_{k-1}^j)	$i-1+j=3q$	$k-1=3p-1$
$3q+1$	$3p-2$	(x_i, u_{k-1}^j)	$i+j=3q+1$	$k-1=3p-3$
$3q+1$	$3p-1$	(x_{i-1}, u_k^j)	$i-1+j=3q$	$k=3p-1$
$3q+2$	$3p$	(x_{i-1}, u_k^j)	$i-1+j=3q+1$	$k=3p$
$3q+2$	$3p-2$	(x_{i-1}, u_{k-1}^j)	$i-1+j=3q+1$	$k-1=3p-3$
$3q+2$	$3p-1$	(x_i, u_{k-1}^j)	$i+j=3q+2$	$k-1=3p-2$

To prove the contrary let $C_m^+ \boxtimes C_n^+$ be an EOD digraph with an EOD set S. If there exists an arc in a tree T_i that is not oriented away from the root, then we have a source in T_i and with that a contradiction with Lemma 1. Hence, all arcs of trees from C_m^+ are oriented away from the root. If cycle C_m is not a directed cycle, then we have a source c_j on C_m for some $j \in [m]$. Because all arcs of T_j are oriented away from the root $r_j = c_j$, we have a source c_j in C_m^+ as well, a contradiction with Lemma 1 again. Hence, C_m^+ is well oriented. Also, C_n^+ must be well oriented by the same arguments. Next we observe a subdigraph $C_m \boxtimes C_n$ of $C_m^+ \boxtimes C_n^+$. By the orientation of all arcs of all the trees, we see that there does not exist an arc from vertices of $(C_m^+ \boxtimes C_n^+) - V(C_m \boxtimes C_n)$ to vertices of $C_m \boxtimes C_n$. Therefore, $C_m \boxtimes C_n$ is an EOD digraph as well and by Theorem 6 we get $m = 3\ell$ and $n = 3k$ for some positive integers ℓ and k. □

The above results give rise to the following conjecture. We believe that it is true, but the proof is a challenge.

Conjecture 1. *The strong product $D \boxtimes F$ is an EOD digraph if and only if $D \cong C_m^+$ and $F \cong C_n^+$ are well oriented, $m = 3\ell$ and $n = 3k$ for some $k, \ell \in \mathbb{N}$.*

5. The Direct and the Lexicographic Product

We conclude this paper with characterizations of the EOD digraphs among the direct and the lexicographic product. They follow from (1) and (2), respectively, and are no surprise. The following result for the direct product is an analogue of the result for the EOD graphs from [8] (under the name of total perfect codes).

Theorem 8. *Let D and F be digraphs. The direct product $D \times F$ is an EOD digraph if and only if D and F are EOD digraphs.*

Proof. Let D and F be EOD digraphs with EOD sets S_D and S_F, respectively. We will show that $S_D \times S_F$ is an EOD set of $D \times F$. By (1) it holds that

$$V(D \times F) \subseteq \bigcup_{(d,f) \in S_D \times S_F} N_{D \times F}^+((d, f)).$$

Suppose there exists a vertex (d_0, f_0) that has two different in-neighbors (d, f) and (d', f') in $S_D \times S_F$. If $d = d'$, then $f \neq f'$, and by (1) we have

$$N^+_{D \times F}((d,f)) \cap N^+_{D \times F}((d', f')) = (N^+_D(d) \times N^+_F(f)) \cap (N^+_D(d) \times N^+_F(f')) = N^+_D(d) \times (N^+_F(f) \cap N^+_F(f')).$$

Thus, f_0 has two different in-neighbors f and f' in S_F. That is a contradiction since S_F in an EOD set of F. If $f = f'$, then $d \neq d'$ and we obtain a contradiction by symmetric arguments. Meaning that $d \neq d'$ and $f \neq f'$. Again by (1) the vertex d_0 has two different in-neighbors d and d' in S_D and f_0 has two different in-neighbors f and f' in S_F, a contradiction with S_D and S_F being EOD sets of D and F, respectively. Therefore, no two vertices from $S_D \times S_F$ have a common out-neighbor, meaning that $D \times F$ is an EOD digraph.

Now let $D \times F$ be an EOD digraph and S be its EOD set. Let $f \in F$ be an arbitrary vertex. Every vertex from D^f has exactly one in-neighbor in S. Denote with S_f the set of all those vertices. We will show that $p_D(S_f)$ is an EOD set of D. Let d and d' be two different vertices from $p_D(S_f)$. Choose $f', f'' \in V(F)$ such that $(d, f'), (d', f'') \in S_f$. If there exists d_0 such that d and d' are its in-neighbors, then (d_0, f) has two in-neighbors (d, f') and (d', f'') in S, a contradiction with S being an EOD set of $D \times F$. By (1) and because S is an EOD set of $D \times F$ it also holds that $V(D) \subseteq \bigcup_{d \in p_D(S_f)} N^+_D(d)$. Therefore, $p_D(S_f)$ is an EOD set of D, meaning that D is an EOD digraph. By symmetric arguments F is also an EOD digraph and with that the proof is completed. $\square$

The result for EOD digraphs among the lexicographic product of digraphs is an analogue to the graph version from [9].

Theorem 9. *Let D and F be digraphs. The lexicographic product $D \circ F$ is an EOD digraph if and only if*

(i) *D is a digraph without arcs and F is an EOD digraph, or*
(ii) *D is an EOD digraph and F contains a sink.*

Proof. Let D be a digraph on n vertices without edges and F be an EOD digraph. Then $D \circ F$ is isomorphic to n copies of F and since F is an EOD digraph, n copies of F also form an EOD digraph.

Now, let D be an EOD digraph, let S_D be its EOD set and let f_0 be a sink in F. We will show that $S_D \times \{f_0\}$ is an EOD set of $D \circ F$. By (2) it holds that $N^+_{D \circ F}((d, f_0)) = N^+_D(d) \times V(F)$ since f_0 is a sink in F. So $\bigcup_{d \in S_D} N^+_{D \circ F}((d, f_0))$ equals $V(D \times F)$. If for $d, d' \in S_D$ and $d \neq d'$ there exists a vertex in $D \circ F$ which in-neighbors are both (d, f_0) and (d', f_0), then there also exists a vertex in D which in-neighbors are both d and d'. A contradiction with S_D being an EOD set of D. Therefore, $D \circ F$ is an EOD digraph.

Conversely, let $D \circ F$ be an EOD digraph, S its EOD set and $(d, f) \in S$ an arbitrary vertex. If f is not a sink in F, then there exists a vertex $f' \in F^d$, such that (d, f) is an in-neighbor of (d, f'). Denote with (d_1, f_1) the unique in-neighbor of (d, f) from S. If $d_1 \neq d$, then (d, f') has both (d, f) and (d_1, f_1) as its in-neighbors, which is not possible. Hence, $d_1 = d$. If d has any out-neighbors, then for every out-neighbor d' of d a vertex (d', f) has both (d, f) and (d_1, f_1) as its in-neighbors, a contradiction. So no d such that $(d, f) \in S$ has any out-neighbors. Since every vertex $(d'', f'') \in V(D \circ F)$ has exactly one in-neighbor $(d, f) \in S$, we conclude that $d'' \neq d$ yields that d has at least one out-neighbor, which is not possible. Therefore, $d'' = d$ and no $d'' \in V(D)$ has any out-neighbors. Meaning that D is a digraph without arcs. To prove that F is an EOD digraph choose an arbitrary F-layer F^d (which always induces a digraph isomorphic to F). Clearly, the vertices in F^d that are also in S form an EOD set of $(D \circ F)[F^d] \cong F$. So F is an EOD digraph and (i) follows.

Now assume f is a sink. Notice that in this case F^d is a subset of all out-neighbors of (d_0, f), where d_0 is an in-neighbor of d. We will prove that $p_D(S)$ is an EOD set of D. Suppose it is not. Then there exist $d, d' \in p_D(S)$ with a common out-neighbor. With this and (2) we have a contradiction with S being an EOD set of $D \circ F$. Meaning that $p_D(S)$ is an EOD set of D and (ii) follows. $\square$

6. Conclusions

In this work we treated the four standard products of digraphs (the Cartesian, the strong, the direct and the lexicographic) with respect to the efficient open domination. The idea is to describe which digraphs among these products are efficient open domination digraphs and to describe them with the properties of their factors. We completely characterized such digraphs among the direct product (Theorem 8) and among the lexicographic product (Theorem 9). For the efficient open domination Cartesian product digraphs the characterizations are given for those for which the first factor has an underlying graph that is a path (Theorems 1, 3 and 4), a cycle (Theorem 2) or a star (Theorem 5). This yields an idea on how to deal with the Cartesian product of digraphs with one fixed factor and an arbitrary second one. Among the efficient open domination strong product of digraphs we characterized those in which both factors have uni-cyclic graphs as their underlying graphs (Theorems 6 and 7). We also conjecture that this are the only strong product digraphs that are the efficient open domination digraphs.

Author Contributions: All authors contributed equally to this work. Conceptualization, D.B. and I.P.; methodology, D.B. and I.P.; formal analysis, D.B. and I.P.; validation, D.B. and I.P.; writing—original draft preparation, D.B. and I.P.; writing—review and editing, D.B. and I.P. All authors have read and agreed to the published version of the manuscript.

Funding: This research was partially funded by Javna Agencija za Raziskovalno Dejavnost RS under grant numbers P1-0297 and J1-9109.

Conflicts of Interest: The authors declare no conflict of interest.

References

1. Hammack, R.; Imrich, W.; Klavžar, S. *Handbook of Product Graphs, Second Edition*; CRC Press, Boca Raton, FL, 2011.
2. Cockayne, E.J.; Hartnell, B.L.; Hedetniemi, S.T.; Laskar, R. Perfect domination in graphs. *J. Comb. Inf. Syst. Sci.* **1993**, *18*, 136–148.
3. Gavlas, H.; Schultz, K. Efficient open domination. *Electron. Notes Discret. Math.* **2002**, *11*, 681–691. [CrossRef]
4. Tamizh Chelvam, T. Efficient open domination in Cayley graphs. *Appl. Math. Lett.* **2012**, *25*, 1560–1564. [CrossRef]
5. Cowen, R.; Hechler, S.H.; Kennedy, J.W.; Steinberg, A. Odd neighborhood transversals on grid graphs. *Discret. Math.* **2007**, *307*, 2200–2208. [CrossRef]
6. Dejter, I.J. Perfect domination in regular grid graphs. *Australas. J. Combin.* **2008**, *42*, 99–114.
7. Klostermeyer, W.F.; Goldwasser, J.L. Total Perfect Codes in Grid Graphs. *Bull. Inst. Combin. Appl.* **2006**, *46*, 61–68.
8. Abay-Asmerom, G.; Hammack, R.H.; Taylor, D.T. Total perfect codes in tensor products of graphs. *Ars Combin.* **2008**, *88*, 129–134.
9. Kuziak, D.; Peterin, I.; Yero. I.G. Efficient open domination in graph products. *Discret. Math. Theoret. Comput. Sci.* **2014**, *16*, 105–120.
10. Kraner Šumenjak, T.; Peterin, I.; Rall, D.F.; Tepeh, A. Partitioning the vertex set of *G* to make $G \square H$ an efficient open domination graph. *Discret. Math. Theoret. Comput. Sci.* **2016**, *18*, #1503.
11. Biggs, N. Perfect codes in graphs. *J. Combin. Theory Ser. B* **1973**, *15*, 289–296. [CrossRef]
12. Bange, D.W.; Barkauskas, A.E.; Slater, P.J. Disjoint dominating sets in trees. Disjoint dominating sets in trees. *Sandia Lab. Rep. SAND* **1978**, *78*, 1087J.
13. Lokshtanov, D.; Pilipczuk, M.; van Leeuwen, E.J. Independence and Efficient Domination on P_6-free Graphs. *ACM Trans. Algorithms* **2017**, *14*, 3. [CrossRef]
14. Brandstädt, A.; Mosca, R. Weighted Efficient Domination for P_6-free Graphs. *Tech. Rep.* **2015**, arXiv:1508.07733v2.
15. Brandstädt, A.; Eschen, E.M.; Friese, E.; Karthick, T. Efficient domination for classes of P_6-free graphs. *Discret. Appl. Math.* **2017**, *233*, 15–27. [CrossRef]
16. Abay-Asmerom, G.; Hammack, R.H.; Taylor, D.T. Perfect *r*-codes in strong products of graphs. *Bull. Inst. Combin. Appl.* **2009**, *55*, 66–72.
17. Jerebic, J.; Klavžar, S.; Špacapan, S. Characterizing *r*-perfect codes in direct products of two and three cycles. *Inf. Process. Lett.* **2005**, *94*, 1–6. [CrossRef]
18. Klavžar, S.; Špacapan, S.; Žerovnik, J. An almost complete description of perfect codes in direct products of cycles. *Adv. Appl. Math.* **2006**, *37*, 2–18. [CrossRef]

19. Žerovnik, J. Perfect codes in direct products of cycles—a complete characterization. *Adv. in Appl. Math.* **2008**, *41*, 197–205. [CrossRef]
20. Taylor, D.T. Perfect *r*-codes in lexicographic products of graphs. *Ars Combin.* **2009**, *93*, 215–223.
21. Mollard, M. On perfect codes in Cartesian products of graphs. *Eur. J. Combin.* **2011**, *32*, 398–403. [CrossRef]
22. Klavžar, S.; Peterin, I.; Yero, I.G. Graphs that are simultaneously efficient open domination and efficient closed domination graphs. *Discret. Appl. Math.* **2017**, *217*, 613–621. [CrossRef]
23. Barkauskas, A.E.; Host, L.H. Finding efficient dominating sets in oriented graphs. *Congr. Numer.* **1993**, *98*, 27–32.
24. Huang, J.; Xu, J.-M. The bondage numbers and efficient dominations of vertex-transitive graphs. *Discret. Math.* **2008**, *308*, 571–582. [CrossRef]
25. Martinez, C.; Beivide, R.; Gabidulin, E. Perfect codes for metrics induced by circulant graphs. *IEEE Trans. Inf. Theory* **2007**, *53*, 3042–3052. [CrossRef]
26. Niepel, Ĺ.; Černý, A. Efficient domination in directed tori and the Vizing's conjecture for directed graphs. *Ars Combin.* **2009**, *91*, 411–422.
27. Schwenk, A.J.; Yue, B.Q. Efficient dominating sets in labeled rooted oriented trees. *Discrete Math.* **2005**, *305*, 276–298. [CrossRef]
28. Schaudt, O. Efficient total domination in digraphs. *J. Discret. Algorithms* **2012**, *15*, 32–42. [CrossRef]
29. Sohn, M.Y.; Chen, X.-G.; Hu, F.-T. On efficiently total dominatable digraphs. *Bull. Malays. Math. Sci. Soc.* **2018**, *41*, 1749–1758. [CrossRef]
30. Peterin, I.; Yero, I.G. Efficient closed domination in digraph products. *J. Combin. Optim.* **2019**, *38*, 130–149. [CrossRef]

Article

Further Results on the Total Roman Domination in Graphs

Abel Cabrera Martínez [1,*], Suitberto Cabrera García [2] and Andrés Carrión García [2]

[1] Departament d'Enginyeria Informàtica i Matemàtiques, Universitat Rovira i Virgili, Av. Països Catalans 26, 43007 Tarragona, Spain

[2] Departamento de Estadística e Investigación Operativa Aplicadas y Calidad, Universitat Politécnica de Valencia, Camino de Vera s/n, 46022 Valencia, Spain; suicabga@eio.upv.es (S.C.G.); acarrion@eio.upv.es (A.C.G.)

* Correspondence: abel.cabrera@urv.cat

Received: 17 February 2020; Accepted: 2 March 2020; Published: 5 March 2020

Abstract: Let G be a graph without isolated vertices. A function $f : V(G) \rightarrow \{0,1,2\}$ is a total Roman dominating function on G if every vertex $v \in V(G)$ for which $f(v) = 0$ is adjacent to at least one vertex $u \in V(G)$ such that $f(u) = 2$, and if the subgraph induced by the set $\{v \in V(G) : f(v) \geq 1\}$ has no isolated vertices. The total Roman domination number of G, denoted $\gamma_{tR}(G)$, is the minimum weight $\omega(f) = \sum_{v \in V(G)} f(v)$ among all total Roman dominating functions f on G. In this article we obtain new tight lower and upper bounds for $\gamma_{tR}(G)$ which improve the well-known bounds $2\gamma(G) \leq \gamma_{tR}(G) \leq 3\gamma(G)$, where $\gamma(G)$ represents the classical domination number. In addition, we characterize the graphs that achieve equality in the previous lower bound and we give necessary conditions for the graphs which satisfy the equality in the upper bound above.

Keywords: total Roman domination; Roman domination; semitotal domination; domination

---

1. Introduction

Domination theory is a classical and interesting topic in theory of graphs, as well as one of the most active areas of research in this topic. The increasing interest in this area is partly explained by the diversity of applications to both theoretical and real-world problems, such as facility location problems, monitoring communication, coding theory, algorithm design, complex ecosystems, electrical networks, among others. A set $D \subseteq V(G)$ of vertices of a graph G is a dominating set if every vertex in $V(G) \setminus D$ is adjacent to at least one vertex in D. The domination number of G, denoted by $\gamma(G)$, is the minimum cardinality among all dominating sets of G. Many variants of the previous concept have appeared in the literature. We refer to [1,2] for numerous results on this issue.

A remarkable variant of the parameter above, and one of the most studied, is as follows. A dominating set D of a graph G without isolated vertices is a total dominating set if the subgraph induced by the vertices of D has no isolated vertex. Notice that any graph with no isolated vertex has a total dominating set, since $D = V(G)$ is such a set. The total domination number of G, denoted by $\gamma_t(G)$, is the minimum cardinality among all total dominating sets of G. More information on total domination in graphs can be found in the survey [3] and the book [4].

Next, we consider another variant of the concept of domination. A semitotal dominating set of a graph G without isolated vertices, is a dominating set D of G such that every vertex in D is within distance two of another vertex of D. The semitotal domination number, denoted by $\gamma_{t2}(G)$, is the minimum cardinality among all semitotal dominating sets of G. This parameter was introduced by Goddard et al. in [5], and was also further studied in [6–8].

For any graph without isolated vertices, we have that every semitotal dominating set is also a dominating set. Similarly, every total dominating set is a semitotal dominating set. Hence, the next inequality chain, given in [5], relates the parameters above.

$$\gamma(G) \leq \gamma_{t2}(G) \leq \gamma_t(G) \tag{1}$$

In the last decades, functions defined on graphs have received much attention in domination theory. This fact may be because the classical (total) domination problem can be studied using functions defined on graphs. Based on this approach, we consider the following concepts, which are also variants of the domination in graphs.

Let $f : V(G) \to \{0, 1, 2\}$ be a function on a graph G. Notice that f generates three sets V_0, V_1 and V_2, where $V_i = \{v \in V(G) \colon f(v) = i\}$ for $i = 0, 1, 2$. In this sense, from now on, we will write $f(V_0^f, V_1^f, V_2^f)$ so as to refer to the function f. Given a set $S \subseteq V(G)$, $f(S) = \sum_{v \in S} f(v)$. We define the *weight* of f as $\omega(f) = f(V(G)) = |V_1^f| + 2|V_2^f|$. In this sense, by an $f(V(G))$-function, we mean a function of weight $f(V(G))$. If the function f is clear from the context, then we will simply write $f(V_0, V_1, V_2)$. We shall also use the following notations: $V_{1,2} = \{v \in V_1 : N(v) \cap V_2 \neq \varnothing\}$ and $V_{1,1} = V_1 \setminus V_{1,2}$.

Roman domination in graphs was formally defined by Cockayne, Dreyer, Hedetniemi, and Hedetniemi [9] motivated, in part, by an article in Scientific American of Ian Stewart entitled "Defend the Roman Empire" [10]. A Roman dominating function (RDF) on a graph G is a function $f(V_0, V_1, V_2)$ satisfying that every vertex $u \in V_0$ is adjacent to at least one vertex $v \in V_2$. The Roman domination number of G, denoted by $\gamma_R(G)$, is the minimum weight among all RDFs on G. Further results on Roman domination can be found for example, in [11–14].

Another kind of functions defined on graphs are the total Roman dominating functions, which were introduced by Liu and Chang [15] and later, studied by Abdollahzadeh Ahangar et al. in [16]. A total Roman dominating function (TRDF) on a graph G without isolated vertices, is an RDF $f(V_0, V_1, V_2)$ such that the set $V_1 \cup V_2$ is a total dominating set of G. The minimum weight among all TRDFs on G is the total Roman domination number of G and it is denoted by $\gamma_{tR}(G)$.

Abdollahzadeh Ahangar et al. [16] give the next relationship between the total Roman domination number and the domination number of a graph: If G is a graph with no isolated vertex, then

$$2\gamma(G) \leq \gamma_{tR}(G) \leq 3\gamma(G). \tag{2}$$

Also, the authors of [16] proposed open problems concerning characterizing the graphs that satisfy the equalities in the inequality chain above. While the families of trees which satisfy these equalities has been characterized in [17], it remains an open problem to characterize graphs in general. In that sense, in this article we study the open problems above. In the next section we first give new lower and upper bounds for this parameter, which improve the bounds given in the Inequality chain (2). Also, in Section 3 we give a characterization for the graphs G that satisfy the equality $\gamma_{tR}(G) = 2\gamma(G)$; and finally, in Section 4 we give some necessary conditions that satisfy the graphs G for which $\gamma_{tR}(G) = 3\gamma(G)$.

Notation

Throughout this article we consider $G = (V(G), E(G))$ as a simple graph of order $n = |V(G)|$. Given a vertex v of G, $N(v)$ and $N[v]$ represent the open neighbourhood and the closed neighbourhood of v, respectively. For a set $D \subseteq V(G)$, its open neighbourhood and closed neighbourhood are $N(D) = \cup_{v \in D} N(v)$ and $N[D] = N(D) \cup D$, respectively. The boundary of the set D is defined as $\partial(D) = N(D) \setminus D$. The private neighbourhood of a vertex v with respect to a set $D \subseteq V(G)$ ($v \in D$), denoted by $pn(v, D)$, is defined by $pn(v, D) = \{u \in V(G). N(u) \cap D = \{v\}\}$. The vertices of $pn(v, D)$ will be called private neighbours of v with respect to D. Given a vertex $v \in D \subseteq V(G)$, $epn(v, D) = pn(v, D) \cap (V(G) \setminus D)$ represent the external private neighbourhood of v with respect to D. Also, and as is commonly defined, $G - D$ denotes the graph obtained from G such that $V(G - D) = V(G) \setminus D$ and $E(G - D) = E(G) \setminus \{uv \in E(G) : u \in D \text{ or } v \in D\}$. The subgraph induced by $D \subseteq V(G)$ is denoted by $G[D]$. For any two vertices u and v, the distance $d(u,v)$ between u and v is the length of a shortest $u - v$ path.

A set X of vertices of G is a packing in G if the closed neighbourhoods of vertices in X are pairwise disjoint, that is, if $N[u] \cap N[v] = \varnothing$, for every pair of different vertices $u, v \in X$.

A leaf vertex of a graph G is a vertex of degree one, and a support vertex of G is a vertex adjacent to a leaf. The set of leaves and support vertices are denoted by $L(G)$ and $S(G)$, respectively. Also, given a set $D \subseteq V(G)$ we denote $I(D)$ as an independent set of maximum cardinality in $G[D]$ such that $|I(D) \cap S(G)|$ is maximum.

Other definitions will be introduced as needed.

2. Main Result

We begin this section with the following useful result of total Roman dominating functions given in [16].

Lemma 1 ([16]). *If G is a graph with no isolated vertex, then there exists a $\gamma_{tR}(G)$-function $f(V_0, V_1, V_2)$ such that either V_2 is a dominating set of G, or the set S of vertices not dominated by V_2 satisfies $G[S] = kK_2$ for some $k \geq 1$, where $S \subseteq V_1$ and $\partial(S) \subseteq V_0$.*

It is known from [9] that for any graph G, $\gamma_R(G) \leq 2\gamma(G)$ and also, from Inequality chain (1) that $\gamma(G) \leq \gamma_{t2}(G)$. Hence, and as consequence of both inequalities above, we deduce that the following result improves the lower and upper bounds given in Inequality chain (2) for the total Roman domination number of graphs.

Theorem 1. *For any graph G with neither isolated vertex nor components isomorphic to K_2,*

$$\gamma_{t2}(G) + \gamma(G) \leq \gamma_{tR}(G) \leq \gamma_R(G) + \gamma(G).$$

Proof. We first prove the lower bound. By Lemma 1, there exists a $\gamma_{tR}(G)$-function $g(V_0^g, V_1^g, V_2^g)$ such that either V_2^g is a dominating set of G, or $V_{1,1}^g$ satisfies $G[V_{1,1}^g] \cong kK_2$ for some $k \geq 1$. Hence, V_2^g is a dominating set of $G - V_{1,1}^g$ and can be extended to a dominating set of G by adding to it the set $I(V_{1,1}^g)$. So $\gamma(G) \leq |V_2^g \cup I(V_{1,1}^g)| = |V_2^g| + |V_{1,1}^g|/2$. Moreover, $V_2^g \cup V_{1,2}^g$ is a total dominating set of $G - V_{1,1}^g$ and it is easy to check that $V_2^g \cup V_{1,2}^g \cup I(V_{1,1}^g)$ is a semitotal dominating set of G. Therefore $\gamma_{t2}(G) \leq |V_2^g \cup V_{1,2}^g \cup I(V_{1,1}^g)| = |V_2^g| + |V_{1,2}^g| + |I(V_{1,1}^g)| = |V_2^g| + |V_{1,2}^g| + |V_{1,1}^g|/2$ and so,

$$\gamma_{t2}(G) + \gamma(G) \leq (|V_2^g| + |V_{1,2}^g| + |V_{1,1}^g|/2) + (|V_2^g| + |V_{1,1}^g|/2) = 2|V_2^g| + |V_1^g| = \gamma_{tR}(G),$$

which completes the proof of the lower bound.

Now, in order to prove the upper bound, let D be a $\gamma(G)$-set and $f(V_0, V_1, V_2)$ be a $\gamma_R(G)$-function. Also, we consider $V_{1,0} = \{v \in V_1 : N(v) \subseteq V_0\}$ and let $f'(V_0', V_1', V_2')$ be a function defined as follows.

(a) For every vertex $x \in (V_{1,0} \cup V_2) \cap D$, choose a vertex $u \in (V_0 \cap N(x)) \setminus D$ (if it exists), and label it as $f'(u) = 1$.
(b) For every vertex $x \in V_0 \cap D$, $f'(x) = 1$.
(c) For any other vertex u not previously labelled, $f'(u) = f(u)$.

Since f is an RDF on G, by construction we have that f' is a TRDF on G. Therefore,

$$
\begin{aligned}
\gamma_{tR}(G) &\leq \omega(f') \\
&\leq |V_1| + 2|V_2| + |(V_{1,0} \cup V_2) \cap D| + |V_0 \cap D| \\
&\leq (|V_1| + 2|V_2|) + |D| \\
&= \gamma_R(G) + \gamma(G),
\end{aligned}
$$

which completes the proof. □

Now, we show a family of graphs $G_{p,q}$ given by Cabrera et al. in [18], which satisfy that $\gamma_{tR}(G_{p,q}) = \gamma_{t2}(G_{p,q}) + \gamma(G_{p,q})$ (observe that $\gamma(G_{p,q}) = p$, $\gamma_{t2}(G_{p,q}) = p + 1$ and $\gamma_{tR}(G_{p,q}) = 2p + 1$). Let p, q be two integers such that $q \geq p \geq 2$. From the complete bipartite graph $K_{p,q}$ and the empty graph N_p, we construct the graph $G_{p,q}$ as follows. We add p new edges which form a matching between the vertices of N_p and the vertices of degree q in $K_{p,q}$. Figure 1 shows the graph $G_{3,4}$ and a $\gamma_{tR}(G_{3,4})$-function $g(V_0, V_1, V_2)$.

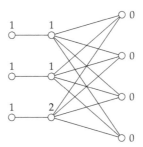

Figure 1. The graph $G_{3,4}$.

Next, we provide some useful properties that satisfies a specific TRDF for the graphs G with $\gamma_{tR}(G) = \gamma_{t2}(G) + \gamma(G)$.

Theorem 2. *For any graph G such that $\gamma_{tR}(G) = \gamma_{t2}(G) + \gamma(G)$, there exists a $\gamma_{tR}(G)$-function $f(V_0, V_1, V_2)$ satisfying the following conditions.*

(i) *Either V_2 is a dominating set of G, or the set $V_{1,1}$ satisfies $G[V_{1,1}] = kK_2$ for some $k \geq 1$, where $\partial(V_{1,1}) \subseteq V_0$.*

(ii) *$V_2 \cup I(V_{1,1})$ is a $\gamma(G)$-set and $V_2 \cup V_{1,2} \cup I(V_{1,1})$ is a $\gamma_{t2}(G)$-set.*

(iii) *$G[V_{1,2}]$ is isomorphic to an empty graph. Furthermore, if $v \in V_{1,2}$, then $|N(v) \cap V_2| = 1$.*

Proof. Let $f(V_0, V_1, V_2)$ be a $\gamma_{tR}(G)$-function that satisfies Lemma 1. Hence, condition (i) holds.

Now, we proceed to prove (ii). First, we notice that $A = V_2 \cup I(V_{1,1})$ and $B = V_2 \cup V_{1,2} \cup I(V_{1,1})$ are a dominating set and a semitotal dominating set, respectively. Hence, $\gamma(G) \leq |A|$ and $\gamma_{t2}(G) \leq |B|$. Since $|A| + |B| = \gamma_{tR}(G)$ and $\gamma_{tR}(G) = \gamma_{t2}(G) + \gamma(G)$, we obtain that $|B| + |A| = \gamma_{t2}(G) + \gamma(G)$. If $|A| > \gamma(G)$, then $|B| < \gamma_{t2}(G)$, which is a contradiction. Therefore, $|A| = \gamma(G)$ and so, $|B| = \gamma_{t2}(G)$, which completes the proof of (ii).

Finally, we proceed to prove (iii). Let $v \in V_{1,2}$. Clearly, $N(v) \cap V_2 \neq \emptyset$. If $N(v) \cap V_{1,2} \neq \emptyset$ or $|N(v) \cap V_2| > 1$, then $(V_2 \cup V_{1,2} \cup I(V_{1,1})) \setminus \{v\}$ is a semitotal dominating set of G, which is a contradiction with the fact that $V_2 \cup V_{1,2} \cup I(V_{1,1})$ is a $\gamma_{t2}(G)$-set by (ii). Therefore, $N(v) \cap V_{1,2} = \emptyset$ and $|N(v) \cap V_2| = 1$, which implies that $G[V_{1,2}]$ is isomorphic to an empty graph, and that $|N(v) \cap V_2| = 1$, which completes the proof. □

We consider again the family of graphs $G_{p,q}$. Let $g(V_0, V_1, V_2)$ be a $\gamma_{tR}(G_{p,q})$-function defined as $V_2 = \{v\}$ and $V_1 = (S(G_{p,q}) \cup L(G_{p,q})) \setminus \{v\}$, for some $v \in S(G)$. Notice that g satisfies the conditions given in Theorem 2. For an example, see the $\gamma_{tR}(G_{3,4})$-function g showed in the Figure 1.

Next, we will show a family of graphs G_r that satisfy the upper bound in the Theorem 1. In this case we have that $\gamma(G_r) = r$, $\gamma_R(G_r) = 2r$ and $\gamma_{tR}(G_r) = 3r$, where $r \geq 2$ is an integer. The graph G_r is constructed from the path graph $P_{3r-2} = v_1 v_2 \cdots v_{3r-2}$ and the empty graph N_2 by taking one copy of P_{3r-2} and r copies of N_2 and adding edges between the vertex v_{3i-2} and the i-th copy of N_2, for $i \in \{1, \ldots, r\}$. Figure 2 shows the graph G_3.

Figure 2. The graph G_3.

3. Graphs G with $\gamma_{tR}(G) = 2\gamma(G)$

We begin this section with a simple characterization, which is a direct consequence of Theorem 1 and the Inequality chains (1) and (2).

Theorem 3. *Let G be a graph with no isolated vertex. Then $\gamma_{tR}(G) = 2\gamma(G)$ if and only if $\gamma_{tR}(G) = \gamma_{t2}(G) + \gamma(G)$ and $\gamma_{t2}(G) = \gamma(G)$.*

We observe that the condition $\gamma_{tR}(G) = \gamma_{t2}(G) + \gamma(G)$ is a necessary condition but is not sufficient to satisfy the equality $\gamma_{tR}(G) = 2\gamma(G)$. For instance, see the graph $G_{3,4}$ shown in Figure 1.

Next, we give another characterization for the graphs G satisfying $\gamma_{tR}(G) = 2\gamma(G)$. It is important to emphasize that this characterization depends only of the existence of a $\gamma(G)$-set which satisfies some specific conditions.

Theorem 4. *Let G be a graph with no isolated vertex. Then $\gamma_{tR}(G) = 2\gamma(G)$ if and only if there exist a $\gamma(G)$-set S and a set $D \subseteq S$ such that*

(a) $G[D]$ *is isomorphic to an empty graph.*
(b) $|epn(v, S)| = 1$, *for every vertex $v \in D$.*
(c) $\gamma(G - D^*) = \gamma_t(G - D^*)$, *where $D^* = \bigcup_{v \in D} epn(v, S) \cup D$.*

Proof. First, we suppose that $\gamma_{tR}(G) = 2\gamma(G)$. By Lemma 1, there exists a $\gamma_{tR}(G)$-function $g(V_0^g, V_1^g, V_2^g)$ such that either V_2^g is a dominating set of G, or $V_{1,1}^g$ satisfies $G[V_{1,1}^g] \cong kK_2$ for some $k \geq 1$. By proceeding analogously as the proof of the lower bound of Theorem 1 and since $\gamma_{tR}(G) = 2\gamma(G) = \gamma_{t2}(G) + \gamma(G)$, we obtain $\gamma(G) = |V_2^g| + |V_{1,1}^g|/2$ and $\gamma_{t2}(G) = |V_2^g| + |V_{1,2}^g| + |V_{1,1}^g|/2$. Therefore $V_{1,2}^g = \varnothing$.

Let D be the set formed by taking one vertex from each K_2-component of $G[V_{1,1}^g]$. Notice that $D \cup V_2^g$ is a dominating set of G. Hence $2\gamma(G) = \gamma_{tR}(G) = |V_1^g| + 2|V_2^g| = 2|D| + 2|V_2^g|$, which implies that $S = D \cup V_2^g$ is a $\gamma(G)$-set. Thus, by construction of sets S and D, it is easy to see that Statements (a) and (b) hold.

Next, we prove Statement (c). Let $D^* = \bigcup_{v \in D} epn(v, S) \cup D$. It is readily seen that from D and any $\gamma(G - D^*)$-set we can construct a dominating set of G, and as $V_{1,2}^g = \varnothing$, we obtain $\frac{1}{2}\gamma_{tR}(G) = \gamma(G) \leq \gamma(G - D^*) + |D| \leq |V_2^g| + \frac{1}{2}|V_{1,1}^g| = \frac{1}{2}\gamma_{tR}(G)$. Thus, we have equalities in the inequality chain above. In particular, $\gamma(G - D^*) = |V_2^g|$. Also, notice that V_2^g is a total dominating set of $G - D^*$ since $V_{1,2}^g = \varnothing$. Hence, we deduce $\gamma_t(G - D^*) \leq |V_2^g| = \gamma(G - D^*)$, which implies $\gamma_t(G - D^*) = \gamma(G - D^*)$, and Statement (c) holds, as desired.

Conversely, we suppose there exist a $\gamma(G)$-set S and a set $D \subseteq S$ such that Statements (a), (b) and (c) hold. Let A_D be a $\gamma_t(G - D^*)$-set. By Statements (a) and (b) we have that $S \setminus D$ is a dominating set of $G - D^*$ and so, by using Statement (c), we deduce that $|A_D| = \gamma(G - D^*) \leq |S \setminus D|$. Moreover, we observe that the function $f(V_0, V_1, V_2)$, defined by $V_1 = D^*$ and $V_2 = A_D$, is a TRDF on G. Therefore, by Inequality chain (2) and statements above, we obtain $2\gamma(G) \leq \gamma_{tR}(G) \leq w(f) = |D^*| + 2|A_D| \leq 2|D| + 2|S \setminus D| = 2|S| = 2\gamma(G)$. Thus, we have equalities in the previous inequality chain. In particular, $\gamma_{tR}(G) = 2\gamma(G)$, which completes the proof. $\square$

4. Some Necessary Conditions for the Graphs G satisfying $\gamma_{tR}(G) = 3\gamma(G)$

Analogously to the section above, we continue now with a simple characterization, which is a direct consequence of Theorem 1 and the well-know inequality $\gamma_R(G) \leq 2\gamma(G)$.

Theorem 5. *Let G be a graph without isolated vertices. Then $\gamma_{tR}(G) = 3\gamma(G)$ if and only if $\gamma_{tR}(G) = \gamma_R(G) + \gamma(G)$ and $\gamma_R(G) = 2\gamma(G)$.*

We want to accentuate that in all the examples in which we have observed that the upper bound of Theorem 1 is achieved, we also have that $\gamma_R(G) = 2\gamma(G)$. In such a sense, we propose the following conjecture, which we could not prove.

Conjecture 1. *Let G be a graph with no isolated vertex. Then $\gamma_{tR}(G) = 3\gamma(G)$ if and only if $\gamma_{tR}(G) = \gamma_R(G) + \gamma(G)$.*

In order to give some necessary conditions for the graphs G satisfying $\gamma_{tR}(G) = 3\gamma(G)$, we shall need the following definition and useful results.

Definition 1. *A graph G satisfies Property $\mathcal{P}$ if for every $\gamma(G)$-set S, there exist no three vertices $x, y, z \in S$ such that*

- *There exists a vertex $y' \in epn(y, S)$ such that $d(x, y') = d(y', z) = 2$.*
- *$|epn(x, S)| = |epn(z, S)| = 2$.*

Notice that the families of graphs $G_{p,q}$ and G_r given in Section 2 satisfy the Property $\mathcal{P}$. Moreover, the Figure 3 shows a graph G that does not satisfy Property $\mathcal{P}$. Observe that the set $S = \{x, y, z\}$ is a $\gamma(G)$-set and also, it is easy to see that $|epn(x, S)| = |epn(z, S)| = 2$ and that the vertex $y' \in epn(y, S)$ satisfies the condition $d(x, y') = d(y', z) = 2$.

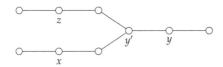

Figure 3. A graph G that does not satisfy the Property $\mathcal{P}$.

Lemma 2. *Let G be a graph and let S be a $\gamma(G)$-set. If S is a packing, then for all $v \in S$ there exists $v' \in S$ such that $d(v, v') = 3$.*

Proof. Suppose there exists a vertex $v \in S$ such that for all vertex $v' \in S \setminus \{v\}$, it is satisfied that $d(v, v') > 3$ (notice that $d(v, v') \geq 3$ because S is a packing). Hence, every vertex at distance two of v is not dominated by S, which is a contradiction. This completes the proof. $\square$

Proposition 1. *If G is a graph such that every $\gamma(G)$-set is a packing, then for every $\gamma(G)$-set S and for every $v \in S$ it is satisfied that $|epn(v, S)| \geq 2$.*

Proof. Let S be a $\gamma(G)$-set and let $v \in S$. Since S is a packing, we have that $epn(v, S) \neq \emptyset$. If $epn(v, S) = \{u\}$, then v is a vertex of degree one. By using Lemma 2, we have that $S' = (S \setminus \{v\}) \cup \{u\}$ is a $\gamma(G)$-set, but is not a packing, contradicting the hypothesis. So $|epn(v, S)| \geq 2$, as desired. □

Theorem 6. *Let G be a graph. If $\gamma_{tR}(G) = 3\gamma(G)$, then the following statements hold.*

(i) $\gamma_R(G) = 2\gamma(G)$.
(ii) S is a packing, for every $\gamma(G)$-set S.
(iii) G satisfies Property $\mathcal{P}$.

Proof. By Theorem 5, Statement (i) follows. Moreover, Abdollahzadeh Ahangar et al. showed in [16] that every $\gamma(G)$-set is a packing, which implies that Statement (ii) holds.

Next we prove Statement (iii). In that sense, we suppose that G does not satisfy Property $\mathcal{P}$. Hence there exist a $\gamma(G)$-set S and three vertices $x, y, z \in S$ satisfying the conditions given in Definition 1. By Statement (ii) and Proposition 1 we have $|epn(v, S)| \geq 2$, for every $v \in S$. Let $x' \in epn(x, S) \setminus N(y')$ and $z' \in epn(z, S) \setminus N(y')$. Now, we consider the function f defined as follows.

(a) For every vertex $u \in (S \setminus \{x, z\}) \cup \{y'\}$, set $f(u) = 2$.
(b) For every vertex $v \in S \setminus \{x, y, z\}$, choose a vertex $v' \in N(v)$, and label it as $f(v') = 1$.
(c) For $u \in \{x, z, x', z'\}$, set $f(u) = 1$.
(d) For any other vertex u not previously labelled, set $f(u) = 0$.

Notice that, by construction, f is a TRDF on G. Therefore,

$$
\begin{aligned}
\gamma_{tR}(G) &\leq w(f) \\
&\leq 2|(S \setminus \{x, z\}) \cup \{y'\}| + |S \setminus \{x, y, z\}| + |\{x, z, x', z'\}| \\
&= 2(|S| - 1) + (|S| - 3) + 4 \\
&= 3|S| - 1 \\
&< 3\gamma(G),
\end{aligned}
$$

which is a contradiction. Hence G satisfies Property $\mathcal{P}$ and the proof is complete. □

5. Conclusions and Open Problems

New results concerning the study of total Roman domination in graphs have been presented in this article. Among the main contributions, the following should be highlighted.

- As the main result, we have provided new lower and upper bounds for the total Roman domination number of graphs, which improve other well-known bounds.
- We have shown a theoretical characterization for the graphs G satisfying $\gamma_{tR}(G) = 2\gamma(G)$.
- We have shown some necessary conditions for the graphs G that satisfy $\gamma_{tR}(G) = 3\gamma(G)$.

On the other hand, and as a consequence of this study, some open problems have arisen. Next, we expose some of the most interesting.

(a) Characterize the graphs G satisfying $\gamma_{tR}(G) = \gamma_{t2}(G) + \gamma(G)$.
(b) Characterize the graphs G satisfying $\gamma_{tR}(G) = \gamma_R(G) + \gamma(G)$.
(c) Settle Conjecture 1.

Author Contributions: All authors contributed equally to this work. Investigation, A.C.M., S.C.G. and A.C.G.; Writing—review & editing, A.C.M., S.C.G. and A.C.G. All authors have read and agreed to the published version of the manuscript.

Funding: This research received no external funding.

References

1. Haynes, T.W.; Hedetniemi, S.T.; Slater, P.J. *Fundamentals of Domination in Graphs*; Chapman and Hall/CRC Pure and Applied Mathematics Series; Marcel Dekker, Inc.: New York, NY, USA, 1998.
2. Haynes, T.W.; Hedetniemi, S.T.; Slater, P.J. *Domination in Graphs: Advanced Topics*; Chapman and Hall/CRC Pure and Applied Mathematics Series; Marcel Dekker, Inc.: New York, NY, USA, 1998.
3. Henning, M. A survey of selected recent results on total domination in graphs. *Discret. Math.* **2009**, *309*, 32–63. [CrossRef]
4. Henning, M.; Yeo, A. *Total Domination in Graphs. Springer Monographs in Mathematics*; Springer: New York, NY, USA, 2013.
5. Goddard, W.; Henning, M.A.; McPillan, C.A. Semitotal domination in graphs. *Util. Math.* **2014**, *94*, 67–81.
6. Henning, M.; Marcon, A.J. Semitotal domination in claw-free cubic graphs. *Ann. Comb.* **2016**, *20*, 799–813. [CrossRef]
7. Henning, M.; Marcon, A.J. Vertices contained in all or in no minimum semitotal dominating set of a tree. *Discuss. Math. Graph Theory* **2016**, *36*, 71–93. [CrossRef]
8. Henning, M.; Pandey, A. Algorithmic aspects of semitotal domination in graphs. *Theor. Comput. Sci.* **2019**, *766*, 46–57. [CrossRef]
9. Cockayne, E.J.; Dreyer, P.A., Jr.; Hedetniemi, S.M.; Hedetniemi, S.T. Roman domination in graphs. *Discret. Math.* **2004**, *278*, 11–22. [CrossRef]
10. Stewart, I. Defend the Roman Empire! *Sci. Am.* **1999**, *281*, 136–138. [CrossRef]
11. Chambers, E.W.; Kinnersley, B.; Prince, N.; West, D.B. Extremal problems for Roman domination. *SIAM J. Discrete Math.* **2009**, *23*, 1575–1586. [CrossRef]
12. Favaron, O.; Karami, H.; Khoeilar, R.; Sheikholeslami, S.M. On the Roman domination number of a graph. *Discret. Math.* **2009**, *309*, 3447–3451. [CrossRef]
13. Liu, C.-H.; Chang, G.J. Upper bounds on Roman domination numbers of graphs. *Discret. Math.* **2012**, *312*, 1386–1391. [CrossRef]
14. Yero, I.G.; Rodríguez-Velázquez, J.A. Roman domination in cartesian product graphs and strong product graphs. *Appl. Anal. Discret. Math.* **2013**, *7*, 262–274.
15. Liu, C.-H.; Chang, G.J. Roman domination on strongly chordal graphs. *J. Comb. Optim.* **2013**, *26*, 608–619. [CrossRef]
16. Abdollahzadeh Ahangar, H.; Henning, M.A.; Samodivkin, V.; Yero, I.G. Total Roman domination in graphs. *Appl. Anal. Discrete Math.* **2016**, *10*, 501–517. [CrossRef]
17. Amjadi, J.; Sheikholeslami, S.M.; Soroudi, M. On the total Roman domination in trees. *Discuss. Math. Graph Theory* **2019**, *39*, 519–532. [CrossRef]
18. Cabrera Martínez, A.; Montejano, L.P.; Rodríguez-Velázquez, J.A. Total Weak Roman Domination in Graphs. *Symmetry* **2019**, *11*, 831. [CrossRef]

Article

On the Total Outer k-Independent Domination Number of Graphs

Abel Cabrera-Martínez [1], Juan Carlos Hernández-Gómez [2,*], Ernesto Parra-Inza [2]
and José María Sigarreta Almira[2]

[1] Departament d'Enginyeria Informàtica i Matemàtiques, Universitat Rovira i Virgili, Av. Països Catalans 26, 43007 Tarragona, Spain; abel.cabrera@urv.cat
[2] Facultad de Matemáticas, Universidad Autónoma de Guerrero, Carlos E. Adame 5, Col. La Garita 39650, Acapulco, Mexico; eparrainza@gmail.com (E.P.-I.); josemariasigarretaalmira@hotmail.com (J.M.S.A.)
* Correspondence: jcarloshg@gmail.com

Received: 23 December 2019; Accepted: 23 January 2020; Published: 5 February 2020

Abstract: A set of vertices of a graph G is a total dominating set if every vertex of G is adjacent to at least one vertex in such a set. We say that a total dominating set D is a total outer k-independent dominating set of G if the maximum degree of the subgraph induced by the vertices that are not in D is less or equal to $k - 1$. The minimum cardinality among all total outer k-independent dominating sets is the total outer k-independent domination number of G. In this article, we introduce this parameter and begin with the study of its combinatorial and computational properties. For instance, we give several closed relationships between this novel parameter and other ones related to domination and independence in graphs. In addition, we give several Nordhaus–Gaddum type results. Finally, we prove that computing the total outer k-independent domination number of a graph G is an NP-hard problem.

Keywords: total outer k-independent domination; total domination; k-independence

---

1. Introduction

Theory of domination in graphs is one of the most important topics in graph theory. In the last few decades, the interest in this area has increased, due to its applications to different fields of science, such as linear algebra, communication networks, social sciences, computational complexity, algorithm design, complex ecosystems, optimization problems, among others (for example, see [1,2]). In this sense, in this important area, a very high number of variants of domination parameters have been developed, which are combinations of two or more parameters. In this article, we center our attention on the study of a new parameter, which is a combination between the following well-known parameters: total domination and k-independence in graphs. In addition, we focus the investigation some computational and combinatorial properties of it.

Throughout this article, we consider simple graphs G. Given a set $D \subseteq V(G)$, and a vertex $v \in V(G)$, $N_D(v)$ denotes the set of neighbors of v in D, that is, $N_D(v) = \{u \in D : uv \in E(G)\}$ and $N_D[v] = N_D(v) \cup \{v\}$. In addition, let $\delta_D(v) = |N_D(v)|$. The parameter $\delta(v) = \delta_{V(G)}(v) = |N_{V(G)}(v)|$ denotes the *degree* of v in G. For short, we will often use $N(v)$ and $N[v]$ instead of $N_{V(G)}(v)$ and $N_{V(G)}[v]$, respectively. The *minimum* and *maximum degrees* of G will be denoted by $\delta(G) = \min_{v \in V(G)}\{\delta(v)\}$ and $\Delta(G) = \max_{v \in V(G)}\{\delta(v)\}$, respectively. A *leaf vertex* of G is a vertex of degree one, and a *support vertex* of G is a vertex adjacent to a leaf vertex. The set of leaves and support vertices will be denoted by $L(G)$ and $S(G)$, respectively. The *subgraph induced* by $X \subseteq V(G)$ will be denoted by $G[X]$. Given two sets $X, Y \subseteq V(G)$, $E(X, Y)$ denotes the set of all edges of G that join a vertex of X and a vertex of Y.

A set of vertices of a graph G is *independent* if the subgraph induced by it is isomorphic to an empty graph. The *independence number* of G is the maximum cardinality among all independent sets of G and is denoted by $\beta(G)$.

A set $D \subseteq V(G)$ is a *dominating set* of G if every vertex in $V(G) \setminus D$ is adjacent to at least one vertex in D. The *domination number* of G is the minimum cardinality among all dominating sets of G, and it is denoted by $\gamma(G)$.

In [3,4], Fink and Jacobson generalized the concepts of dominating and independent sets. For an integer $k \geq 1$, we say that a set $X \subseteq V(G)$ is *k-independent* if the maximum degree of the subgraph induced by the vertices of X is less than or equal to $k - 1$, that is, $\Delta(G[X]) \leq k - 1$. The *k-independence number* of G is the maximum cardinality among all k-independent sets of G and is denoted by $\beta_k(G)$. A $\beta_k(G)$-*set* is a k-independent set of cardinality $\beta_k(G)$. Thus, when $k = 1$, the 1-independence number is the classical independence number. Moreover, we say that a set $D \subseteq V(G)$ is *k-dominating* if every vertex in $V(G) \setminus D$ has at least k neighbors in D. The *k-domination number* of G is the minimum cardinality among all k-dominating sets of G and is denoted by $\gamma_k(G)$. A k-dominating set of cardinality $\gamma_k(G)$ is called a $\gamma_k(G)$-*set*. For more information on k-independence and k-domination, we suggest the relatively recent survey [5].

A dominating set $D \subseteq V(G)$ is a *total dominating set* of G if the subgraph induced by the vertices of D has no isolated vertex. The *total domination number* of G is the minimum cardinality among all total dominating sets of G and is denoted by $\gamma_t(G)$. A total dominating set of cardinality $\gamma_t(G)$ is called $\gamma_t(G)$-*set*. For more information on total domination, we suggest the survey [6] and the book [7].

A *total outer k-independent dominating set* (or TOkID set, for short) is a total dominating set $D \subseteq V(G)$ such that $V(G) \setminus D$ is a k-independent set. The minimum cardinality among all TOkID sets is the *total outer k-independent domination number* of G and is denoted by $\gamma_{t,oi}^k(G)$. A TOkID set of cardinality $\gamma_{t,oi}^k(G)$ is a $\gamma_{t,oi}^k(G)$-*set*. When $k = 1$, a TOkID set is a *total outer-independent dominating set*, that is, a total dominating set D such that the subgraph induced by $V(G) \setminus D$ is isomorphic to an empty graph. This last concept was introduced in [8] and also barely looked at in [9] under the name of total co-independent domination number. Recently, it was analyzed in [10–12].

Given a graph G with no isolated vertex, in order to have a TOkID set D of G, any vertex of $V(G) \setminus D$ must have at least one neighbor in D and must have at most $k - 1$ neighbors in $V(G) \setminus D$. Hence, $1 \leq k \leq \Delta(G)$.

Moreover, we observe that, if $H_1, H_2, \ldots, H_r$ with $r \geq 2$ are the components of a non-connected graph H with no isolated vertex, then any TOkID set of H is formed by a TOkID set in each component H_i, for $i = 1, \ldots, r$. In the following remark, we expose the quotation above, and, as a consequence, in the paper, we only study the TOkID sets of nontrivial connected graphs.

Remark 1. *Let H be a non-connected graph with no isolated vertex. If $H_1, H_2, \ldots, H_r$ with $r \geq 2$, are the components of H, then*

$$\gamma_{t,oi}^k(H) = \sum_{i=1}^{r} \gamma_{t,oi}^k(H_i).$$

The remainder of this article is structured as follows. Section 2 introduces primary combinatorial and computational results. For instance, we show that the problem of finding the total outer k-independent domination number of a graph is NP-hard. In addition, we give the exact value of this parameter for some specific families of graphs, and we expose general bounds and discuss the extreme cases. Finally, Section 3 is dedicated to giving several Nordhaus–Gaddum type results concerning the parameter $\gamma_{t,oi}^k(G)$.

2. Primary Combinatorial and Computational Results

It is natural to think that, due to the concept of "TOkID set", the total outer k-independent domination number is related to the total domination number and the k-independence number. This simple quotation leads to the following result.

Theorem 1. *If G is a connected graph of order n, then*

$$\gamma^k_{t,oi}(G) \geq \max\{\gamma_t(G), n - \beta_k(G)\}.$$

Moreover, it is not difficult to see that, for any nontrivial connected graph G, any TO$(k-1)$ID set is a TOkID set, where $2 \leq k \leq \Delta(G)$. Therefore, the following inequality chain holds.

Proposition 1. *If G is a connected graph of order n and maximum degree Δ, then*

$$2 \leq \gamma_t(G) = \gamma^\Delta_{t,oi}(G) \leq \gamma^{\Delta-1}_{t,oi}(G) \leq \cdots \leq \gamma_{t,oi}(G) \leq n.$$

The following remark is an immediate consequence of the proposition above.

Remark 2. *Let G be any connected graph. If $\gamma^k_{t,oi}(G) = \gamma_t(G)$, then $\gamma^j_{t,oi}(G) = \gamma_t(G)$ for every $j \in \{k, \ldots, \Delta(G)\}$.*

Next, we give a theoretical characterization of the graphs that have equal TOkID and TO$(k-1)$ID numbers. For this, we need some extra terminology and notation. For any $\gamma^k_{t,oi}(G)$-set D, let A^k_D be the set of vertices defined as follows:

$$A^k_D = \left\{v \in V(G) \setminus D : \delta_{V(G)\setminus D}(v) = k - 1\right\}.$$

Lemma 1. *Let G be a nontrivial connected graph. For any $\gamma^k_{t,oi}(G)$-set D with $k \geq 2$,*

$$\gamma^{k-1}_{t,oi}(G) \leq \gamma^k_{t,oi}(G) + |A^k_D|.$$

Proof. Let D be any $\gamma^k_{t,oi}(G)$-set. Notice that $D \cup A^k_D$ is a TO$(k-1)$ID set of G. Thus, $\gamma^{k-1}_{t,oi}(G) \leq |D \cup A^k_D| = \gamma^k_{t,oi}(G) + |A^k_D|$. □

Theorem 2. *Let G be a connected graph. For an integer $k \geq 2$, $\gamma^k_{t,oi}(G) = \gamma^{k-1}_{t,oi}(G)$ if and only if $A^k_D = \emptyset$ for some $\gamma^k_{t,oi}(G)$-set D.*

Proof. Suppose that $\gamma^k_{t,oi}(G) = \gamma^{k-1}_{t,oi}(G)$ and let D be a $\gamma^{k-1}_{t,oi}(G)$-set. Thus, $\Delta(G[V(G) \setminus D]) \leq k - 2$. Since every TO$(k-1)$ID set is a TO$k$ID set, it follows that D is also a TOkID set of G of cardinality $\gamma^k_{t,oi}(G)$. Hence, D is also a $\gamma^k_{t,oi}(G)$-set and satisfies that $A^k_D = \emptyset$. Conversely, if there exists a $\gamma^k_{t,oi}(G)$-set D such that $A^k_D = \emptyset$, then, by Proposition 1 and Lemma 1, the result follows. □

Now, we give an example of a subfamily of graphs given by Cabrera et al. in [13], in which the lower bound of Theorem 1 is achieved for the graphs of this family, and also the equivalence of Theorem 2 is satisfied. To this end, we need to introduce the family of graphs $\mathcal{F}$. Before this, we shall need the following operations for vertices or induced paths P_3 of a graph G. Note that these operations were already presented in [12].

Addition of t pendant vertices: Given a vertex x, add t new vertices $y_1, \ldots, y_t$ and the edges xy_i for every $i \in \{1, \ldots, t\}$.

Inflation of size q: Given an induced path $P_3 = uvw$ of G, in which $\delta(v) = 2$, remove the vertex v and the two incident edges, and replace them with q vertices $v_1, \ldots, v_q$ and edges uv_i, v_iw for every $i \in \{1, \ldots, q\}$.

From the cycle C_6, we obtain a graph $H \in \mathcal{F}$ by making the following sequence of operations.

(i) Apply the operation "*Addition of t_i pendant vertices*", $t_i \geq 1$ and $i \in \{1, 2, 3\}$, to all vertices of a $\beta(C_6)$-set $S = \{v_1, v_2, v_3\}$, respectively.

(ii) Apply the operation "*Inflation of size q_i*" with $q_i \geq 1$ and $i \in \{1, 2, 3\}$ to the three possible paths of order three between v_1, v_2, v_3.

Figure 1 shows an example of a graph belonging to the family $\mathcal{F}$. Next, we expose a result which relates $\gamma_t(H)$ and $\gamma_{t,oi}(H)$ for graphs $H \in \mathcal{F}$.

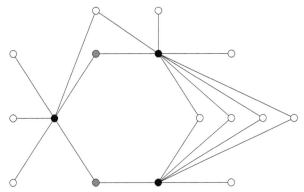

Figure 1. A graph $H \in \mathcal{F}$ where the three black-colored vertices form a $\beta(C_6)$-set and the two gray-colored vertices form a possible set to be added to the black-colored vertices to get a $\gamma_t(H)$-set.

Remark 3. *If $H \in \mathcal{F}$, then $\gamma_t(H) = \gamma_{t,oi}(H) = 5$.*

According to the remark above, we can easily check that, for any graph $H \in \mathcal{F}$, $\gamma_t(H) = \gamma_{t,oi}^{\Delta}(H) = \gamma_{t,oi}^{\Delta-1}(H) = \cdots = \gamma_{t,oi}(H)$. Since every TO$k$ID set is also a total dominating set and $\gamma_t(H) = \gamma_{t,oi}^k(H)$ by equality chain above, we have that every $\gamma_{t,oi}^k(H)$-set is also a $\gamma_t(H)$-set too. Hence, if $k \geq 2$, then $A_D^k = \emptyset$ for every $\gamma_{t,oi}^k(H)$-set D.

Now, we consider the decision problem associated with total outer k-independent domination number of graphs.

> TOTAL OUTER k-INDEPENDENT DOMINATION PROBLEM (TOkID PROBLEM)
> INSTANCE: A nontrivial connected graph G and a positive integer r
> PROBLEM: Deciding whether $\gamma_{t,oi}^k(G)$ is less than r

We will show that the TOkID PROBLEM is NP-Complete by making a reduction from a known decision problem concerning the k-independence number of graphs, which was solved in 1989 by Jacobson and Peters [14]. In this article, the authors showed that the problem of determining the number $\beta_k(G)$ for an arbitrary graph G is NP-Complete.

Next, we define a family of graphs, which we will need to make the reduction. Fixing a positive integer k, the graph H_k is obtained from a path P_2, by adding four copies of K_k, and joining with an edge each vertex of P_2 with all the vertices from two of such copies. (see Figure 2I). Let G be a connected graph with $|V(G)| = n$ and let $H_k^{(1)}, \ldots, H_k^{(n)}$ be n graphs isomorphic to the graph H_k. We construct the graph $G_{n,k}$ by adding edges between the ith-vertex of G and one vertex of maximum degree of the ith-graph $H_k^{(i)}$. See Figure 2II for an example.

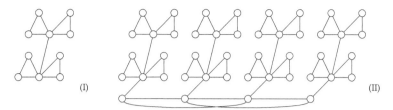

Figure 2. The graph H_2 (**I**) and a graph $G_{4,2}$ (**II**) where G is a complete graph minus one edge.

Lemma 2. *If G is a connected graph of order n and any positive integer $k \leq \Delta(G)$, then*

$$\beta_k(G_{n,k}) = |V(G_{n,k})| - 3n + \beta_k(G).$$

Proof. Let G be a nontrivial connected graph such that $|V(G)| = n$ and let $G_{n,k}$ be the graph described above ($1 \leq k \leq \Delta(G)$). We define $u^{(i)}, v^{(i)}$ as the two vertices of maximum degree in the copy $H_k^{(i)}$ of the graph H_k used to construct $G_{n,k}$ and let A be a $\beta_k(G)$-set. Notice that $A \cup \{\bigcup_{i=1}^n V(H_k^{(i)}) \setminus \{u^{(i)}, v^{(i)}\}\}$ is a k-independent set of $G_{n,k}$. Hence, $\beta_k(G_{n,k}) \geq |V(G_{n,k})| - 3n + \beta_k(G)$.

On the other hand, let S be a $\beta_k(G_{n,k})$-set. It is straightforward to see that $|S \cap V(H_k^{(i)})| \leq |V(H_k^{(i)})| - 2$ for every $1 \leq i \leq n$ and that $|S \cap V(G)| \leq \beta_k(G)$. Therefore,

$$
\begin{aligned}
\beta_k(G_{n,k}) &= |S| = |(S \cap V(G)) \cup \{\bigcup_{i=1}^n S \cap V(H_k^{(i)})\}| \\
&\leq |S \cap V(G)| + \sum_{i=1}^n (|V(H_k^{(i)})| - 2) \\
&= |V(G_{n,k})| - 3n + \beta_k(G),
\end{aligned}
$$

which completes the proof. □

The following theorem shows the NP-completeness of the TO*k*ID PROBLEM.

Theorem 3. *TOkID PROBLEM is NP-complete.*

Proof. The TO*k*ID PROBLEM belongs to NP, since we can check in polynomial time that a given set has cardinality at most r and is a TO*k*ID set. Let $G_{n,k}$ and $u^{(i)}, v^{(i)}$ be the graph and the vertices described in the lemma above, respectively. Now, we will prove that $\gamma_{t,oi}^k(G_{n,k}) = 3n - \beta_k(G)$.

Let A be a $\beta_k(G)$-set and let $D = (V(G) \setminus A) \cup \{\bigcup_{i=1}^n \{u^{(i)}, v^{(i)}\}\}$. Notice that D is a total dominating set of $G_{n,k}$ and $V(G_{n,k}) \setminus D$ is a k-independent set. Thus, D is a TO*k*ID set of $G_{n,k}$ and, as a consequence,

$$\gamma_{t,oi}^k(G_{n,k}) \leq |D| = n - |A| + \left|\bigcup_{i=1}^n \{u^{(i)}, v^{(i)}\}\right| = 3n - \beta_k(G).$$

Moreover, by Theorem 1 and Lemma 2, we obtain that $\gamma_{t,oi}^k(G_{n,k}) \geq 3n - \beta_k(G)$. Therefore, $\gamma_{t,oi}^k(G_{n,k}) = 3n - \beta_k(G)$.

Now, for $j = 3n - h$, it is readily seen that $\gamma_{t,oi}^k(G_{n,k}) \leq j$ if and only if $\beta_k(G) \geq h$, which completes the reduction. Hence, TO*k*ID PROBLEM is NP-complete. □

The next result is an immediate consequence of the previous theorem.

Corollary 1. *The problem of computing the total outer k-independent domination number of a nontrivial connected graph is NP-hard.*

According to the complexity results above, it is desirable to bound the total outer k-independent domination number or compute its exact value for several families of graphs. We next center our attention on this second goal. We will use the notation P_n, C_n, K_n, S_n, $S_{r,n-r}$, N_n and $W_n = N_1 + C_{n-1}$ for path graphs, cycle graphs, complete graphs, star graphs, double star graphs, empty graphs and wheel graphs of order n, respectively. In addition, we use the notation $K_{r,s}$ for the bipartite complete graph and, without loss of generality, we always assume that $r \leq s$.

Remark 4 ([7])**.** *For any integer $n \geq 3$, $\gamma_t(P_n) = \gamma_t(C_n) = \lfloor \frac{n}{2} \rfloor + \lceil \frac{n}{4} \rceil - \lfloor \frac{n}{4} \rfloor$.*

Proposition 2. *The following equalities hold for any integer $n \geq 3$.*

(i) $\gamma_{t,oi}(P_n) = \lfloor \frac{2n}{3} \rfloor$ *and* $\gamma_{t,oi}^2(P_n) = \lfloor \frac{n}{2} \rfloor + \lceil \frac{n}{4} \rceil - \lfloor \frac{n}{4} \rfloor$.

(ii) $\gamma_{t,oi}(C_n) = \lfloor \frac{2n+2}{3} \rfloor$ *and* $\gamma_{t,oi}^2(C_n) = \lfloor \frac{n}{2} \rfloor + \lceil \frac{n}{4} \rceil - \lfloor \frac{n}{4} \rfloor$.

(iii) $\gamma_{t,oi}^k(K_n) = \begin{cases} 2 & \text{if } k = n-1, \\ n-k & \text{otherwise.} \end{cases}$

(iv) $\gamma_{t,oi}^k(S_n) = \gamma_{t,oi}^k(S_{r,n-r}) = 2$.

(v) $\gamma_{t,oi}^k(W_n) = \begin{cases} \lceil \frac{n+1}{2} \rceil & \text{if } k = 1, \\ \lceil \frac{n+2}{3} \rceil & \text{if } k = 2, \\ 2 & \text{otherwise.} \end{cases}$

(vi) $\gamma_{t,oi}^k(K_{r,s}) = \begin{cases} \min\{r+1, r+s-2k+2\} & \text{if } k \leq r, \\ \min\{r+1, s-k+2\} & \text{otherwise.} \end{cases}$

Proof. From Proposition 1 and Remark 4, we deduce (i) and (ii). The equalities (iii)–(v) are straightforward. Now, we proceed to prove (vi). Let $K_{r,s}$ be the bipartite complete graph with partite sets V_r and V_s of cardinality r and s, respectively. Let $v \in V_s$. Notice that $V_r \cup \{v\}$ is a TOkID set of $K_{r,s}$. Hence, $\gamma_{t,oi}^k(K_{r,s}) \leq |V_r \cup \{v\}| = r+1$. If $\gamma_{t,oi}^k(K_{r,s}) = r+1$, then we are done. Thus, we assume that $\gamma_{t,oi}^k(K_{r,s}) \leq r$. Next, we analyze two cases.

Case 1. $k \leq r$. Let $X \subseteq V(K_{r,s})$ such that $|X \cap V_r| = r - (k-1)$ and $|X \cap V_s| = s - (k-1)$. Notice that X is a TOkID set of $K_{r,s}$. Hence, $\gamma_{t,oi}^k(K_{r,s}) \leq |X| = r+s-2k+2$. Now, let D be a $\gamma_{t,oi}^k(K_{r,s})$-set. Since $D \cap V_r \neq \emptyset$, $D \cap V_s \neq \emptyset$ and $|D| \leq r$, we have that $|D \cap V_r| \geq r - (k-1)$ and $|D \cap V_s| \geq s - (k-1)$. Thus, $\gamma_{t,oi}^k(K_{r,s}) = |D| \geq r+s-2(k-1)$. Therefore, $\gamma_{t,oi}^k(K_{r,s}) = r+s-2k+2$.

Case 2. $k > r$. Let $X \subseteq V(K_{r,s})$ such that $|X \cap V_r| = 1$ and $|X \cap V_s| = s - (k-1)$. Notice that X is a TOkID set of $K_{r,s}$. Hence, $\gamma_{t,oi}^k(K_{r,s}) \leq |X| = s-k+2$. Now, let D be a $\gamma_{t,oi}^k(K_{r,s})$-set. Since $D \cap V_r \neq \emptyset$, $D \cap V_s \neq \emptyset$ and $|D| > r$, we have that $|D \cap V_r| \geq 1$ and $|D \cap V_s| \geq s - (k-1)$. Thus, $\gamma_{t,oi}^k(K_{r,s}) = |D| \geq s-k+2$. Therefore, $\gamma_{t,oi}^k(K_{r,s}) = s-k+2$. □

Let G and H be two graphs of order n_G and n_H, respectively. The corona product graph $G \odot H$ is defined as the graph obtained from G and H, by taking one copy of G and n_G copies of H and joining by an edge every vertex from the ith-copy of H with the ith-vertex of G. For every $x \in V(G)$, H_x will denote the copy of H in $G \odot H$ associated with x.

Next, we study the total outer k-independent domination number of corona product graphs. Before, we shall need the following useful lemmas.

Lemma 3. *If G and H are two graphs with no isolated vertex, then, for any positive integer $k \leq \Delta(H)$,*

$$\beta_k(G \odot H) = n_G \beta_k(H).$$

Proof. Let S be a $\beta_k(H)$-set. For any $x \in V(G)$, let S^x be the copy of S associated with H_x. Since $\bigcup_{x \in V(G)} S^x$ is a k-independent set of $G \odot H$, we have that $\beta_k(G \odot H) \geq |\bigcup_{x \in V(G)} S^x| = n_G \beta_k(H)$. Now, we suppose that $\beta_k(G \odot H) > n_G \beta_k(H)$ and let D be a $\beta_k(G \odot H)$-set. Thus, there exists a vertex

$v \in V(G)$ such that $|D \cap (V(H_v) \cup \{v\})| > \beta_k(H)$. This can only happen if $v \in D$, which implies that $|D \cap (V(H_v)| \leq k - 1$, contradicting the fact that $|D \cap (V(H_v) \cup \{v\})| > \beta_k(H)$ since $\beta_k(H) \geq k$. Therefore, $\beta_k(G \odot H) = n_G \beta_k(H)$, which completes the proof. $\square$

Lemma 4. *If G and H are two graphs with no isolated vertex, then*

$$\gamma_t(G \odot H) = n_G.$$

Proof. Notice that $V(G)$ is a total dominating set of $G \odot H$. Hence, $\gamma_t(G \odot H) \leq |V(G)| = n_G$. Moreover, we observe that each copy of H contains at least one vertex in any total dominating set of $G \odot H$. Thus, $\gamma_t(G \odot H) \geq n_G$, which completes the proof. $\square$

Theorem 4. *If G is a graph with no isolated vertex, then, for every graph H with no isolated vertex,*

$$\gamma_{t,oi}^k(G \odot H) = \begin{cases} n_G & \text{if } \Delta(H) \leq k - 1, \\ n_G(n_H - \beta_k(H) + 1) & \text{otherwise.} \end{cases}$$

Proof. If $\Delta(H) \leq k - 1$, then it is straightforward to see that $V(G)$ is a TOkID set of $G \odot H$. Hence, by Lemma 4 and the statement above, we have that $\gamma_{t,oi}^k(G \odot H) \leq |V(G)| = n_G = \gamma_t(G \odot H)$. Therefore, Theorem 1 leads to $\gamma_{t,oi}^k(G \odot H) = n_G$.

From now on, we assume that $k \leq \Delta(H)$. Let S be a $\beta_k(H)$-set. For any $x \in V(G)$, let S^x be the copy of S associated with H_x. Since $R = \cup_{x \in V(G)} S^x$ is a k-independent set of $G \odot H$, by Lemma 3, we deduce that R is a $\beta_k(G \odot H)$-set. Moreover, we observe that $V(G \odot H) \setminus R$ is a total dominating set of $G \odot H$. Thus, $V(G \odot H) \setminus R$ is a TOkID set of $G \odot H$ and so $\gamma_{t,oi}^k(G \odot H) \leq |V(G \odot H) \setminus R| = |V(G \odot H)| - \beta_k(G \odot H) = n_G(n_H + 1) - n_G \beta_k(H) = n_G(n_H - \beta_k(H) + 1)$. The proof is completed by Theorem 1. $\square$

Now, we continue the article giving relationships between the total outer k-independent domination number and other parameters of a graph.

Theorem 5 ([15]). *If G is a connected graph of order $n \geq 3$ and maximum degree $\Delta(G) \leq n - 2$, then $\gamma_t(G) \leq n - \Delta(G)$.*

Theorem 6. *If G is a connected graph of order n and size m, then*

$$\frac{2m - n(k - 2)}{3\Delta(G) - k} \leq \gamma_{t,oi}^k(G) \leq n - k + 1.$$

Furthermore, $\gamma_{t,oi}^k(G) = n - k + 1$ if and only if $k = \Delta(G) = n - 1$.

Proof. Let D be a $\gamma_{t,oi}^k(G)$-set. Since D is also a total dominating set of G, each vertex in $V(G) \setminus D$ is adjacent to at least one vertex in D. Hence, $(n - |D|) \leq |E(D, V(G) \setminus D)| \leq |D|(\Delta(G) - 1)$. In addition, as $V(G) \setminus D$ is a k-independent set, we have that $|E(V(G) \setminus D, V(G) \setminus D)| \leq \frac{(n - |D|)(k - 1)}{2}$. Since $|E(D, D)| \leq \frac{|D|\Delta(G) - |E(D, V(G) \setminus D)|}{2} \leq \frac{|D|\Delta(G) - (n - |D|)}{2}$, we obtain

$$
\begin{aligned}
m &= |E(D, V(G) \setminus D)| + |E(D, D)| + |E(V(G) \setminus D, V(G) \setminus D)| \\
&\leq |D|(\Delta(G) - 1) + \frac{|D|\Delta(G) - (n - |D|)}{2} + \frac{(n - |D|)(k - 1)}{2},
\end{aligned}
$$

which is equivalent to $2m \leq |D|(3\Delta(G) - k) + n(k - 2)$. Therefore, $\gamma_{t,oi}^k(G) = |D| \geq \frac{2m - n(k-2)}{3\Delta(G) - k}$, which completes the proof of the lower bound.

In order to prove the upper bound, we first suppose that $1 \le k < \Delta(G)$. Let v be a vertex of maximum degree and let S_k be a set of k vertices adjacent to v. Clearly, the set S_k is k-independent. If $D = V(G) \setminus S_k$ is a total dominating set, then D is a TOkID set. Hence, $\gamma_{t,oi}^k(G) \le |D| = n - k < n - k + 1$. Now, we assume that D is not a total dominating set of G. Since G is connected, it can only happen when $S_k \cap S(G) \ne \emptyset$. Let $S_k^s = S_k \cap S(G)$ and consider the set $D' = (D \setminus (N(S_k^s) \cap L(G))) \cup S_k^s$. Observe that D' is a total dominating set of G of cardinality at most $|D|$ and $V(G) \setminus D'$ is k-independent. Hence, D' is a TOkID set of G and so, $\gamma_{t,oi}^k(G) \le |D'| \le |D| = n - k < n - k + 1$.

Now, we suppose that $k = \Delta(G) < n - 1$. Hence, by Proposition 1 and Theorem 5, we have that $\gamma_{t,oi}^k(G) = \gamma_t(G) \le n - \Delta(G) = n - k < n - k + 1$.

Finally, we assume that $k = \Delta(G) = n - 1$. Thus, $\gamma_t(G) = 2$ and again, by Proposition 1, it follows that $\gamma_{t,oi}^k(G) = \gamma_t(G) = 2 = n - \Delta(G) + 1 = n - k + 1$. Conversely, if $\gamma_{t,oi}^k(G) = n - k + 1$, then, by previous cases ($1 \le k < \Delta(G)$ and $k = \Delta(G) < n - 1$), we deduce that $k = \Delta(G) = n - 1$, which completes the proof. □

The lower bound above is tight. For instance, it is achieved for the cycle C_{4t} with $k = 2$, where, by Proposition 2(ii), we obtain $\gamma_{t,oi}^2(C_{4t}) = 2t$.

The following result is a direct consequence of Theorems 1 and 6.

Corollary 2. *Let G be a nontrivial connected graph of order n. Let k be an integer such that $\beta_k(G) = k$. If $k < \Delta(G)$ or $\Delta(G) < n - 1$, then $\gamma_{t,oi}^k(G) = n - k$.*

Next, we give an upper bound for the total outer k-independent domination number of a graph.

Theorem 7. *If G is a connected graph of order n, then for any positive integer $k \le \delta(G)$,*

$$\gamma_{t,oi}^k(G) \le 2(n - \beta_k(G)) - \delta(G) + k.$$

Proof. Let S be a $\beta_k(G)$-set. Since S is k-independent, then $V(G) \setminus S$ is a $(\delta(G) - k + 1)$-dominating set of G. Now, we fix a vertex $v \in S$ and let A be the set of isolated vertices of $G[V(G) \setminus (S \cup N(v))]$. Let A' be a subset of S of minimum cardinality such that $N(x) \cap A' \ne \emptyset$ for every $x \in A$. Clearly, $|A'| \le |A|$. Moreover, notice that the set $(V(G) \setminus S) \cup A' \cup \{v\}$ is a TOkID set of G. Hence,

$$
\begin{aligned}
\gamma_{t,oi}^k(G) &\le |(V(G) \setminus S) \cup A' \cup \{v\}| \\
&\le |V(G) \setminus S| + |A'| + 1 \\
&\le |V(G) \setminus S| + |A| + 1 \\
&= (n - \beta_k(G)) + (n - \beta_k(G) - (\delta(G) - k + 1)) + 1 \\
&= 2(n - \beta_k(G)) - \delta(G) + k,
\end{aligned}
$$

which completes the proof. □

We remark that the upper bound given in Theorem 7 is tight. For example, it is achieved for the graph $H_k = (k+1)K_k + N_{k+1}$, where $k \ge 2$ is an integer. It is easy to check that $\beta_k(H_k) = (k+1)k$, $|V(H_k)| = (k+1)^2$, $\delta(H_k) = 2k$ and $\gamma_{t,oi}^k(H_k) = k + 2$. The graph H_2, for example, is illustrated in Figure 3.

Figure 3. The graph $H_2 = 3K_2 + N_3$.

Our next result provides a lower bound for the total outer k-independent domination number in terms of the order, minimum degree, and the maximum degree of a graph.

Theorem 8. *If G is a connected graph of order n, then for any positive integer $k \leq \delta(G)$,*

$$\gamma^k_{t,oi}(G) \geq \max\left\{\delta(G) - k + 1, \frac{n(\delta(G) - k + 1)}{\Delta(G) + \delta(G) - k}\right\}.$$

Furthermore, if $\gamma^k_{t,oi}(G) = \delta(G) - k + 1$, then $G \cong G_1 + G_2$, where G_1 is a graph with no isolated vertex of order $\delta(G) - k + 1$ and G_2 is a $(k-1)$-regular graph of order $n - \delta(G) + k - 1$.

Proof. Let D be a $\gamma^k_{t,oi}(G)$-set. If $D = V(G)$, then, by Theorem 13(iii), we have that $k = 1$ and $G \cong P_2$. Hence, the bound is satisfied. Now, we assume that $V(G) \setminus D \neq \emptyset$. Since every vertex in $V(G) \setminus D$ has at least $\delta(G) - k + 1$ neighbors in D, we obtain that $\gamma^k_{t,oi}(G) = |D| \geq \delta(G) - k + 1$. In addition, since every vertex in D has at most $\Delta(G) - 1$ neighbors in $V(G) \setminus D$, we deduce that

$$|D|(\Delta(G) - 1) \geq |V(G) \setminus D|(\delta(G) - k + 1)$$
$$\gamma^k_{t,oi}(G)(\Delta(G) - 1) \geq (n - \gamma^k_{t,oi}(G))(\delta(G) - k + 1)$$
$$\gamma^k_{t,oi}(G)(\Delta(G) + \delta(G) - k) \geq n(\delta(G) - k + 1)$$
$$\gamma^k_{t,oi}(G) \geq \frac{n(\delta(G) - k + 1)}{\Delta(G) + \delta(G) - k}$$

which implies that the bound is satisfied.

Now, we assume that $|D| = \delta(G) - k + 1$. Since D is also a total dominating set of G, we have that $G_1 = G[D]$ is a graph with no isolated vertex of order $\delta(G) - k + 1$. Let $v \in V(G) \setminus D$. If $\delta(v) > \delta(G)$, then $\delta_D(v) > \delta(G) - k + 1$ as $V(G) \setminus D$ is k-independent, which is a contradiction. Hence, for every vertex $x \in V(G) \setminus D$, it satisfies that $\delta(x) = \delta(G)$ and, consequently, $\delta_{V(G) \setminus D}(x) = k - 1$. Thus, $G_2 = G[V(G) \setminus D]$ is a $(k-1)$-regular graph of order $n - \delta(G) + k - 1$ and $G \cong G_1 + G_2$, which completes the proof. $\square$

For any integer $k \geq 3$, let $\mathcal{G}_{2k,k-1}$ be the family of $(k-1)$-regular graphs of order $2k$, and let $G = P_2 + G_k$, where $G_k \in \mathcal{G}_{2k,k-1}$. Observe that $\mathcal{G}_{2k,k-1} \subseteq T[F \circ_1 P_2]$, where $\Delta(F) \leq k - 1$. Hence, by Theorem 13(i), we have that $\gamma^k_{t,oi}(G) = 2$. In addition, one can check that $|V(G)| = 2k + 2$, $\Delta(G) = 2k + 1$, and $\delta(G) = k + 1$, concluding that the lower bound given in the previous theorem is tight, and it is achieved for the graph G. Recall that, for any integer $k \geq 3$, the family $\mathcal{G}_{2k,k-1}$ is not empty. Next, we give an example of a graph $F_k \in \mathcal{G}_{2k,k-1}$. Let F_k be the graph with vertex set $V(F_k) = \{v_1, \ldots, v_k, u_1, \ldots, u_k\}$ and edge set $E(F_k) = \{v_i u_j : i \in \{1, \ldots k\}, j \in \{i, \ldots, i + k - 1\}\}$, where the subscripts are taken modulo k. It is not difficult to see that the graph F_k is a $(k-1)$-regular graph of order $2k$, as desired. The graph F_4, for example, is illustrated in Figure 4.

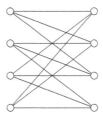

Figure 4. The graph F_4.

In order to derive another results, we need to state the following results.

Theorem 9. *Let G be a graph.*

(i)   [16] *If $k \leq \delta(G)$, then $\beta_k(G) + \gamma_{\delta(G)-k+1}(G) \leq n$.*
(ii)   [3] *If $2 \leq k \leq \Delta(G)$, then $\gamma_k(G) \geq \gamma(G) + k - 2$.*

The following result is a direct consequence of combining Theorems 1 and 9(i).

Theorem 10. *If G is a connected graph, then for any positive integer $k \leq \delta(G)$,*

$$\gamma_{t,oi}^k(G) \geq \gamma_{\delta(G)-k+1}(G).$$

We remark that the lower bound given in the theorem above is sharp. For example, it is achieved for any complete graph K_n with $n \geq 3$ and $1 \leq k \leq n - 2$.

From Theorems 10 and 9(ii), we immediately have the next theorem.

Theorem 11. *If G is a connected graph, then for any positive integer $2 \leq k \leq \delta(G)$,*

$$\gamma_{t,oi}^k(G) \geq \gamma(G) + \delta(G) - k - 1.$$

To conclude this section, we proceed to characterize all graphs achieving the extreme values given in Proposition 1. Before this, we shall need the following result and notation.

Theorem 12 ([8]). *Let G be a graph of order n. Then, $\gamma_{t,oi}(G) = n - 1$ if and only if $G \in \{P_3, C_4, C_5\}$ or G is a complete graph with at least three vertices.*

We define the k-join operation between two graphs G and H, and denoted by $G \circ_k H$, as the disjoint union of G and H by joining each vertex of G to k or $k + 1$ vertices of H. For each integer positive k and any graphs G and H, the family of all graphs obtained by the operation above is denoted by $T[G \circ_k H]$.

Theorem 13. *Let G be a connected graph of order n. Then, the following statement holds.*

(i) $\gamma_{t,oi}^k(G) = 2$ *if and only if $G \in T[F \circ_1 P_2]$, where F is some graph with $\Delta(F) \leq k - 1$.*
(ii)   *For $n \geq 3$, we have that $\gamma_{t,oi}^k(G) = n - 1$ if and only if either $k = 1$ and $G \in \{K_n, P_3, C_4, C_5\}$ or $k = 2$ and $G \in \{P_3, C_3\}$.*
(iii) $\gamma_{t,oi}^k(G) = n$ *if and only if $k = 1$ and G is the path P_2.*

Proof. We first proceed to prove (i). Suppose that $\gamma_{t,oi}^k(G) = 2$ and let D be a $\gamma_{t,oi}^k(G)$-set. Clearly, D induces a path P_2. Moreover, $V(G) \setminus D$ is a k-independent set, which implies that the subgraph induced by $V(G) \setminus D$, namely F, has maximum degree $\Delta(F) \leq k - 1$. In addition, as D is a total dominating set, every vertex in $V(G) \setminus D$ is adjacent to one or two vertices in D, i.e., $1 \leq \delta_D(v) \leq 2$ for every $v \in V(G) \setminus D$. Therefore, $G \in T[F \circ_1 P_2]$, where F is some graph with $\Delta(F) \leq k - 1$. The necessary condition is straightforward and so the proof of (i) holds.

We now proceed to prove (ii). If either $k = 1$ and $G \in \{K_n, P_3, C_4, C_5\}$ or $k = 2$ and $G \in \{P_3, C_3\}$, then it is easy to see that $\gamma_{t,oi}^k(G) = n - 1$. Hence, we assume that G is a connected graph satisfying $\gamma_{t,oi}^k(G) = n - 1$. By Theorem 6, we obtain that $k \leq 2$ and, if $k = 2$, then $k = \Delta(G) = n - 1$. If $k = 1$, then, by Theorem 12, we give that $G \in \{K_n, P_3, C_4, C_5\}$. Moreover, if $k = 2$, then $\Delta = 2$ and $n = 3$. Hence, G is either P_3 or C_3, which completes the proof of (ii).

Finally, we proceed to prove (iii). If $k = 1$ and $G = P_2$, then it is straightforward that $\gamma_{t,oi}^k(G) = n$. Conversely, if G is a connected graph such that $\gamma_{t,oi}^k(G) = n$, then, by Theorem 6, we obtain that $k = \Delta(G) = 1$ and $n = 2$. Hence, G is the path P_2, which completes the proof. □

3. Nordhaus–Gaddum Type Inequalities

In 1956, Nordhaus and Gaddum published an article [17], where it gave lower and upper bounds on the sum and product of the chromatic numbers of a graph and its complement. From this research idea, these types of inequalities was defined as Nordhaus–Gaddum type inequalities, and have been well studied for several domination parameters. We suggest a recent survey [18]. In the present section, we initiate the study of Nordhaus–Gaddum type inequalities for the total outer k-independence domination number.

We first establish a lower and upper bounds on the sum of the total outer k-independence domination numbers of a graph and its complement. Before this, we remark that in this section we involve the study of not connected graphs. However, it is necessary to assume that both G and $\overline{G}$ have no isolated vertices. This last condition implies that $n \geq 4$. In addition, we assume that $1 \leq k \leq \min\{\Delta(G), \Delta(\overline{G})\}$.

Lemma 5. *For any integer $m \geq 3$,*

$$\gamma_{t,oi}(\overline{mK_2}) = 2m - 2.$$

Proof. Let u and v be two adjacent vertices of mK_2. Notice that $V(\overline{mK_2}) \setminus \{u, v\}$ is a TO1ID set of $\overline{mK_2}$. Hence, $\gamma_{t,oi}(\overline{mK_2}) \leq |V(\overline{mK_2}) \setminus \{u, v\}| = 2m - 2$. Now, suppose that $\gamma_{t,oi}(\overline{mK_2}) < 2m - 2$ and let D be a $\gamma_{t,oi}(\overline{mK_2})$-set. Observe that $|V(\overline{mK_2}) \setminus D| \geq 3$ and any three vertices in $V(\overline{mK_2}) \setminus D$ contain a path P_3, which is a contradiction since $V(\overline{mK_2}) \setminus D$ is an independent set. Therefore, $\gamma_{t,oi}(\overline{mK_2}) = 2m - 2$, which completes the proof. □

Theorem 14. *For any graph G of order $n \geq 4$ such that neither G nor $\overline{G}$ contains isolated vertices,*

$$\max\{4, n - 2k + 1\} \leq \gamma_{t,oi}^k(G) + \gamma_{t,oi}^k(\overline{G}) \leq 2n - k.$$

Furthermore,

(i) $\gamma_{t,oi}^k(G) + \gamma_{t,oi}^k(\overline{G}) = 4$ *if and only if* $\gamma_{t,oi}^k(G) = \gamma_{t,oi}^k(\overline{G}) = 2$.
(ii) $\gamma_{t,oi}^k(G) + \gamma_{t,oi}^k(\overline{G}) = 2n - k$ *if and only if* $k = 1$ *and* $G \in \{C_4, \overline{C_4}\}$.
(iii) $\gamma_{t,oi}^k(G) + \gamma_{t,oi}^k(\overline{G}) = 2n - k - 1$ *if and only if* $k = 1$ *and* $G \in \{mK_2, \overline{mK_2}\}$, *with* $m \geq 3$.

Proof. First, we prove the lower bound. Since $\gamma_{t,oi}^k(G) \geq 2$ for any graph G without isolated vertices, the trivial lower bound follows and also (i) is straightforward. Now, let D and $\overline{D}$ be a $\gamma_{t,oi}^k(G)$-set and a $\gamma_{t,oi}^k(\overline{G})$-set, respectively. As $V(G) \setminus D$ and $V(G) \setminus \overline{D}$ are k-independent in G and $\overline{G}$, respectively, we have that $\delta_{V(G) \setminus D}(x) \leq k - 1$ and $\delta_{V(G) \setminus \overline{D}}(x) \leq k - 1$ for every $x \in (V(G) \setminus D) \cap (V(G) \setminus \overline{D})$. Hence, $|(V(G) \setminus D) \cap (V(G) \setminus \overline{D})| \leq |N_{V(G) \setminus D}(x)| + |N_{V(G) \setminus \overline{D}}(x)| + 1 \leq 2k - 1$, and, as a consequence,

$$n - (|D| + |\overline{D}|) \leq n - |D \cup \overline{D}| = |(V(G) \setminus D) \cap (V(G) \setminus \overline{D})| \leq 2k - 1,$$

which implies that $n - 2k + 1 \leq \gamma_{t,oi}^k(G) + \gamma_{t,oi}^k(\overline{G})$, as desired.

Next, we prove the upper bound. Suppose that $\gamma_{t,oi}^k(G) + \gamma_{t,oi}^k(\overline{G}) > 2n - k$. Notice that either G or $\overline{G}$ is connected. By symmetry, we assume that G is connected. Since $n \geq 4$ and $\Delta(G) < n - 1$, by Theorem 6, we have that $\gamma_{t,oi}^k(G) \leq n - k$. This implies that $\gamma_{t,oi}^k(\overline{G}) > n$, which is a contradiction. Therefore, the upper bound follows.

Now, we proceed to prove (ii). If $k = 1$ and $G \in \{C_4, \overline{C_4}\}$, then it is straightforward to observe that $\gamma_{t,oi}^k(G) + \gamma_{t,oi}^k(\overline{G}) = 2n - k$. Conversely, we assume that $\gamma_{t,oi}^k(G) + \gamma_{t,oi}^k(\overline{G}) = 2n - k$. Since G is connected, Theorem 6 leads to $\gamma_{t,oi}^k(G) = n - k$ and $\gamma_{t,oi}^k(\overline{G}) = n$. Hence, by Theorem 13(iii), it follows that $\overline{G}$ consists of disjoint copies of K_2. Since $k \leq \Delta(mK_2) = 1$, we have that k can only take the value 1 and so $\gamma_{t,oi}^1(\overline{mK_2}) = n - 1$. This implies, by Theorem 13(ii), that $m = 2$. Therefore, $k = 1$ and $G \in \{C_4, \overline{C_4}\}$, which completes the proof of (ii).

Finally, we proceed to prove (iii). First, we suppose that $\gamma_{t,oi}^k(G) + \gamma_{t,oi}^k(\overline{G}) = 2n - k - 1$. Again, as G is connected, we have that $(\gamma_{t,oi}^k(G), \gamma_{t,oi}^k(\overline{G})) = (n - k, n - 1)$ or $(\gamma_{t,oi}^k(G), \gamma_{t,oi}^k(\overline{G})) = (n - k - 1, n)$. Hence, we analyze these two cases.

Case 1. $(\gamma_{t,oi}^k(G), \gamma_{t,oi}^k(\overline{G})) = (n - k, n - 1)$. If $\gamma_{t,oi}^k(\overline{G}) = n - 1$, then by Theorem 13(ii), we have that ($k = 1$ and $\overline{G}$ is isomorphic to $mK_2 \cup H$, where $H \in \{K_r, P_3, C_4, C_5\}$) or ($k = 2$ and $\overline{G}$ is isomorphic to $mK_2 \cup H$, where $H \in \{P_3, C_3\}$). In both cases, we can construct a TOkID set of G of cardinality $n - k - 1$, which contradicts the condition $\gamma_{t,oi}^k(G) = n - k$.

Case 2. $(\gamma_{t,oi}^k(G), \gamma_{t,oi}^k(\overline{G})) = (n - k - 1, n)$. If $\gamma_{t,oi}^k(\overline{G}) = n$, then by Theorem 13(iii) we have that $k = 1$ and $\overline{G}$ is isomorphic to mK_2, with $m \geq 3$. Moreover, Lemma 5 leads to $\gamma_{t,oi}^k(G) = \gamma_{t,oi}^k(\overline{mK_2}) = \gamma_{t,oi}(\overline{mK_2}) = 2m - 2 = n - 2 = n - k - 1$, as desired.

On the other hand, we suppose that $k = 1$ and $G \in \{mK_2, \overline{mK_2}\}$, with $m \geq 3$. By symmetry, we consider that $G = \overline{mK_2}$. Theorem 13(iii) and Lemma 5 lead to $(\gamma_{t,oi}^k(G), \gamma_{t,oi}^k(\overline{G})) = (n - k - 1, n)$. Hence, $\gamma_{t,oi}^k(G) + \gamma_{t,oi}^k(\overline{G}) = 2n - k - 1$, which completes the proof. $\square$

Next, we show that the upper bounds in Theorem 14 can be improved if we assume that both G and $\overline{G}$ are connected graphs.

Theorem 15. *If G is a graph of order $n \geq 4$ such that both G and $\overline{G}$ are connected, then*

$$\gamma_{t,oi}^k(G) + \gamma_{t,oi}^k(\overline{G}) \leq 2(n - k).$$

Proof. Notice that, if both G and $\overline{G}$ are connected, then $k \leq \min\{\Delta(G), \Delta(\overline{G})\} < n - 1$, and by Theorem 6 we have that $(\gamma_{t,oi}^k(G), \gamma_{t,oi}^k(\overline{G})) \leq (n - k, n - k)$. Hence, $\gamma_{t,oi}^k(G) + \gamma_{t,oi}^k(\overline{G}) \leq 2(n - k)$. $\square$

Next, we give Nordhaus–Gaddum type inequalities for the product of the TOkID numbers of a graph and its complement.

Theorem 16. *If G is a graph of order $n \geq 5$ such that neither G nor $\overline{G}$ contains isolated vertices, then*

$$\max\{4, 2n - 2(2k + 1)\} \leq \gamma_{t,oi}^k(G) \cdot \gamma_{t,oi}^k(\overline{G}) \leq (n - k)(n - 1).$$

Furthermore,

(i) $\gamma_{t,oi}^k(G) \cdot \gamma_{t,oi}^k(\overline{G}) = 4$ *if and only if* $\gamma_{t,oi}^k(G) = \gamma_{t,oi}^k(\overline{G}) = 2$.
(ii) $\gamma_{t,oi}^k(G) \cdot \gamma_{t,oi}^k(\overline{G}) = (n - k)(n - 1)$ *if and only if* $k = 1$ *and* $G \cong C_5$.

Proof. We first prove the upper bound. Since either G or $\overline{G}$ is connected (by symmetry, we assume that G is connected) and $\max\{\Delta(G), \Delta(\overline{G})\} < n - 1$, we deduce by Theorem 6 that $\gamma_{t,oi}^k(G) \leq n - k$. Therefore, $\gamma_{t,oi}^k(G) \cdot \gamma_{t,oi}^k(\overline{G}) \leq (n - k)n$.

Suppose now that there exists a graph G of order n for which $\gamma_{t,oi}^k(G) \cdot \gamma_{t,oi}^k(\overline{G}) = (n - k)n$. Without loss of generality, we assume that $\gamma_{t,oi}^k(G) = n - k$ and $\gamma_{t,oi}^k(\overline{G}) = n$. Thus, by Theorem 13(iii), we have that $k = 1$ and $\overline{G}$ consists of disjoint copies of K_2, which is a contradiction with the equality above $\gamma_{t,oi}^k(G) = n - k = n - 1$ by Lemma 5.

As a consequence, $\gamma_{t,oi}^k(G) \cdot \gamma_{t,oi}^k(\overline{G}) < (n - k)n$, which implies

$$\gamma_{t,oi}^k(G) \cdot \gamma_{t,oi}^k(\overline{G}) \leq (n - k)(n - 1), \tag{1}$$

as desired.

Now, we suppose that the equality in the inequality (1) holds. Hence, either $(\gamma_{t,oi}^k(G), \gamma_{t,oi}^k(\overline{G})) = (n - k, n - 1)$ or $(\gamma_{t,oi}^k(G), \gamma_{t,oi}^k(\overline{G})) = (n - 1, n - k)$. Without loss of generality, we may assume that

$(\gamma_{t,oi}^k(G), \gamma_{t,oi}^k(\overline{G})) = (n-k, n-1)$. By Theorem 13(ii), we have that either $(k = 1$ and $\overline{G} \cong t_1K_2 + G'$, where $G' \in \{K_n, P_3, C_4, C_5\})$ or $(k = 2$ and $\overline{G} \cong t_2K_2 + G''$, where $G'' \in \{P_3, C_3\})$. In both cases, if $t_1, t_2 \geq 1$, then we can construct a TOkID set of G of cardinality $n-k-1$, which contradicts the condition $\gamma_{t,oi}^k(G) = n-k$. Since $n \geq 5$, we obtain that $k = 1$ and $G \cong C_5$. The other hand is straightforward to see, which completes the proof of statement (ii).

In order to prove the lower bound, by Theorem 14, we have

$$\gamma_{t,oi}^k(G) + \gamma_{t,oi}^k(\overline{G}) \geq \max\{4, n-2k+1\}.$$

Now, we minimize $\gamma_{t,oi}^k(G) \cdot \gamma_{t,oi}^k(\overline{G})$ subject to $\gamma_{t,oi}^k(G) + \gamma_{t,oi}^k(\overline{G}) = \max\{4, n-2k+1\}$. If $\gamma_{t,oi}^k(G) + \gamma_{t,oi}^k(\overline{G}) = 4$, then, by Theorem 14(i), we obtain the equivalence with the condition $\gamma_{t,oi}^k(G) = \gamma_{t,oi}^k(\overline{G}) = 2$. Therefore, $\gamma_{t,oi}^k(G) \cdot \gamma_{t,oi}^k(\overline{G}) \geq 4$ and statement (i) holds. On the other hand, if $\gamma_{t,oi}^k(G) + \gamma_{t,oi}^k(\overline{G}) = n-2k+1$, then we obtain either $(\gamma_{t,oi}^k(G), \gamma_{t,oi}^k(\overline{G})) = (2, n-2k-1)$ or $(\gamma_{t,oi}^k(G), \gamma_{t,oi}^k(\overline{G})) = (n-2k-1, 2)$. Therefore, $\gamma_{t,oi}^k(G) \cdot \gamma_{t,oi}^k(\overline{G}) \geq 2n - 2(2k+1)$, which completes the proof. $\square$

4. Conclusions and Open Problems

In this paper, we have introduced and studied the total outer k-independent domination number of graphs. Among the main contributions, we emphasize the following.

- We have shown the close relationship that exists between the total outer k-independent domination number and other domination parameters such as domination number, total domination number, k-domination number, and k-independence number.
- We have obtained general bounds for the parameter and discussed the sharpness of them.
- In a specific section of the article, we focused on the study of Nordhaus–Gaddum type inequalities for the total outer k-independence domination number.
- We have shown that the problem of finding the total outer k-independent domination number of a graph is NP-hard.

In order to continue with this new line of research, we propose some open problems, which we consider to be interesting.

(a) Characterize the graphs G of order n such that $\gamma_{t,oi}^k(G) = \gamma_t(G)$ and $\gamma_{t,oi}^k(G) = n - \beta_k(G)$.
(b) Since the problem of finding $\gamma_{t,oi}^k(G)$ is NP-hard, is there a polynomial-time algorithm for finding $\gamma_{t,oi}^k(T)$ for any tree T?
(c) To find possible practical applications to the parameter $\gamma_{t,oi}^k(G)$ studied.

Author Contributions: All authors contributed equally to this work. All authors have read and agreed to the published version of the manuscript.

Funding: This paper was supported in part by two grants from the Ministerio de Economía y Competitividad, Agencia Estatal de Investigacioìn (AEI) and Fondo Europeo de Desarrollo Regional (FEDER) (MTM2016-78227-C2-1-P and MTM2015-69323-REDT), Spain.

Acknowledgments: We would like to thank the referees for their careful reading of the manuscript and several useful comments that have helped us to improve the presentation of the paper.

Conflicts of Interest: The authors declare no conflict of interest.

References

1. Farber, M.R. *Applications of Linear Programming Duality to Problems Involving Independence and Domination*; Simon Fraser University, Computing Science: Burnaby, BC, Canada, 1981.
2. Gupta, P. Domination in Graph with Application. *Indian J. Res.* **2013**, *2*, 115–117.
3. Fink, J.F.; Jacobson, M.S. n-Domination in Graphs. In *Graph Theory with Applications to Algorithms and Computer Science*; John Wiley and Sons: New York, NY, USA, 1985; pp. 283–300.

4. Fink, J.F.; Jacobson, M.S. *n*-Domination, *n*-Dependence and Forbidden Subgraphs. In *Graph Theory with Applications to Algorithms and Computer Science*; John Wiley and Sons: New York, NY, USA, 1985; pp. 301–311.

5. Chellali, M.; Favaron, O.; Hansberg A.; Volkmann, L. *k*-Domination and *k*-Independence in Graphs: A Survey. *Graphs Comb.* **2012**, *28*, 1–55. [CrossRef]

6. Henning, M.A. A survey of selected recent results on total domination in graphs. *Discret. Math.* **2009**, *309*, 32–63. [CrossRef]

7. Henning, M.A.; Yeo, A. *Total Domination in Graphs. Springer Monographs in Mathematics*; Springer: New York, NY, USA, 2013.

8. Krzywkowski, M. Total Outer-Independent Domination in Graphs. Manuscript. 2014. Available online: http://citeseerx.ist.psu.edu/viewdoc/download?doi=10.1.1.704.9143&rep=rep1&type=pdf (accessed on 22 January 2020).

9. Soner, N.D.; Murthy, B.V.D.; Deepak, G. Total co-independent domination in graphs. *Appl. Math. Sci.* **2012**, *6*, 6545–6551.

10. Cabrera Martínez, A.; Cabrera García, S.; Peterin, I.; Yero, I.G. Total co-independent domination number of some graph operations. **2019**, submitted.

11. Cabrera Martínez, A.; Hernández Mira, F.A.; Sigarreta, J.M.; Yero, I.G. A note on total co-independent domination in trees. **2017**, submitted.

12. Cabrera Martínez, A.; Hernández Mira, F.A.; Sigarreta, J.M.; Yero, I.G. On computational and combinatorial properties of the total co-independent domination number of graphs. *Comput. J.* **2019**, *62*, 97–108. [CrossRef]

13. Cabrera Martínez, A.; Kuziak D.; Yero, I.G. Outer-independent total Roman domination in graphs. *Discret. Appl. Math.* **2019**, *269*, 107–119. [CrossRef]

14. Jacobson, M.S.; Peters, K. Complexity questions for *n*-domination and related parameters. *Congr. Numer.* **1989**, *68*, 7–22.

15. Cockayne, E.J.; Dawes, R.M.; Hedetniemi, S.T. Total domination in graphs. *Networks* **1980**, *10*, 211–219. [CrossRef]

16. Jacobson, M.S.; Peters, K.; Rall, D.F. On *n*-irredundance and *n*-domination. *Ars Combin.* **1990**, *29B*, 151–160.

17. Nordhaus E.A.; Gaddum, J. On complementary graphs, *Am. Math. Mon.* **1956**, *63*, 175–177. [CrossRef]

18. Aouchiche, M.; Hansen, P. A survey of Nordhaus–Gaddum type relations. *Discret. Appl. Math.* **2013**, *161*, 466–546. [CrossRef] .

Article

Independent Domination Stable Trees and Unicyclic Graphs

Pu Wu [1], Huiqin Jiang [1], Sakineh Nazari-Moghaddam [2], Seyed Mahmoud Sheikholeslami [2], Zehui Shao [1,*] and Lutz Volkmann [3]

[1]   Institute of Computing Science and Technology, Guangzhou University, Guangzhou 510006, China
[2]   Department of Mathematics, Azarbaijan Shahid Madani University, Tabriz 5375171379, Iran
[3]   Lehrstuhl II für Mathematik, RWTH Aachen University, 52056 Aachen, Germany
*   Correspondence: zshao@gzhu.edu.cn

Received: 1 August 2019; Accepted: 2 September 2019; Published: 5 September 2019

Abstract: A set $S \subseteq V(G)$ in a graph G is a *dominating set* if S dominates all vertices in G, where we say a vertex dominates each vertex in its closed neighbourhood. A set is independent if it is pairwise non-adjacent. The minimum cardinality of an independent dominating set on a graph G is called the *independent domination number $i(G)$*. A graph G is ID-stable if the independent domination number of G is not changed when any vertex is removed. In this paper, we study basic properties of ID-stable graphs and we characterize all ID-stable trees and unicyclic graphs. In addition, we establish bounds on the order of ID-stable trees.

Keywords: independent domination; stable graph; tree; unicyclic graph

1. Introduction

Throughout this paper, $V(G)$ and edge set $E(G)$ (briefly V, E) are used to denote the vertex set and edge set of G, respectively. For every vertex $v \in V(G)$, the *open neighborhood* of v is the set $N_G(v) = N(v) = \{u \in V(G) \mid uv \in E(G)\}$, and its *closed neighborhood* is the set $N_G[v] = N[v] = N(v) \cup \{v\}$. The *degree* of a vertex $v \in V$ is $d_G(v) = |N(v)|$. A *leaf* of G is a vertex with degree one, and a *support vertex* is a vertex adjacent to a leaf. The set of all leaves adjacent to a vertex v is denoted by $L(v)$. For two vertices u and v, the *distance* $d_G(u, v)$ from u to v is the number of the edges of a shortest uv-path in G. The *diameter* diam(G) of a graph G is the greatest distance among a pair of vertices of G. Assume T is a rooted tree and $v \in V(T)$, let $C(v)$ and $D(v)$ denote the set of children and descendants of v, respectively, and $D[v] = D(v) \cup \{v\}$. The *maximal subtree* at v, denoted by T_v, is the subgraph of T induced by $D[v]$, and is denoted by T_v. For a graph G, let $I(G)$ be the set of vertices with degree 1. The path and cycle on n vertices are denote by P_n and C_n, respectively.

A set $S \subseteq V$ in a graph G is a *dominating set* if every vertex of G is either in S or adjacent to a vertex of S. The *domination number* $\gamma(G)$ equals the minimum cardinality of a dominating set in G. There are many variants of the dominating set which are studied extensively, such as the independent dominating set [1], total domination [2,3], Roman domination [4,5], semitotal domination [6,7], etc. For a comprehensive treatment of domination in graphs, see the monographs by Haynes, Hedetniemi, and Slater [8,9].

A set is *independent* if it is pairwise non-adjacent. The minimum cardinality among all independent dominating sets on a graph G called the *independent domination number* $i(G)$ of G. An $i(G)$-set is an independent dominating set of G of cardinality $i(G)$. This variation of graph domination has been studied extensively in the literature; see for example the books [8,9], and the readers can consult the new survey of Goddard and Henning [1].

The removal of a vertex from a graph can increase the independent domination number, decrease the independent domination number, or leave it unchanged. A graph G is independent domination vertex-critical or *i*-vertex-critical if $i(G - v) < i(G)$ for every $v \in V(G)$. The independent domination vertex-critical graphs have been studied by Ao [10] and Edwards [11] and elsewhere [12–14]. Here we focus on the case where the removal of any vertex leave the independent domination number unchanged.

A graph G is independent domination stable (ID-stable) if the independent domination number of G is not changed when any vertex is removed. The domination stable problem consists of characterize graphs whose domination number (a type of domination number, e.g. total domination number, Roman domination number) remains unchanged under removal of any vertex or edge, or addition of any edge [2,15–17].

In this paper, we study basic properties of ID-stable graphs and we characterize all ID-stable trees and unicyclic graphs. In addition, we establish bounds on the order of ID-stable trees.

We make use of the following results in this paper.

Proposition 1 ([1]). *For* $n \geq 3$, $i(P_n) = i(C_n) = \lceil \frac{n}{3} \rceil$.

The next result is an immediate consequence of Proposition 1.

Corollary 1. *If* $n \geq 3$, *then* C_n *is an ID-stable graph if and only if* $n \not\equiv 1 \pmod 3$.

In the next sections, we will use the following notations:
For a graph G, let:

$$W(G) = \{u \in V(G) \mid \text{there exists an } i(G)\text{-set containing } u\}$$

and:

$$W^{1,1}(G) = \{(u,v) \mid u,v \in V(G) \text{ and there exists an } i(G)\text{-set containing both of } u \text{ and } v\}.$$

2. Basic Properties

In this section, we study the basic properties of the ID-stable graph, and we construct new ID-stable graphs from an old one.

Proposition 2. *If* G *is an ID-stable graph, then every support vertex in* G *is adjacent to exactly one leaf.*

Proof. Let G be an ID-stable graph. Suppose, to the contrary, that G has a support vertex x with $|L(x)| \geq 2$, and let $y, z \in L(x)$. If G has an $i(G)$-set S such that $x \notin S$, then $y, z \in S$, and clearly, $S - \{y\}$ is an independent dominating set of $G - y$ yielding $i(G - y) < i(G)$, which is a contradiction. Hence, we assume that every $i(G)$-set contains x. Now, consider the graph $G - x$, and let D be an $i(G - x)$-set. Since each vertex in $L(x)$ is isolated in $G - x$, D contains all vertices in $L(x)$. Clearly, D is an independent dominating set of G such that $x \notin D$. It follows from the assumption that $i(G - x) = |D| > i(G)$, a contradiction again. This completes the proof. □

Proposition 3. *If* G *is an ID-stable graph, then* G *does not have two adjacent support vertices.*

Proof. Let G be an ID-stable graph. Suppose, to the contrary, that there exist two adjacent support vertices x, y in G. Assume that $L(x) = \{x'\}$, $L(y) = \{y'\}$, and let S be an $i(G)$-set. Then, $x' \in S$ or $y' \in S$. Assume, without loss of generality, that $y' \in S$. Then, $y \notin S$. If $(N_G(y) - \{y'\}) \cap S \neq \emptyset$, then $S - \{y'\}$ is an independent dominating set of $G - y'$, which leads to a contradiction. Hence, $(N_G(y) - \{y'\}) \cap S = \emptyset$. In particular, $x \notin S$, and so, $x' \in S$. Now, $(S - \{y', x'\}) \cup \{y\}$ is an independent dominating set of $G - x'$, which leads to a contradiction. □

The spider S_q is the graph obtained from the star $K_{1,q}$ by subdividing its edges once. Clearly, $i(S_q) = q$. Assume that $V(S_q) = \{s\} \cup \{a_i, b_i | i = 1, 2, \ldots, q\}$ and $E(S_q) = \{sa_i, a_i b_i | i = 1, 2, \ldots, q\}$. The vertex s is called the *head*; the vertices a_i are called the *knees*; and the vertices b_i are called the *feet* of the spider for $1 \leq i \leq q$.

Proposition 4. *Let G be a graph and $v \in V(G)$. Let G' be the graph obtained from G by adding a spider S_q ($q \geq 1$) and possibly joining the head s to v. Then, $i(G') = i(G) + q$.*

Proof. Clearly, any $i(G)$-set can be extended to an independent dominating set of G' by adding $a_1, \ldots, a_q$, and so, $i(G') \leq i(G) + q$.

Now, we show that $i(G') \geq i(G) + q$. Let S be an $i(G')$-set. To dominate b_i, we must have $|S \cap \{a_i, b_i\}| \geq 1$ for each i. If $s \notin S$ or $sv \notin E(G')$, then the set $S - V(S_q)$ is an independent dominating set of G, and this implies that $i(G') \geq i(G) + q$. Suppose that $s \in S$ and $sv \in E(G')$. It follows that $\{b_1, \ldots, b_q\} \subseteq S$ and $S \cap N_G[v] = \emptyset$. Then, the set $(S - \{s, b_1, \ldots, b_q\}) \cup \{v\}$ is an independent dominating set of G yielding $i(G') \geq i(G) + q$. Thus, $i(G') = i(G) + q$, and the proof is complete. $\square$

Proposition 5. *Let G be an ID-stable graph. Then:*

1. *if $u \in W(G)$ and G' is a graph obtained from G by adding a spider S_1 with head s and an edge us, then G' is an ID-stable graph,*

2. *if $u \in V(G)$ and G' is a graph obtained from G by adding a spider S_q ($q \geq 2$) with head s and an edge us, then G' is an ID-stable graph.*

Proof. Our arguments apply equally well to both parts, so we prove them simultaneously. Let $v \in V(G')$ be an arbitrary vertex. If $v \in V(G)$, then we have $i(G - v) = i(G)$ because G is an ID-stable graph, and by Proposition 4, we have

$$i(G' - v) = i(G - v) + q = i(G) + q = i(G').$$

Assume that $v \in V(S_q)$. We consider three cases.

Case 1. $v = s$.

Then, clearly, $G' - v$ is the union of G with qK_2 ($q \geq 1$), and so, $i(G' - v) = i(G) + q$. It follows from Proposition 4 that $i(G' - v) = i(G')$.

Case 2. $v = a_i$ for some $i \in \{1, 2, \ldots, q\}$.

Assume, without loss of generality, that $v = a_q$. First, we prove (1). Clearly, we have $G' - v = (G + us) \cup K_1$. Obviously, any $i(G)$-set containing u can be extended to an independent dominating set of $G' - v$ by adding b_1, and so, $i(G' - v) \leq i(G) + 1 = i(G')$. On the other hand, any $i(G' - v)$-set is obviously an independent dominating set of G', and so, $i(G' - v) \geq i(G')$, yielding $i(G' - v) = i(G')$. Now, we prove (2). Clearly, any $i(G)$-set can be extended to an independent dominating set of $G' - v$ by adding $\{b_q, a_1, \ldots, a_{q-1}\}$, and so, $i(G' - v) \leq i(G) + q = i(G')$. Furthermore, any $i(G' - v)$-set is obviously an independent dominating set of G', and so, $i(G' - v) \geq i(G')$. Thus, $i(G' - v) = i(G')$.

Case 3. $v = b_i$ for some $i \in \{1, 2, \ldots, q\}$.

Assume, without loss of generality, that $v = b_1$. Obviously, any $i(G)$-set can be extended to an independent dominating set of $G' - v$ by adding $\{a_1, \ldots, a_q\}$, and so, $i(G' - v) \leq i(G) + q = i(G')$. Now, let S' be an $i(G' - v)$-set. If $a_1 \in S'$, then S' is obviously an independent dominating set of G', and so, $i(G' - v) \geq i(G')$. Assume that $a_1 \notin S'$. Then, $s \in S'$. If $(N_{G'}(u) - \{s\}) \cap S' \neq \emptyset$, then $(S' - \{s\}) \cup \{a_1\}$ is an independent dominating set of G', and so, $i(G' - v) \geq i(G')$. Suppose that $(N_{G'}(u) - \{s\}) \cap S' = \emptyset$. Then, $S' - \{s, b_2, \ldots, b_q\}$ is an independent dominating set of $G - u$, and since G is an ID-stable graph, we deduce that $i(G' - v) = (|S'| - q) + q \geq i(G) + q = i(G')$. Hence, $i(G' - v) = i(G')$. Therefore, G' is an ID-stable, and the proof is complete. $\square$

Let k_1 and k_2 be non-negative integers, and let H_{k_1,k_2} be the graph obtained from the star $K_{1,3}$ centered at s with $V(K_{1,3}) = \{s,a,b,c\}$ by attaching k_1 pendent paths P_2 to a and k_2 pendent paths P_2 to b (see, e.g., Figure 1). For each $1 \leq i \leq k_1$, the vertex set of ith P_2 is $\{r_i, t_i\}$ with $ar_i \in E(H_{k_1,k_2})$, and for each $1 \leq j \leq k_2$, the vertex set of jth P_2 is $\{p_j, q_j\}$ with $bp_j \in E(H_{k_1,k_2})$.

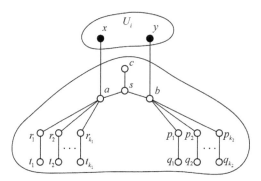

Figure 1. The operations $\mathcal{O}_3$, or $\mathcal{O}_4$, or $\mathcal{O}_5$.

Proposition 6. *Let G be a graph and $x, y \in V(G)$ (possibly $x = y$). Let G' be the graph obtained from G by adding a graph H_{k_1,k_2} and adding possibly the edges xa or yb. Then, $i(G') = i(G) + k_1 + k_2 + 1$.*

Proof. Clearly, any $i(G)$-set can be extended to an independent dominating set of G' by adding $s, r_1, \ldots, r_{k_1}, p_1, \ldots, p_{k_2}$, and so, $i(G') \leq i(G) + k_1 + k_2 + 1$.

Now, we show that $i(G') \geq i(G) + k_1 + k_2 + 1$. Let S be an $i(G')$-set such that $|S \cap \{a,b\}|$ is as small as possible. To dominate c, t_i $(1 \leq i \leq k_1)$ and q_j $(1 \leq j \leq k_2)$, we must have $|S \cap \{s,c\}| \geq 1$, $|S \cap \{r_i, t_i\}| \geq 1$ $(1 \leq i \leq k_1)$ and $|S \cap \{p_j, q_j\}| \geq 1$ $(1 \leq j \leq k_2)$. We claim that $|S \cap \{a,b\}| = 0$. Suppose, on the contrary, that $|S \cap \{a,b\}| \geq 1$. We consider the following cases.

Case 4. $|S \cap \{a,b\}| = 1$.

Assume without loss of generality that $a \in S$ and $b \notin S$. Then, we must have $c \in S$ and $t_1, \ldots, t_{k_1} \in S$ if $k_1 \geq 1$. If $xa \notin E(G')$ or $S \cap N_G(x) \neq \emptyset$, then the set $(S - \{a,c\}) \cup \{s\}$ is an independent dominating set of G' of size less that $i(G')$, which is a contradiction. Hence, $xa \in E(G')$ or $S \cap N_G(x) = \emptyset$, but then the set $(S - \{a\}) \cup \{x\}$ is an $i(G')$-set, which contradicts the choice of S.

Case 5. $|S \cap \{a,b\}| = 2$.

Then, we must have $c \in S$, $\{t_1, \ldots, t_{k_1}\} \subseteq S$ if $k_1 \geq 1$ and $\{q_1, \ldots, q_{k_2}\} \subseteq S$ if $k_2 \geq 1$. If $S \cap N_G[x] \neq \emptyset$ and $S \cap N_G[y] \neq \emptyset$, then $(S - \{a,b,c\}) \cup \{s\}$ is an independent dominating set of G' of size $i(G') - 2$, which is a contradiction. Assume without loss of generality that $S \cap N_G[x] = \emptyset$. If $x = y$, then $(S - \{a,b,c\}) \cup \{x,s\}$ is an independent dominating set of G' of size $i(G') - 1$, a contradiction again. Hence, $x \neq y$. Now, to dominate x, we must have $xa \in E(G')$, but then the set $(S - \{a\}) \cup \{x\}$ is an $i(G)'$-set, contradicting the choice of S.

Therefore $a, b \notin S$. Now, the set $S \cap V(G)$ is an independent dominating set of G, and this implies that $i(G') \geq i(G) + k_1 + k_2 + 1$. Thus, $i(G') = i(G) + k_1 + k_2 + 1$, and the proof is complete. □

Proposition 7. *Let G be an ID-stable graph. Then:*

(a) *if $(x,y) \in W^{1,1}(G)$ and G' is a graph obtained from G by adding $H_{0,0}$ and adding the edges xa, yb, then G' is an ID-stable graph,*

(b) *if $x \in W(C)$, $y \in V(G)$, and G' is a graph obtained from G by adding H_{0,k_2} $(k_2 \geq 1)$ and adding the edges xa, yb, then G' is an ID-stable graph,*

(c) *if $x, y \in V(G)$ and G' is a graph obtained from G by adding H_{k_1,k_2} $(k_1, k_2 \geq 1)$ and adding the edges xa, yb, then G' is an ID-stable graph.*

Proof. Let v be a vertex in G'. If $v \in V(G)$, then by Proposition 6, we have $i(G' - v) = i(G - v) + k_1 + k_2 + 1$. Since G is an ID-stable graph, we have $i(G - v) = i(G)$, and so, $i(G' - v) = i(G) + k_1 + k_2 + 1 = i(G')$. Assume that $v \notin V(G)$. We consider the following cases.

Case 6. $v = s$.

Clearly, any $i(G' - v)$-set is an independent dominating set of G', and so, $i(G' - v) \geq i(G')$. In the case (a), any $i(G)$-set containing x, y can be extended to an independent dominating set of $G' - v$ by adding c, and so, $i(G' - v) \leq i(G) + 1 = i(G')$. In the case (b), any $i(G)$-set containing x can be extended to an independent dominating set of $G' - v$ by adding $c, p_1, \ldots, p_{k_2}$, and so, $i(G' - v) \leq i(G) + k_2 + 1 = i(G')$. In the case (c), any $i(G)$-set can be extended to an independent dominating set of $G' - v$ by adding $c, p_1, \ldots, p_{k_2}, r_1, \ldots, r_{k_1}$, and so, $i(G' - v) \leq i(G) + k_1 + k_2 + 1 = i(G')$. Thus, $i(G' - v) = i(G')$.

Case 7. $v = a$ (the case $v = b$ is similar).

It is easy to see that there exists an $i(G' - v)$-set containing s. On the other hand, any $i(G' - v)$-set containing s is an independent dominating set of G', and so, $i(G' - v) \geq i(G')$. Using an argument similar to that described in Case 6, we obtain $i(G' - v) = i(G')$.

Case 8. $v = c$.

Obviously, any $i(G)$-set can be extended to an independent dominating set of $G' - v$ by adding the vertices $s, r_1, \ldots, r_{k_1}$ if $k_1 \geq 1$ and $p_1, \ldots, p_{k_2}$ if $k_2 \geq 1$, and so, $i(G' - v) \leq i(G) + k_1 + k_2 + 1 = i(G')$. Now, let S be an $i(G' - v)$-set. To dominate s, t_i ($1 \leq i \leq k_1$) and q_j ($1 \leq j \leq k_2$), we must have $|S \cap \{a, b, s\}| \geq 1$, $|S \cap \{r_i, t_i\}| \geq 1$ for $1 \leq i \leq k_1$ and $|S \cap \{p_j, q_j\}| \geq 1$ for $1 \leq j \leq k_2$. If $s \in S$, then S is obviously an independent dominating set of G', and so, $i(G' - v) \geq i(G')$. Assume that $s \notin S$. Then, $a \in S$ or $b \in S$. Assume, without loss of generality, that $a \in S$. If $b \notin S$, then $S - V(H_{k_1, k_2})$ is an independent dominating set of $G - x$, and since G is an independent domination stable graph, we have $i(G' - v) = (|S| - k_1 - k_2 - 1) + k_1 + k_2 + 1 \geq i(G) + k_1 + k_2 + 1 = i(G')$. Let $b \in S$. This implies that $\{q_1, \ldots, q_{k_2}\} \subseteq S$ if $k_2 \geq 1$. If $(N(y) - \{b\}) \cap S \neq \emptyset$, then the set $S - \{b\}$ if $k_2 = 0$, and the set $(S - \{b, q_1, \ldots, q_{k_2}\}) \cup \{p_1, \ldots, p_{k_2}\}$ if $k_2 \geq 1$ is an independent dominating set of $G' - v$, which leads to a contradiction. Hence, $(N(y) - \{b\}) \cap S = \emptyset$, and similarly, $(N(x) - \{a\}) \cap S = \emptyset$. Then, $(S - V(H_{k_1, k_2})) \cup \{y\}$ is an independent dominating set of $G - x$, and since G is an ID-stable graph, we deduce that $i(G' - v) = (|S| - k_1 - k_2 - 1) + k_1 + k_2 + 1 \geq i(G) + k_1 + k_2 + 1 = i(G')$. Therefore, $i(G' - v) = i(G')$.

Case 9. $v = r_i$ for some $i \in \{1, 2, \ldots, k_1\}$ or $v = p_j$ for some $j \in \{1, 2, \ldots, k_2\}$.

Assume, without loss of generality, that $v = r_1$. Obviously, any $i(G)$-set can be extended to an independent dominating set of $G' - v$ by adding $s, t_1, r_2, \ldots, r_{k_1}$ and $p_1, \ldots, p_{k_2}$ if $k_2 \geq 1$, and so, $i(G' - v) \leq i(G) + k_1 + k_2 + 1 = i(G')$. On the other hand, any $i(G' - v)$-set is obviously an independent dominating set of G', and so, $i(G' - v) \geq i(G')$. Therefore, $i(G' - v) = i(G')$.

Case 10. $v = t_i$ for some $i \in \{1, 2, \ldots, k_1\}$ or $v = q_j$ for some $j \in \{1, 2, \ldots, k_2\}$.

Assume, without loss of generality that $v = t_1$. Clearly, any $i(G)$-set can be extended to an independent dominating set of $G' - v$ by adding the vertices $s, r_1, \ldots, r_{k_1}$ and $p_1, \ldots, p_{k_2}$ if $k_2 \geq 1$, and so, $i(G' - v) \leq i(G) + k_1 + k_2 + 1 = i(G')$. To prove the inverse inequality, let S be an $i(G' - v)$-set. To dominate c, t_i ($2 \leq i \leq k_1$) and q_j ($1 \leq j \leq k_2$), we must have $|S \cap \{c, s\}| \geq 1$, $|S \cap \{r_i, t_i\}| \geq 1$ for $2 \leq i \leq k_1$ and $|S \cap \{p_j, q_j\}| \geq 1$ for $1 \leq j \leq k_2$. If $r_1 \in S$, then S is obviously an independent dominating set of G', and so, $i(G' - v) \geq i(G')$. Assume that $r_1 \notin S'$. It follows that $a \in S$ yielding $c, t_i \in S$ for $2 \leq i \leq k_2$. If $b \notin S$, then we may assume that $p_1, \ldots, p_{k_2} \in S$, and clearly, the set $S - V(H_{k_1, k_2})$ is an independent dominating set of $G - x$. Since G is an ID-stable graph, we obtain $i(G' - v) = (|S| - k_1 - k_2 - 1) + k_1 + k_2 + 1 \geq i(G) + k_1 + k_2 + 1 = i(G')$. Let $b \in S$. Then, $q_1, \ldots, q_{k_2} \in S$ if $k_2 \geq 1$. It is easy to see that $(N(y) - \{b\}) \cap S = \emptyset$. If $(N(x) - \{a\}) \cap S \neq \emptyset$, then $(S - \{a\}) \cup \{r_1\}$ is an independent dominating set of G', and so, $i(G' - v) \geq i(G')$. Suppose that $(N(x) - \{a\}) \cap S = \emptyset$. Then, $(S - V(H_{k_1, k_2})) \cup \{y\}$ is an independent dominating set of $G - x$, and since G is an ID-stable graph, we have $i(G' - v) = (|S| - k_1 - k_2 - 1) + k_1 + k_2 + 1 \geq i(G) + k_1 + k_2 + 1 = i(G')$. Hence, $i(G' - v) = i(G')$. Thus, G' is an ID-stable graph, and the proof is complete. □

Let $\mathbb{N}$ be the set of non-negative integers, $n \geq 3$ and $Q \in \mathbb{N}^n$ with $Q = (q_1, q_2, \ldots, q_n)$. Let $D(Q) = \{i \mid q_i > 0\}$. For any i with $q_i > 0$ and $q_{i+1} = 0$, if $q_j = 0$ for $j = i+1, i+2, \ldots, i+k$ and $q_{i+k+1} > 0$ where the subscript is taken modulo n, we define $H(Q, i) = k$. For example, if $Q = (0, 2, 0, 1, 3, 0, 1, 2, 0, 0)$, then $H(Q, 2) = 1$, $H(Q, 5) = 1$ and $H(Q, 8) = 3$.

The graph $C(n, Q)$ (resp. $P(n, Q)$) is the graph obtained from $C_n = (v_1 v_2 \ldots v_n)$ (resp. $P_n = v_1 v_2 \ldots v_n$) by attaching q_i disjoint pendent paths P_2 to v_i. If $q_i > 0$, then let $H_{v_i} = \{v_{i+1}, \ldots, v_{i+H(Q,i)}\}$, and assume for any $1 \leq j \leq q_i$, the vertex set of jth P_2 attached to v_i is $\{v_{i,j,a}, v_{i,j,b}\}$ with leaf $v_{i,j,b}$ (see Figure 2).

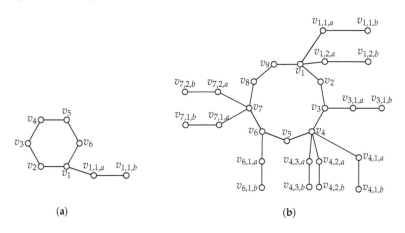

(a)   (b)

Figure 2. (a) The graph $C(6, (1, 0, 0, 0, 0, 0))$; (b) the graph $C(9, (2, 0, 1, 3, 0, 1, 2, 0, 0))$.

Proposition 8. *Let G be a graph, and $x, y \in V(G)$ (possibly $x = y$). If G' is a graph obtained from G by adding $H = P(n, (0, 0, k_1, 0, \ldots, 0, k_2, 0, 0))$, where $n \equiv 0 \pmod 6$, $k_1 \geq 0, k_2 \geq 0$, and adding possibly the edges xv_3 and yv_{n-2}, then $i(G') = i(G) + k_1 + k_2 + \frac{n}{3}$.*

Proof. Clearly, any $i(G)$-set can be extended to an independent dominating set of G' by adding v_{3i-1} $(1 \leq i \leq \frac{n}{3})$, $v_{3,j,a}$ $(1 \leq j \leq k_1)$ and $v_{n-2,j,a}$ $(1 \leq j \leq k_2)$, and so, $i(G') \leq i(G) + k_1 + k_2 + \frac{n}{3}$.

Now, we show that $i(G') \geq i(G) + k_1 + k_2 + \frac{n}{3}$. Let S be an $i(G')$-set. To dominate the vertices v_1, v_n, v_{3i-1} $(2 \leq i \leq \frac{n}{3} - 1)$, $v_{3,j,b}$ $(1 \leq j \leq k_1)$ and $v_{n-2,j,a}$ $(1 \leq j \leq k_2)$, we must have $|S \cap \{v_1, v_2\}| \geq 1$, $|S \cap \{v_{n-1}, v_n\}| \geq 1$, $|S \cap \{v_{3i-2}, v_{3i-1}, v_{3i}\}| \geq 1$ $(2 \leq i \leq \frac{n}{3} - 1)$, $|S \cap \{v_{3,j,a}, v_{3,j,b}\}| \geq 1$ $(1 \leq j \leq k_1)$, and $|S \cap \{v_{n-2,j,a}, v_{n-2,j,b}\}| \geq 1$ $(1 \leq j \leq k_2)$. We may assume without loss of generality that $\{v_{3i-1} \mid 2 \leq i \leq \frac{n}{3} - 1\} \subseteq S$. If $v_3, v_{n-2} \notin S$, then the set $S \cap V(G)$ is an independent dominating set of G, and this implies that $i(G') \geq i(G) + k_1 + k_2 + \frac{n}{3}$. Assume without loss of generality that $v_3 \in S$. Then, we must have $\{v_{3,1,b}, \ldots, v_{3,k_1,b}\} \subseteq S$ and $S \cap N_G(v_3) = \emptyset$. If v_3 is not adjacent to x or $N_G(x) \cap S \neq \emptyset$, then the set $S' = (S - \{v_1, v_2, v_3, v_{3,1,b}, \ldots, v_{3,k_1,b}\}) \cup \{v_2, v_{3,1,a}, \ldots, v_{3,k_1,a}\}$ is an independent dominating set of G' of size $i(G') - 1$, a contradiction. Hence, $v_3 x \in E(G')$, $N_G(x) \cap S \neq \emptyset$, and so, $x \notin S$. If $v_{n-2} \notin S$, then the set $(S - V(H)) \cup \{x\}$ is an independent dominating set of G, yielding $i(G') \geq i(G) + k_1 + k_2 + \frac{n}{3}$. Assume that $v_{n-2} \in S$. Then, we have $\{v_{n-2,1,b}, \ldots, v_{n-2,k_2,b}\} \subseteq S$ and $S \cap N_G(v_{n-2}) = \emptyset$. Using the above arguments, we have $v_{n-2} y \in E(G')$, $y \notin S$, and $N_G(y) \cap S = \emptyset$. If $x = y$ or x and y are adjacent in G, then the set $(S - V(H)) \cup \{x, v_2, v_5, \ldots, v_{n-2}, v_{3,1,a}, \ldots, v_{3,k_1,a}, v_{n-2,1,a}, \ldots, v_{n-2,k_2,a}\}$ is an independent dominating set of G' of size $i(G') - 1$, which is a contradiction. Hence, $x \neq y$ and x and y are not adjacent in G. Now, the set

$(S - V(H)) \cup \{x, y\}$ is an independent dominating set of G, implying that $i(G') \geq i(G) + k_1 + k_2 + \frac{n}{3}$. Therefore, $i(G') = i(G) + k_1 + k_2 + \frac{n}{3}$, and the proof is complete. $\square$

Proposition 9. *Let G be an ID-stable graph. If $x, y \in V(G)$ and G' is a graph obtained from G by adding $P(6, (0, 0, k_1, k_2, 0, 0))$ and adding the edges xv_3, yv_4, then G' is an ID-stable graph.*

Proof. Let v be a vertex in G'. If $v \in V(G)$, then by Proposition 8 and the fact that G is an ID-stable graph, we obtain:

$$i(G' - v) = i(G - v) + k_1 + k_2 + 2 = i(G) + k_1 + k_2 + 2 = i(G').$$

Let $v \notin V(G)$. We consider the following cases.

Case 11. $v \in \{v_2, v_5, v_{3,j,a}, v_{4,k,a} \mid 1 \leq j \leq k_1 \text{ and } 1 \leq k \leq k_2\}$.
As in Case 9 in Proposition 7, we have $i(G' - v) = i(G')$.

Case 12. $v \in \{v_1, v_6, v_{3,j,b}, v_{4,k,b} \mid 1 \leq j \leq k_1 \text{ and } 1 \leq k \leq k_2\}$.
As in Case 10 in Proposition 7, we have $i(G' - v) = i(G')$.

Case 13. $v \in \{v_3, v_4\}$.
We may assume, without loss of generality, that $v = v_3$. Clearly, any $i(G' - v)$-set containing v_2 is an independent dominating set of G', and so, $i(G' - v) \geq i(G')$. On the other hand, any $i(G)$-set can be extended to an independent dominating set of $G' - v$ by adding $\{v_2, v_5, v_{3,j,a}, v_{4,l,a} \mid 1 \leq j \leq k_1 \text{ and } 1 \leq l \leq k_2\}$, and Proposition 8 yields $i(G' - v) \leq i(G) + k_1 + k_2 + 2 = i(G')$. $\square$

Proposition 10. *Let $Q = (q_1, q_2, \ldots, q_n) \in \mathbb{N}^n$ such that $|D(Q)| \geq 2$ and $H(Q, i) \geq 1$ for each $i \in D(Q)$. If $H(Q, i) \equiv 1 \pmod 3$ for some $i \in D(Q)$ or $H(i, Q) \equiv 2 \pmod 3$ for each $i \in D(Q)$, or $H(Q, i) \equiv 0 \pmod 3$ and $H(Q, j) \equiv 0 \pmod 3$ for some $i, j \in D(Q)$, then the graph $C(n, Q)$ is not an ID-stable graph.*

Proof. Suppose, to the contrary, that $G = C(n, Q)$ is an ID-stable graph. If G has an $i(G)$-set S containing v_i for some $i \in D(Q)$, then $S - \{v_{i,1,b}\}$ is an independent dominating stable set for $G - v_{i,1,b}$, which leads to a contradiction. Hence, for any $i(G)$-set S and any $i \in D(Q)$, we have $v_i \notin S$. Assume that $D(Q) = \{i_1, i_2, \ldots, i_r\}$. Now, we show that:

$$i(G) = \sum_{j=1}^{r} q_{i_j} + \sum_{j=1}^{r} \left\lceil \frac{H(i_j, Q)}{3} \right\rceil.$$

For $1 \leq j \leq r$, let P_{i_j} be the path $v_{i_j+1} v_{i_j+2} \cdots v_{i_j + H(Q, i_j)}$, and let S_j be an $i(P_{i_j})$-set. Clearly, the set $I = \cup_{j=1}^{r} (S_{i_j} \cup \{v_{i_j,k,a} \mid 1 \leq k \leq q_{i_j}\})$ is an independent dominating set of G, and we conclude from Proposition 1 that $i(G) \leq \sum_{j=1}^{r} q_{i_j} + \sum_{j=1}^{r} \left\lceil \frac{H(i_j, Q)}{3} \right\rceil$. To prove the inverse inequality, let S be an $i(G)$-set. To dominate the vertices $v_{i_j,k,b}$ for $1 \leq j \leq r$ and $1 \leq k \leq q_{i_j}$, we must have $|S \cap \{v_{i_j,k,a}, v_{i_j,k,b}\}| \geq 1$, and since $S \cap \{v_{i_1}, \ldots, v_{i_r}\} = \varnothing$, we must have $|S \cap H_{v_{i_j}}| \geq \left\lceil \frac{H(i_j, Q)}{3} \right\rceil$ for each j, by Proposition 1. This implies that $i(G) = |S| \geq \sum_{j=1}^{r} (d_G(v_{i_j}) - 2) + \sum_{j=1}^{r} \left\lceil \frac{H(i_j, Q)}{3} \right\rceil$. Hence, $i(G) = \sum_{j=1}^{r} q_{i_j}) + \sum_{j=1}^{r} \left\lceil \frac{H(i_j, Q)}{3} \right\rceil$.

If $H(Q, i_j) \equiv 1 \pmod 3$ for some $i_j \in D(Q)$, say $j = 1$, then the set $(I - (S_{i_1} \cup \{v_{i_1,k,a} \mid 1 \leq k \leq q_{i_1}\})) \cup (\{v_{i_1,k,b} \mid 1 \leq k \leq q_{i_1}\} \cup \{v_{i_1+3s} \mid 0 \leq s \leq \lceil \frac{q_{i_1}}{3} \rceil - 1\})$ when $q_{i_r} \equiv 0 \pmod 3$, the set $(I - (S_{i_1} \cup S_{i_2} \cup \{v_{i_1,k,a} \mid 1 \leq k \leq q_{i_1}\})) \cup (\{v_{i_1,k,b} \mid 1 \leq k \leq q_{i_1}\} \cup \{v_{i_1+3s} \mid 0 \leq s \leq \lceil \frac{q_{i_1}}{3} \rceil\} \cup \{v_{i_1+3s+1} \mid 0 \leq s \leq \lceil \frac{q_{i_1}}{3} \rceil - 1\})$ when $q_{i_r} \equiv 2 \pmod 3$, and the set $(I - (S_{i_1} \cup S_{i_2} \cup \{v_{i_1,k,a} \mid 1 \leq k \leq q_{i_1}\})) \cup (\{v_{i_1,k,b} \mid 1 \leq k \leq q_{i_1}\} \cup \{v_{i_1+3s} \mid 0 \leq s \leq \lceil \frac{q_{i_1}}{3} \rceil\}) \cup \{v_{i_r+q_{i_r}-1}, v_{i_r+3s+1} \mid 0 \leq s \leq \lceil \frac{q_{i_r}}{3} \rceil - 2\})$ when $q_{i_r} \equiv 1 \pmod 3$ is an $i(G)$-set, which is a contradiction. Thus, $H(Q, i_j) \not\equiv 1 \pmod 3$ for each $i_j \in D(Q)$.

Suppose $H(i, Q) \equiv 2 \pmod 3$ for each $i \in D(Q)$. Then, clearly, $n = \sum_{j=1}^{r} \left\lceil \frac{H(i_j, Q)}{3} \right\rceil$, and the set $\{v_{i_1+3s} \mid 0 \le i \le \lceil \frac{n}{3} \rceil - 1\} \cup \{v_{i_j, k, b} \mid 1 \le k \le q_{i_j}\}$) is an independent dominating set of G, which leads to a contradiction again.

Finally let, without loss of generality, $H(Q, i_1) \equiv 0 \pmod 3$ and $H(Q, i_\ell) \equiv 0 \pmod 3$ for some $i_1, i_\ell \in D(Q)$ and $H(Q, i_j) \equiv 2 \pmod 3$ for each $i_j \in D(Q) - \{i_j, i_\ell\}$. If $|D(Q)| = 2$, then it is not hard to see that $i(G - v_{i_\ell+2}) > i(G)$, which is a contradiction. Assume that $|D(Q)| \ge 3$. By symmetry, we may assume that $\ell \ge 3$. Let $G' = G - v_{i_\ell+2}$, and let S' be an $i(G')$-set such that $|S' \cap \{v_{i_1}, \ldots, v_{i_r}\}|$ is as large as possible. Since G is an independent domination stable graph, we have $i(G) = i(G')$. It is not hard to see that the set:

$$D_1 = \left(\{v_{i_2}, \ldots, v_{i_\ell}\} \cup \left(\bigcup_{j=2}^{\ell-1} \{v_{i_j+3k} \mid 1 \le k \le \left\lfloor \frac{H(i_j, Q) - 1}{3} \right\rfloor \} \right) \right)$$

is a subset of S'. It follows that $D_2 = \cup_{j=2}^{\ell-1} \{v_{i_j, k, b} \mid 1 \le k \le q_{i_j}\} \subseteq S'$. We may also assume that $\{v_{i_1+3s-1} \mid 1 \le s \le \left\lfloor \frac{H(i_1, Q)}{3} \right\rfloor\} \subseteq S'$. Let $D_3 = \cup_{j=2}^{\ell} \{v_{i_j, k, a} \mid 1 \le k \le q_{i_j}\}$. Clearly, the set:

$$(S' - (D_1 \cup D_2)) \cup \{v_{i_\ell}\} \cup D_3 \cup \left(\bigcup_{j=2}^{\ell} \{v_{i_j+3k+1} \mid 0 \le k \le \left\lfloor \frac{H(i_j, Q) - 1}{3} \right\rfloor \} \right)$$

is an independent dominating set of G of cardinality $|S'| = i(G)$ containing v_{i_ℓ}, which is a contradiction. This completes the proof. $\square$

3. Independent Domination Stable Trees

In this section, we give a constructive characterization of all ID-stable trees.

In order to present our constructive characterization, we define a family of trees as follows. Let $\mathcal{T}$ be the family of trees T that can be obtained from a sequence $T_1, T_2, \ldots, T_k$ of trees for some $k \ge 1$, where T_1 is P_2 and $T = T_k$. If $k \ge 2$, T_{i+1} can be obtained from T_i by one of the following operations.

Operation $\mathcal{T}_1$: If $u \in W(T_i)$, then $\mathcal{T}_1$ adds a spider S_1 with head s and an edge us to obtain T_{i+1} (see Figure 3).

Operation $\mathcal{T}_2$: If $u \in V(T_i)$, then $\mathcal{T}_2$ adds a spider S_q ($q \ge 2$) with head s and an edge us to obtain T_{i+1} (see Figure 3).

Theorem 1. *If $T \in \mathcal{T}$, then T is an ID-stable tree.*

Proof. If T is P_2, then obviously T is an ID-stable tree. Suppose now that $T \in \mathcal{T}$. Then there exists a sequence of trees $T_1, T_2, \ldots, T_k$ ($k \ge 1$) such that T_1 is P_2, and if $k \ge 2$, then T_{i+1} can be obtained from T_i by one of the Operations $\mathcal{T}_1$ or $\mathcal{T}_2$. We proceed by induction on the number of operations used to construct T. If $k = 1$, the result is trivial. Assume the result holds for each tree $T \in \mathcal{T}$ which can be obtained from a sequence of operations of length $k - 1$ and let $T' = T_{k-1}$. By the induction hypothesis, T' is an ID-stable tree. Since $T = T_k$ is obtained by one of the Operations $\mathcal{T}_1$ or $\mathcal{T}_2$ from T', we conclude from the Proposition 5 that T is an ID-stable tree. $\square$

Next, we characterize all ID-stable trees.

Theorem 2. *Let T be a tree of order $n \ge 2$. Then, T is an ID-stable tree if and only if $T \in \mathcal{T}$.*

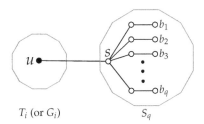

Figure 3. The operations: $\mathcal{T}_1$ or $\mathcal{T}_2$.

Proof. According to Theorem 1, we need only to prove necessity. Let T be an ID-stable tree of order $n \geq 2$. The proof is by induction on n. If $n = 2$, then $T = P_2 \in \mathcal{T}$. Let $n \geq 3$, and let the statement hold for all ID-stable trees of order less than n. Assume that T is an ID-stable tree of order n. By Propositions 2 and 3, we deduce that $\mathrm{diam}(T) \geq 4$. Let $v_1 v_2 \ldots v_k$ ($k \geq 5$) be a diametrical path in T and root T at v_k. By Proposition 2, any support vertex adjacent to v_3 has degree two. In particular $d_T(v_2) = 2$. By Proposition 3, v_3 is not a support vertex, and so, $T_{v_3} = S_{d_T(v_3)-1}$. Let $T' = T - T_{v_3}$. Since T is an ID-stable tree, we deduce from Proposition 4 that for any vertex $v \in V(T')$,

$$i(T' - v) + d_T(v_3) - 1 = i(T - v) = i(T) = i(T') + d_T(v_3) - 1$$

and this implies that $i(T' - v) = i(T')$. Hence, T' is an ID-stable tree. It follows from the induction hypothesis that $T' \in \mathcal{T}$. If $d_T(v_3) \geq 3$, then $T \in \mathcal{T}$ since T can be obtained from T' by operation $\mathcal{T}_2$.

Assume that $d_T(v_3) = 2$. By Proposition 4, we have $i(T') + 1 = i(T)$. Since T is an ID-stable tree, we have $i(T - v_2) = i(T)$. Let S be an $i(T - v_2)$-set. Clearly, $v_1 \in S$. If $v_3 \in S$, then $S - \{v_1\}$ is an independent dominating set of $T - v_1$, which is a contradiction. Hence, $v_3 \notin S$, and this implies that $v_4 \in S$. Now, $S - \{v_1\}$ is an independent dominating set of T', and we deduce from $i(T') + 1 = i(T)$ that $S - \{v_1\}$ is an $i(T')$-set. Thus, $v_4 \in W(T')$. Now, T can be obtained from T' by operation $\mathcal{T}_1$, and so, $T \in \mathcal{T}$. This completes the proof. □

4. Independent Domination Stable Unicyclic Graphs

In this section, we give a constructive characterization of all ID-stable unicyclic graphs. We start with introducing the following families of graphs.

- $\mathcal{J}_1 = \{C_n | n \geq 3 \text{ and } n \not\equiv 1 \pmod{\text{three}}\}$.
- $\mathcal{J}_2 = \{C(3k+1, (q_1, 0, 0, \ldots, 0)) | k \geq 1 \text{ and } q_1 \geq 2\}$.
- $\mathcal{J}_3$ is the family of graphs $C(n, Q)$ where $Q = (q_1, \ldots, q_n) \in \mathbb{N}^n$ satisfies (i) $D(Q) \geq 2$, (ii) $H(Q, i) \not\equiv 1 \pmod 3$ for each $i \in D(Q)$, and (iii) $H(Q, i) \equiv 0 \pmod 3$ for exactly one $i \in D(Q)$.
- $\mathcal{J}_4$ is the family of graphs obtained from $P(6, (0, 0, k_1, k_2, 0, 0))$ ($k_1 \geq 0, k_2 \geq 0$) by adding a new vertex w, joining w to v_3, v_4, and adding a pendant edge at w (see, e.g., the graph of the second column and the fifth row in Figure A2 (Appendix A)).
- $\mathcal{J} = \mathcal{J}_1 \cup \mathcal{J}_2 \cup \mathcal{J}_3 \cup \mathcal{J}_4 \cup \mathcal{T}$.

Next, we show that each graph in $\mathcal{J}$ is an ID-stable graph. By Corollary 1 and Theorem 1, any graph in the family $\mathcal{T} \cup \mathcal{J}_1$ is an independent domination stable graph.

Proposition 11. *If $G \in \mathcal{J}_2$, then G is an ID-stable graph.*

Proof. Let $G \in \mathcal{J}_2$. First, we show that $i(G) = k + q_1$. Clearly, the set $\{v_{3i} \mid 1 \leq i \leq k\} \cup \{v_{1,j,a} \mid 1 \leq j \leq q_1\}$ is an independent dominating set of G yielding $i(G) \leq k + q_1$. To prove the inverse inequality, let S be an $i(G)$-set. To dominate $v_{1,j,b}$, we must have $|S \cap \{v_{1,j,a}, v_{1,j,b}\}| \geq 1$ for each $j \in \{1, \ldots, q_1\}$. On the other hand, to dominate the vertices v_{3i} ($1 \leq i \leq k$), we must have $|S \cap \{v_{3i-1}, v_{3i}, v_{3i+1}\}| \geq 1$ for each $i \in \{1, \ldots, k\}$, and this implies that $i(G) \geq k + q_1$. Hence, $i(G) = k + q_1$.

Next we show that G is an ID-stable graph. Let $v \in G$. If $v = v_1$, then $G = P_{3k} \cup q_1 K_2$, and by Proposition 1, we have $i(G - v) = i(P_{3k}) + i(q_1 K_2) = k + q_1 = i(G)$. If $v = v_{1,j,a}$ for some $1 \le j \le q_1$, then $G = K_1 \cup C(3k + 1, (q_1 - 1, 0, 0, \ldots, 0))$, and as above, we have $i(G - v) = k + q_1 = i(G)$. Suppose that $v = v_{1,j,b}$ for some $1 \le j \le q_1$, say $j = 1$. Clearly, the set $\{v_{3i} \mid 1 \le i \le k\} \cup \{v_{1,j,a} \mid 1 \le j \le q_1\}$ is an independent dominating set of G yielding $i(G - v) \le k + q_1 = i(G)$. To prove $i(G - v) \ge k + q_1$, let S' be an $i(G - v)$-set. To dominate $v_{1,j,a}$, we must have $|S' \cap \{v_{1,j,a}, v_1\}| \ge 1$, and to dominate the vertex $v_{1,j,b}$, we must have $|S' \cap \{v_{1,j,a}, v_{1,j,b}\}| \ge 1$ for each $j \in \{2, \ldots, q_1\}$. On the other hand, to dominate the vertices in $V(C_n) - \{v_1, v_2, v_3\}$, S' must contain at least $k - 1$ vertices in $\{v_2, \ldots, v_n\}$, and so, $i(G - v) \ge k + q_1$. Hence, $i(G - v) = i(G)$ in this case. Let now $v = v_i$ ($i \ne 1$). Clearly, any $i(P_{3k})$-set of $P_{3k} = v_{i-1} \ldots v_1 v_n \ldots v_{i+1}$ can be extended to an independent dominating set of $G - v$ by adding $v_{1,j,a}$ for $j = 1, 2, \ldots, q_1$, and so, $i(G - v) \le i(P_{3k}) + q_1 = k + q_1 = i(G)$. On the other hand, if S is an $i(G - v)$-set, then to dominate the vertices in $\{v_{1,j,b} \mid 1 \le j \le q_1\}$, we must have $|S \cap \{v_{1,j,a}, v_{1,j,b} \mid 1 \le j \le q_1\}| \ge q_1$, and to dominate the vertices in $V(C_n) - \{v_i, v_1\}$, we must have $|S \cap (V(C_n) - \{v_i\})| \ge k$. Thus, $i(G - v) = |S| \ge k + q_1 = i(G)$, and hence, G is an ID-stable graph. $\square$

Theorem 3. *Let $G = C(n, Q)$ where $n \ge 3$ and $D(Q) = 1$. Then, G is an ID-stable graph if and only if $G \in \mathcal{J}_2$.*

Proof. According to Proposition 11, we only need to prove necessity. Let G be an independent domination stable graph. Assume, without loss of generality, that $Q = (q_1, 0 \ldots, 0)$ where $q_1 \ge 1$. As Proposition 11, we can see that $i(G) = \lceil \frac{n-1}{3} \rceil + q_1$. If $n \not\equiv 1 \pmod 3$, then the set $\{v_{3i+1} \mid 0 \le i \le \lceil \frac{n-1}{3} \rceil - 1\} \cup \{v_{1,j,a} \mid 2 \le j \le q_1\}$ is an independent dominating set of $G - v_{1,1,b}$ of size $i(G) - 1$, which is a contradiction. Assume that $n \equiv 1 \pmod 3$. If $q_1 = 1$, then clearly $G - v_{1,1,a} = K_1 \cup C_n$, and by Proposition 1, we have $i(G) = i(C_n) + 1 = \lceil \frac{n-1}{3} \rceil + 2$, which is a contradiction. Therefore, $q_1 \ge 2$, and so, $G \in \mathcal{J}_2$. $\square$

Proposition 12. *If $G \in \mathcal{J}_3$, then G is an independent domination stable graph.*

Proof. Let $G = C(n, Q) \in \mathcal{J}_3$, and let $\omega = \sum_{j=1}^r q_{i_j} + \sum_{j=1}^r \lceil \frac{H(Q,i_j)}{3} \rceil$. Assume that $D(Q) = \{i_1, \ldots, i_r\}$, and suppose, without loss of generality, that $H(Q, i_1) \equiv 0 \pmod 3$. Let $S' = \cup_{j=1}^r \{v_{i_j,s,a} \mid 1 \le s \le q_{i_j}\}$, $S'' = \cup_{j=2}^r \{v_{i_j,s,b} \mid 1 \le s \le q_{i_j}\}$, $S_j^p = \{v_{i_j+3k+p} \mid 0 \le k \le \lceil \frac{H(Q,i_j)}{3} \rceil - 1\}$ for $j \in \{1, \ldots, r\}$ and $p \in \{1, 2, 3\}$.

First, we show that $i(G) = \omega$. Clearly, the set $S = (\cup_{j=1}^r S_j^2) \cup S'$ is an $i(G)$-set, and so, $i(G) \le \omega$. To prove the inverse inequality, let T be an $i(G)$-set. To dominate the vertices $v_{i_j,s,b}$, we must have $|T \cap \{v_{i_j,s,a}, v_{i_j,s,b}\}| \ge 1$ for each $1 \le j \le r$ and $1 \le s \le q_{i_j}$. Now, to dominate the vertices v_{i_1+3k+2}, we must have $|T \cap \{v_{i_1+3k+1}, v_{i_1+3k+2}, v_{i_1+3k+3}\}| \ge 1$ for $0 \le k \le \lceil \frac{H(Q,i_j)}{3} \rceil - 1$, and to dominate the vertices $v_{i_j+2}, \ldots, v_{i_{j+1}-1}$, we must have $|T \cap \{v_{i_j+1}, v_{i_j+2}, \ldots, v_{i_{j+1}-1}, v_{i_{j+1}}\}| \ge 1$ for each $j \in \{2, \ldots, r\}$ yielding $i(G) \ge \omega$. Thus, $i(G) = \omega$ as desired.

Now, we show that G is an independent domination stable graph. Let $v \in V(G)$. Consider the following cases.

Case 14. $v \in S'$.

Clearly, any $i(G - v)$-set is an independent dominating set of G, and so, $i(G - v) \ge i(G)$. On the other hand, $(\cup_{j=1}^r S_j^2) \cup S'' \cup \{v_{i_1,s,b} \mid 1 \le s \le q_{i_1}\}$ is an independent dominating set of $G - v$, and hence, $i(G) \ge i(G - v)$. Thus, $i(G) = i(G - v)$ in this case.

Case 15. $v \in \{v_{i_1}, \ldots, v_{i_r}\}$.

Suppose, without loss of generality, that $v = v_{i_1}$. Obviously, S is an independent dominating set of $G - v$, and hence, $i(G) \ge i(G - v)$. Let D be an $i(G - v)$-set such that $|D \cap \{v_{i_1,j,a} \mid 1 \le j \le q_1\}|$ is as large as possible. Then, $\{v_{i_1,j,a} \mid 1 \leq j \leq q_1\} \subseteq D$. As above, we can see that $|D| = i(G - v) \geq i(G)$. Therefore, $i(G) = i(G - v)$ in this case.

Case 16. $v \in S''$.

Assume, without loss of generality, that $v = v_{i_1,1,b}$. Clearly, S is an independent dominating set of $G - v$, and hence, $i(G) \geq i(G - v)$. To prove the inverse inequality, let T be a $i(G - v)$-set. As above, we have $|T \cap \{v_{i_1,s,a}, v_{i_1,s,b}\}| \geq 1$ for $2 \leq s \leq q_{i_1}$, and $|T \cap \{v_{i_j,s,a}, v_{i_j,s,b}\}| \geq 1$ for each $2 \leq j \leq r$ and $1 \leq s \leq q_{i_j}$. Furthermore, we must have $|T \cap \{v_{i_1}, v_{i_1,1,a}\}| \geq 1$. Now, to dominate the vertices $v_{i_1+2}, \ldots, v_{i_2-1}$, we must have $|T \cap \{v_{i_1+1}, \ldots, v_{i_2-1}\}| \geq \frac{H(Q,i_1)}{3}$, and to dominate the vertices $v_{i_r+1}, \ldots, v_{i_1-2}$, we must have $|T \cap \{v_{i_r}, v_{i_r+1}, \ldots, v_{i_1-2}, v_{i_1-1}\}| \geq \frac{H(Q,i_r)}{3}$. Repeating this process, we must have $|T \cap \{v_{i_j}, v_{i_j+1}, \ldots, v_{i_{j+1}-2}, v_{i_{j+1}-1}\}| \geq \frac{H(Q,i_j)}{3}$ for each $2 \leq j \leq r - 1$. It follows that $|T| \geq i(G)$, and so, $i(G) = i(G - v)$.

Case 17. $v \in S_1^1$ (the case $v \in S_1^3$ is similar).

Assume that $v = v_{i_1+3k+1}$. Clearly, the set $(\cup_{j=2}^{r} S_j^3) \cup \{v_{i_1+3t+2} \mid 0 \leq t \leq k-1\} \cup \{v_{i_1+3t} \mid k+1 \leq t \leq \left\lceil \frac{H(Q,i_1)-3k-1}{3} \right\rceil\}$ is an independent dominating set of $G - v$ of size $i(G)$, and so, $i(G) \geq i(G - v)$. To prove the inverse inequality, let T be an $i(G - v)$-set. As above, we have $|T \cap \{v_{i_j,s,a}, v_{i_j,s,b}\}| \geq 1$ for each $1 \leq j \leq r$ and $1 \leq s \leq q_{i_j}$, and $|T \cap \{v_{i_j+1}, \ldots, v_{i_{j+1}-1}, v_{i_{j+1}}\}| \geq \frac{H(Q,i_j)}{3}$ for $2 \leq j \leq r$. Now to dominate the vertices v_{i_1+j} $(1 \leq j \leq 3k)$, we must have $|T \cap \{v_{i_1+1}, \ldots, v_{i_1+3k}\}| \geq k$, and to dominate the vertices $v_{i_1+3k+2}, \ldots, v_{i_2-1}$, we must have $|T \cap \{v_{i_2+3k+2}, \ldots, v_{i_2-1}, v_{i_2}\}| \geq \frac{H(Q,i_1)}{3} - k$. This implies that $|T| \geq i(G)$, and so, $i(G) = i(G - v)$.

Case 18. $v \in S_1^2$. Assume that $v = v_{i_1+3k+2}$. Clearly, the set $(\cup_{j=2}^{r} S_j^3) \cup \{v_{i_1+3t+3} \mid 0 \leq t \leq k-1\} \cup \{v_{i_1+3t+1} \mid k+1 \leq t \leq \left\lceil \frac{H(Q,i_1)-3k-2}{3} \right\rceil\}$ is an independent dominating set of $G - v$ of size $i(G)$, and so, $i(G) \geq i(G - v)$. To prove the inverse inequality, let T be an $i(G - v)$-set. As above, we have $|T \cap \{v_{i_j,s,a}, v_{i_j,s,b}\}| \geq 1$ for each $1 \leq j \leq r$ and $1 \leq s \leq q_{i_j}$, and $|T \cap \{v_{i_j+2}, \ldots, v_{i_{j+1}-1}, v_{i_{j+1}}\}| \geq \frac{H(Q,i_j)}{3}$ for $2 \leq j \leq r$. If $k = 0$, then to dominate the vertices $v_{i_1+3}, \ldots, v_{i_2-1}$, we must have $|T \cap \{v_{i_2+3}, \ldots, v_{i_2-1}, v_{i_2}\}| \geq \frac{H(Q,i_1)}{3}$ yielding $|T| \geq i(G)$. If $k \geq 1$, then to dominate the vertices $v_{i_1+1}, \ldots, v_{i_1+3k+1}$, we must have $|T \cap \{v_{i_1+2}, \ldots, v_{i_1+3k+1}\}| \geq k$, and to dominate the vertices $v_{i_1+3k+2}, \ldots, v_{i_2-1}$, we must have $|T \cap \{v_{i_2+3k+2}, \ldots, v_{i_2-1}, v_{i_2}\}| \geq \frac{H(Q,i_1)}{3} - k$, so $|T| \geq i(G)$. Therefore, $i(G) = i(G - v)$.

Case 19. $v \in \cup_{j=2}^{r} S_j^1$ (the case $v \in \cup_{j=2}^{r} S_j^3$ is similar).

Suppose, without loss of generality, that $v = v_{i_2+3k+1}$. Clearly, the set $S_1^2 \cup (\cup_{j=3}^{r} S_j^2) \cup \{v_{i_2+3t+2} \mid 0 \leq t \leq k-1\} \cup \{v_{i_3}, v_{i_2+3t} \mid k+1 \leq t \leq \left\lceil \frac{H(Q,i_2)-3k-1}{3} \right\rceil\}$ is an independent dominating set of $G - v$ of size $i(G)$, and so, $i(G) \geq i(G - v)$. Now, we show that $i(G - v) \geq i(G)$. Let T be a $i(G - v)$-set. As above, we have $|T \cap \{v_{i_j,s,a}, v_{i_j,s,b}\}| \geq 1$ for each $1 \leq j \leq r$ and $1 \leq s \leq q_{i_j}$, and $|T \cap \{v_{i_1+1}, v_{i_1+2}, \ldots, v_{i_2-1}\}| \geq \frac{H(Q,i_1)}{3}$. Furthermore, to dominate the vertices $v_{i_j+2}, \ldots, v_{i_{j+1}-1}$, we must have $|T \cap \{v_{i_j+2}, \ldots, v_{i_{j+1}-1}, v_{i_{j+1}}\}| \geq \frac{H(Q,i_j)}{3}$ for $3 \leq j \leq r$. Now, to dominate the vertices $v_{i_2+1}, \ldots, v_{i_2+3k}$, we must have $|T \cap \{v_{i_2+1}, \ldots, v_{i_2+3k}\}| \geq k$, and to dominate the vertices $v_{i_2+3k+2}, \ldots, v_{i_3-1}$, we must have $|T \cap \{v_{i_2+3k+2}, \ldots, v_{i_3-1}, v_{i_3}\}| \geq \frac{H(Q,i_2)}{3} - k$. This implies that $|T| \geq i(G)$, yielding $i(G) = i(G - v)$.

Case 20. $v \in \cup_{j=2}^{r} S_j^2$.

Suppose, without loss of generality, that $v = v_{i_2+3k+2}$. Clearly, the set $S_1^2 \cup (\cup_{j=3}^{r} S_j^2) \cup \{v_{i_2+3t} \mid 0 \leq t \leq k\} \cup \{v_{i_2+3t+1} \mid k+1 \leq t \leq \left\lceil \frac{H(Q,i_2)-3k-2}{3} \right\rceil\}$ is an independent dominating set of $G - v$ of size $i(G)$, and so, $i(G) \geq i(G - v)$. To prove the inverse inequality, let T be an $i(G - v)$-set. As above, we have $|T \cap \{v_{i_j,s,a}, v_{i_j,s,b}\}| \geq 1$ for each $1 \leq j \leq r$ and $1 \leq s \leq q_{i_j}$, and $|T \cap \{v_{i_1+1}, v_{i_1+2}, \ldots, v_{i_2-1}\}| \geq \frac{H(Q,i_1)}{3}$. Furthermore, to dominate the vertices $v_{i_j+2}, \ldots, v_{i_{j+1}-1}$, we must have $|T \cap \{v_{i_j+2}, \ldots, v_{i_{j+1}-1}, v_{i_{j+1}}\}| \geq \frac{H(Q, i_j)}{3}$ for $3 \leq j \leq r$. Now, to dominate the vertices $v_{i_2+1}, \ldots, v_{i_2+3k+1}$, we must have $|T \cap \{v_{i_2}, \ldots, v_{i_2+3k+1}\}| \geq k+1$, and to dominate the vertices $v_{i_2+3k+3}, \ldots, v_{i_3-1}$, we must have $|T \cap \{v_{i_2+3k+3}, \ldots, v_{i_3-1}\}| \geq \frac{H(Q, i_2)}{3} - k - 1$. This implies that $|T| \geq i(G)$, and so, $i(G) = i(G - v)$.

Thus, G is an independent domination stable graph, and the proof is complete. $\square$

The proof of the next result is straightforward and therefore omitted.

Proposition 13. *If $G \in \mathcal{J}_4$, then G is an independent domination stable graph.*

In order to present our constructive characterization of independent domination stable unicyclic graphs, we define a family of graphs as follows. Let $\mathcal{G}$ be the family of graphs G that can be obtained from a sequence $G_1, G_2, \ldots, G_k$ of graphs for some $k \geq 1$, where $G_1 \in \mathcal{J} - \mathcal{T}$ if $k = 1$ and $G_1 \in \mathcal{J}$ if $k \geq 2$, and $G = G_k$. If $k \geq 2$, G_{i+1} can be obtained from G_i by one of the following operations.

Operation $\mathcal{O}_1$: If $u \in W(G_i)$, then $\mathcal{O}_1$ adds a spider S_1 with head s and an edge us to obtain G_{i+1} (see Figure 3).
Operation $\mathcal{O}_2$: If $u \in V(G_i)$, then $\mathcal{O}_2$ adds a spider S_q $(q \geq 2)$ with head s and an edge us to obtain G_{i+1} (see Figure 3).
Operation $\mathcal{O}_3$: If G_i is a tree and $(x, y) \in W^{1,1}(G_i)$, then $\mathcal{O}_3$ adds a graph H_{k_1, k_2} $(k_1 = k_2 = 0)$ and edges ax, by to obtain G_{i+1} (see Figure 1).
Operation $\mathcal{O}_4$: If G_i is a tree, $x \in W(G_i)$ and $y \in V(G_i)$, then $\mathcal{O}_4$ adds a graph H_{k_1, k_2} $(k_1 = 0, k_2 \geq 1)$ and edges ax, by to obtain G_{i+1} (see Figure 1).
Operation $\mathcal{O}_5$: If G_i is a tree, $x, y \in V(G_i)$, then $\mathcal{O}_5$ adds a graph H_{k_1, k_2} $(k_1 \geq 1, k_2 \geq 1)$ and edges ax, by to obtain G_{i+1} (see Figure 1).
Operation $\mathcal{O}_6$: If G_i is a tree, $x, y \in V(G_i)$, then $\mathcal{O}_6$ adds a graph $P(6, (0, 0, k_1, k_2, 0, 0))$ $(k_1 \geq 0, k_2 \geq 0)$ and edges v_3x, v_4y to obtain G_{i+1} (see Figure 4).

Theorem 4. *Let $G \in \mathcal{G}$ be a graph of order $n \geq 3$. Then, G is an independent domination stable graph.*

Proof. Suppose that $G \in \mathcal{G}$. Then, there exists a sequence of graphs $G_1, G_2, \ldots, G_k$ $(k \geq 1)$ such that $G_1 \in \mathcal{J} - \mathcal{T}$ if $k = 1$ and $G_1 \in \mathcal{J}$ if $k \geq 2$, and if $k \geq 2$, then G_{i+1} can be obtained from G_i by one of the operations $\mathcal{O}_1, \mathcal{O}_2, \cdots, \mathcal{O}_6$. We proceed by induction on the number of operations used to construct G. If $k = 1$, the result holds by Propositions 11, 12, and 13. Assume that the result holds for each graph $G \in \mathcal{G}$, which can be obtained from a sequence of operations of length $k - 1$, and let $G' = G_{k-1}$. By the induction hypothesis, G' is an independent domination stable graph. Since $G = G_k$ is obtained by one of the operations $\mathcal{O}_1, \mathcal{O}_2, \cdots, \mathcal{O}_6$ from G', we conclude from Propositions 5, 7, and 9 that G is an independent domination stable unicyclic graph. $\square$

Theorem 5. *Let G be a unicyclic graph of order $n \geq 3$. Then, G is an ID-stable graph if and only if $G \in \mathcal{G}$.*

Proof. According to Theorem 4, we need only to prove necessity. Let G be an ID-stable unicyclic graph of order $n \geq 3$. The proof is by induction on n. Let $n \geq 11$, and let the statement hold for all ID-stable unicyclic graphs of order less than n. Assume that G is an ID-stable unicyclic graph of order n. Let $C = (v_1 v_2 \ldots v_p)$ be the unique cycle of G. If G is a cycle, then $p = n$, and Proposition 1 implies that $G \in \mathcal{J}_3 \subseteq \mathcal{G}$. Now, we consider the case $p < n$. Choose a vertex $u \in V(G) - V(C)$ such that the distance between the vertex u and the set $V(C)$ is as large as possible. Assume that $v_1 u_1 u_2 \cdots u_\ell u$ is the shortest $(u, V(C))$-path. If $\ell \geq 2$, then similar to the proof of Theorem 2, G can be obtained from G_{k-1} by one of the operations $\mathcal{O}_1$ or $\mathcal{O}_2$, and so, $G \in \mathcal{G}$. Assume that $\ell \leq 1$.

First, assume v_i is not a support vertex for each $i \in \{1, \ldots, p\}$. Then, $G = C(n, Q)$ for some $Q \in \mathcal{N}^n$. If $D(Q) = 0$, then it follows from Corollary 1 that $G \in \mathcal{J}_1$. If $D(Q) = 1$, then it follows from Theorem 3 that $G \in \mathcal{J}_2$. If $D(Q) \geq 2$, then we conclude from Propositions 10 and 12 that $G \in \mathcal{J}_3$.

Now, suppose that v_i is a support vertex for some $i \in \{1, \ldots, p\}$, say $i = 2$. Assume c is a leaf adjacent to v_2. We conclude from Propositions 2 and 3 that v_2 is not a strong support vertex and is not adjacent to a support vertex. It follows that $d_G(v_2) = 3$ and that v_1, v_3 are not support vertices. Let k_1 be the number of pendant paths of length two beginning at v_1 and k_2 be the number of pendant paths of length two beginning at v_3. Let G' be the graph obtained from G by removing v_1, v_2, v_3 and the vertices of all pendant paths at v_1, v_3. By Proposition 6, we have $i(G) = i(G') + k_1 + k_2 + 1$. If G' is not an ID-stable graph, then $i(G' - v) \neq i(G')$ for some vertex $v \in V(G')$, and it follows from Proposition 6 that $i(G - v) = i(G' - v) + k_1 + k_2 + 1 \neq i(G') + k_1 + k_2 + 1 = i(G)$, which is a contradiction. Hence, G' is an ID-stable graph, and by the induction hypothesis, we have $G' \in \mathcal{G}$. If $k_1 \geq 1, k_2 \geq 1$, then T can be obtained from G' by operation $\mathcal{O}_5$, and so, $G \in \mathcal{G}$. Assume that $k_1 = k_2 = 0$. Then, we have $d_G(v_1) = d_G(v_3) = 2$. Let S be a $i(G - v_2)$-set. Since G is an ID-stable graph, we have $i(G) = i(G - v_2)$. To dominate the vertices c, v_1, v_3, we must have $c \in S, |s \cap \{v_1, v_n\}| \geq 1$ and $|s \cap \{v_3, v_4\}| \geq 1$. Suppose, without loss of generality, that $v_4, v_n \in S$. Then, $S - \{c\}$ is an $i(G')$-set containing v_4, v_n, and so, $(v_3, v_n) \in W^{1,1}$. Now, T can be obtained from G' by operation $\mathcal{O}_3$, and so, $G \in \mathcal{G}$. Finally, let $k_1 = 0$ and $k_2 \geq 1$. As above, we can see that $v_4 \in W(G')$, and since T can be obtained from G' by operation $\mathcal{O}_4$, we have $T \in \mathcal{G}$. This completes the proof. $\square$

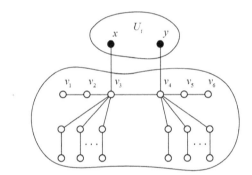

Figure 4. The operation $\mathcal{O}_6$.

5. Bounds

In this section, we provide sharp bounds on ID-stable trees. First, we present a lower bound and characterize all extremal trees. Let $\mathfrak{T}_1$ be the family of trees T that can be obtained from a sequence T_1, $T_2, \ldots, T_k$ of trees for some $k \geq 1$, where T_1 is P_2 and $T = T_k$. If $k \geq 2$, then all but at most one of T_{i+1} can be obtained from T_i by operation $\mathcal{T}_1$, and that one (if any) can be obtained from T_i by operation $\mathcal{T}_2$ for $q = 2$.

Theorem 6. *Let T be an ID-stable tree of order $n \geq 2$. Then:*

$$i(T) \geq \left\lceil \frac{n}{3} \right\rceil$$

with equality if and only if $T \in \mathfrak{T}_1$.

Proof. By Theorem 2, we have $T \in \mathcal{T}$. Thus, there exists a sequence of trees $T_1, T_2, \ldots, T_k$ ($k \geq 1$) such that T_1 is P_2, and if $k \geq 2$, then T_{i+1} can be obtained from T_i by one of the operations $\mathcal{T}_1$ or $\mathcal{T}_2$. We proceed by induction on the number of operations used to construct T. If $k = 1$, the result is trivial.

Assume the result holds for each tree $T \in \mathcal{T}$, which can be obtained from a sequence of operations of length $k - 1$, and let $T' = T_{k-1}$. By Proposition 4 and the induction hypothesis, we obtain:

$$i(T) = i(T') + i(S_q) \geq \left\lceil \frac{n - 2q - 1}{3} \right\rceil + \left\lceil \frac{2q + 1}{3} \right\rceil \geq \left\lceil \frac{n}{3} \right\rceil. \tag{1}$$

The equality holds if and only if $i(T') = \left\lceil \frac{n-2q-1}{3} \right\rceil$ and $i(S_q) = \left\lceil \frac{2q+1}{3} \right\rceil$. It follows from the induction hypothesis that $T' \in \mathcal{T}_1$. Furthermore, we deduce from $i(S_q) = \left\lceil \frac{2q+1}{3} \right\rceil$ that $q \leq 3$. First, let $q = 3$. It follows from Equation (1) that:

$$\left\lceil \frac{n - 7}{3} \right\rceil + \left\lceil \frac{7}{3} \right\rceil = \left\lceil \frac{n}{3} \right\rceil$$

yielding $n \equiv 1 \pmod 3$. This implies that $3 | n(T')$, which is a contradiction by construction of trees in $\mathcal{T}_1$. Hence, $q \leq 2$. If T_{i+1} is obtained from T_i by operation $\mathcal{T}_1$ for each $2 \leq i \leq k - 1$, then clearly, $T \in \mathcal{T}_1$. Assume that one of the T_{i+1}'s is obtained from T_i by operation $\mathcal{T}_2$ for $q = 2$. Then, clearly, $n(T') = n - 2q - 1 = 3(k - 1) + 1$. If $q = 2$, then $n(T) = 3(k - 1) + 6$, and we have $\left\lceil \frac{n-2q-1}{3} \right\rceil + \left\lceil \frac{2q+1}{3} \right\rceil = k + 2 > k + 1 = \left\lceil \frac{n(T)}{3} \right\rceil$, which is a contradiction. Thus, $q = 1$, and this implies that $T \in \mathcal{T}_1$. □

Let $\mathcal{F}_1$ be the family of all spiders S_q for $q \geq 2$, $\mathcal{F}_2$ be the family of trees obtained from two spiders S_p and S_q by joining their heads, $\mathcal{F}_3$ be the family of trees obtained from two spiders S_p and S_q by joining the head of S_p to a knee of S_q, and $\mathcal{F}_4$ be the family of trees obtained from two spiders S_p and S_q by joining the head of S_p to a foot of S_q where $p \geq q = 2$ or $p, q \geq 3$. For example, the trees obtained by $\mathcal{F}_2$, $\mathcal{F}_3$, and $\mathcal{F}_4$ when $p = q = 3$ are illustrated in Figure 5.

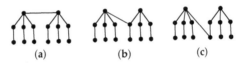

(a) (b) (c)

Figure 5. (a) Tree $\mathcal{F}_2$; (b) tree $\mathcal{F}_3$; (c) tree $\mathcal{F}_4$.

The next result is an immediate consequence of Proposition 4.

Observation 1. *If $T \in \cup_{i=1}^{4} \mathcal{F}_i$, then $i(T) = \lceil \frac{n-2}{2} \rceil$.*

Theorem 7. *Let T be an ID-stable tree of order $n \geq 5$. Then:*

$$i(T) \leq \left\lceil \frac{n - 2}{2} \right\rceil$$

with equality if and only if $T \in \cup_{i=1}^{4} \mathcal{F}_i$.

Proof. The proof is by induction on n. If $n = 5$, then by Propositions 2 and 3, we have $T = P_5$, and the result holds. Let $n \geq 6$, and let the statement hold for all ID-stable trees of order less than n. Assume that T is an ID-stable tree of order n. By Propositions 2 and 3, we deduce that $\mathrm{diam}(T) \geq 4$. If $\mathrm{diam}(T) = 4$, then by Propositions 2 and 3, T is the healthy spider $Spider(d_T(v_3))$, and so, $i(T) = d_T(v_3) = \left\lceil \frac{n(T) - 2}{2} \right\rceil$ and $T \in \mathcal{F}_1$. Suppose that $\mathrm{diam}(T) \geq 5$. Let $v_1 v_2 \ldots v_k$ ($k \geq 5$) be a diametrical path in T such that $d_T(v_3)$ is as large as possible and root T at v_k. By Propositions 2 and 3, we have $d_T(v_2) = 2$ and that v_3 is not a support vertex. Hence, $T_{v_3} = S_{d_T(v_3)-1}$. Assume that

$p = d_T(v_3) - 1$. Let $T' = T - T_{v_3}$. Since T is an ID-stable tree, we deduce from Proposition 4 that for any vertex $v \in V(T')$,

$$i(T' - v) + p = i(T - v) = i(T) = i(T') + p$$

and this implies that $i(T' - v) = i(T')$. Hence, T' is an ID-stable tree. It follows from the induction hypothesis that $i(T') \leq \left\lceil \frac{n-2p-3}{2} \right\rceil$, and hence,

$$
\begin{aligned}
i(T) &\leq i(T') + i(S_p) \\
&\leq \left\lceil \frac{n - 2p - 3}{2} \right\rceil + p \\
&= \left\lceil \frac{n - 3}{2} \right\rceil \\
&\leq \left\lceil \frac{n - 2}{2} \right\rceil.
\end{aligned}
$$

The equality holds if and only if $\mathrm{diam}(T) = 4$ or $\mathrm{diam}(T) \geq 5$ and $i(T') = \left\lceil \frac{n(T')-2}{2} \right\rceil = \left\lceil \frac{n-2p-3}{2} \right\rceil$ and n is even, and this if and only if $T \in \mathcal{F}_1$ or $\mathrm{diam}(T) \geq 5$ and $T' \in \mathcal{F}_1$ by the induction hypothesis. Thus, the equality holds if and only if $T \in \cup_{i=1}^4 \mathcal{F}_i$, and the proof is complete. □

6. Conclusions

In this note, we studied the ID-stable graphs. Some basic properties of ID-stable graphs were presented and new independent domination stable graphs constructed from an old one. We also characterized all independent domination stable trees and unicyclic graphs. In addition, we proved that for any tree T of order $n \geq 5$, $\left\lceil \frac{n}{3} \right\rceil \leq i(T) \leq \left\lceil \frac{n-2}{2} \right\rceil$, and we characterized all trees attaining the lower and upper bound. An interesting problem is to find sharp lower and upper bounds on the independent domination number of ID-stable graphs. The other problem is to characterize all ID-stable bicyclic graphs. Another problem is to study algorithm running times to decide independent domination graphs.

Author Contributions: Z.S. and S.M.S. contributed to the supervision, methodology, validation, project administration, and formal analysis. P.W., H.J., S.N.-M., and L.V. contributed to the investigation, resources, and some computations and wrote the initial draft of the paper, which was investigated and approved by Z.S. S.M.S. wrote the final draft.

Funding: This work is supported by the Natural Science Foundation of Guangdong Province under Grant 2018A0303130115, the Science and Technology Program of Guangzhou (No. 201904010493), and the Specialized Fund for Science and Technology Platform and Talent Team Project of Guizhou Province (No. QianKeHePingTaiRenCai [2016]5609).

Conflicts of Interest: The authors declare no conflict of interest.

Appendix A

Appendix A.1. Trees

By applying the constructive method as above, we obtain all ID-stable trees with order up to 12, and the statistics of the number of trees with different orders is presented in Table A1.

We list all the independent domination stable trees with orders from 5 to 12 in Figure A1.

Appendix A.2. Unicyclic Graphs

By applying the constructive method as above, we obtain all independent domination stable unicyclic graphs with order from 3 to 10, and the statistics of the number of unicyclic graphs with different orders is presented in Table A2.

We here list all the independent domination stable unicyclic graphs with orders from 3 to 10 in Figure A2.

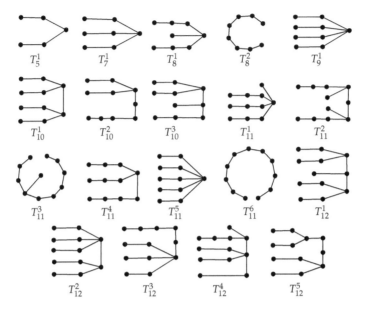

Figure A1. Independent domination stable trees with orders from 5 to 12.

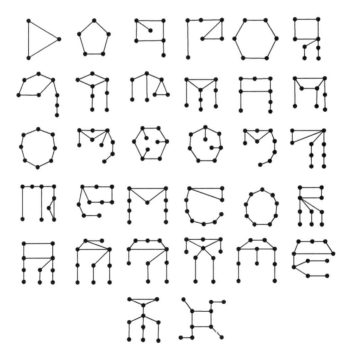

Figure A2. All independent domination stable unicyclic graphs of orders from 3 to 10.

Table A1. The number of independent domination stable trees with different orders.

Order	2	3	4	5	6	7	8	9	10	11	12
Number	1	0	0	1	0	1	2	1	3	4	5

Table A2. The number of independent domination stable unicyclic graphs with different orders.

Order	3	4	5	6	7	8	9	10
Number	1	0	1	3	0	8	10	9

References

1. Goddard, W.; Henning, M.A. Independent domination in graphs: A survey and recent results. *Discret. Math.* **2013**, *313*, 839–854. [CrossRef]
2. Desormeaux, W.J.; Haynes, T.W.; Henning, M.A. Total domination stable graphs upon edge addition. *Discret. Math.* **2010**, *310*, 3446–3454. [CrossRef]
3. Zhu, E.; Liu, C.; Deng, F.; Rao, Y. On upper total domination versus upper domination in graphs. *Graphs Comb.* **2019**, *35*, 767–778. [CrossRef]
4. Cockayne, E.J.; Dreyer, P.A., Jr.; Hedetniemi, S.M.; Hedetniemi, S.T. Roman domination in graphs. *Discret. Math.* **2004**, *278*, 11–22. [CrossRef]
5. Zhu, E.; Shao, Z. Extremal problems on weak Roman domination number. *Inf. Process. Lett.* **2018**, *138*, 12–18. [CrossRef]
6. Zhu, E.; Shao, Z.; Xu, J. Semitotal domination in claw-free cubic graphs. *Graphs Comb.* **2017**, *33*, 1119–1130. [CrossRef]
7. Zhu, E.; Liu, C. On the semitotal domination number of line graphs. *Discret. Appl. Math.* **2019**, *254*, 295–298. [CrossRef]
8. Haynes, T.W.; Hedetniemi, S.T.; Slater, P.J. *Fundamentals of Domination in Graphs*; CRC Press: Boca Raton, FL, USA, 1998.
9. Haynes, T.W.; Hedetniemi, S.; Slater, P. *Domination in Graphs: Volume 2: Advanced Topics*; CRC Press: Boca Raton, FL, USA, 1998.
10. Ao, S. Independent Domination Critical Graphs. Ph.D. Thesis, University of Victoria, Victoria, BC, Canada, 1994.
11. Edwards, M. Vertex-Criticality and Bicriticality for Independent Domination and Total Domination in Graphs. Ph.D. Thesis, University of Victoria, Victoria, BC, Canada, 2015.
12. Edwards, M.; Finbow, A.; MacGillivray, G.; Nasserasr, S. Independent domination bicritical graphs. *Australas. J. Comb.* **2018**, *72*, 446–471.
13. Edwards, M.; MacGillivray, G. The diameter of total domination and independent domination vertex-critical graphs. *Australas. J. Comb.* **2012**, *52*, 33–40.
14. Ananchuen, N.; Ruangthampisan, S.; Ananchuen, W.; Caccetta, L. On minimum cutsets in independent domination vertex-critical graphs. *Australas. J. Comb.* **2018**, *71*, 369–380.
15. Chellali, M.; Haynes, T.W. Double domination stable graphs upon edge removal. *Australas. J. Comb.* **2010**, *47*, 157–164.
16. Desormeaux, W.J.; Haynes, T.W.; Henning, M.A. An extremal problem for total domination stable graphs upon edge removal. *Discret. Appl. Math.* **2011**, *159*, 1048–1052. [CrossRef]
17. Desormeaux, W.J.; Haynes, T.W.; Henning, M.A. Total domination changing and stable graphs upon vertex removal. *Discret. Appl. Math.* **2011**, *159*, 1548–1554. [CrossRef]

Article

The Strong Resolving Graph and the Strong Metric Dimension of Cactus Graphs

Dorota Kuziak

Departamento de Estadística e Investigación Operativa, Universidad de Cádiz, 11003 Cádiz, Spain;
dorota.kuziak@uca.es

Received: 12 July 2020; Accepted: 21 July 2020; Published: 2 August 2020

Abstract: A vertex w of a connected graph G strongly resolves two distinct vertices $u, v \in V(G)$, if there is a shortest u, w path containing v, or a shortest v, w path containing u. A set S of vertices of G is a *strong resolving set* for G if every two distinct vertices of G are strongly resolved by a vertex of S. The smallest cardinality of a strong resolving set for G is called the *strong metric dimension* of G. To study the strong metric dimension of graphs, a very important role is played by a structure of graphs called the strong resolving graph In this work, we obtain the strong metric dimension of some families of cactus graphs, and along the way, we give several structural properties of the strong resolving graphs of the studied families of cactus graphs.

Keywords: strong resolving graph; strong metric dimension; strong resolving set; cactus graphs; unicyclic graphs

MSC: 05C12

1. Introduction

Topics concerning metric dimension and related parameters in graphs are nowadays very common in the research community, probably based on its applicability to diverse practical problems of identification of nodes in networks. One can find in the literature a large number of works dealing with this topic, both from the applied and theoretical points of views. A popular research line in this subject concerns studying different variants of metric dimension in graphs, which have had their beginnings in the seminal standard metric dimension concept. Some of the most recent ones are probably the edge metric dimension [1], the mixed metric dimension [2], the k-metric antidimension [3], the strong partition dimension [4], and the multiset dimension [5,6], just to cite a few recent and remarkable cases. One other interesting version is the strong metric dimension [7], which is now relatively well studied, although a few open questions on this are still open. A fairly complete study on results and open questions concerning the strong metric dimension of graphs can be found in [8].

One significant reason for the interest of several researchers in the strong metric dimension of graphs concerns the closed relationship that exists between such parameter and the very well known vertex cover number of graphs (and thus with the independence number, based on the Gallai's Theorem). To see this relationship, for a given graph G, the construction of a new related graph, called strong resolving graph, was required. This graph transformation clearly raised some other related questions on the transformation itself. That is for instance, given a graph G: can some properties of the strong resolving graph of G be deduced? or; can we realize every graph H as the strong resolving graph of another graph H'? These ones and several other questions were dealt with in [9], which was the first work paying specific attention to the strong resolving graphs of graphs as a special graph transformation. See also [10], where an open problem from [9] was settled.

Clearly, and as we will further notice, a good knowledge of the strong resolving graph of a graph brings important contributions to studying the strong metric dimension of graphs. In this sense, this work is precisely aimed to study the strong resolving graphs and the strong metric dimension of cactus graphs, with some emphasis on different special structures of such cactus graphs. As one will also note through our exposition, strong resolving graphs are very challenging for those graphs having a large number of induced cycles. Thus, cactus graphs represent a significant example of such a situation. With this work, we also contribute to some open problems presented in [9].

The study of the strong metric dimension of some classes of cactus graphs was started in [11,12] where the authors presented some general results for the strong metric dimension of corona product graph and rooted product graphs, respectively. Clear definitions of these two graph products can be found in [8]. A corona product graph or a rooted product graph can have the structure of a cactus graph, depending on which are the graphs used as factors in the product. For instance, if G is a cycle and H is a graph whose components are only singleton vertices or complete graphs K_2, then it happens that the corona product graph $G \odot H$ is a cactus graphs. To generate a rooted product graph that is a cactus graph, we may consider for example two graphs G and H which are paths or cycles.

On the other hand, we must mention that the strong metric dimension of unicyclic graphs (which is a cactus graph too) was studied in [13]. There, among other results, several relationships between the strong metric dimension of a unicyclic graph and that of its complement were given. A few other sporadic results can be found in some other articles dealing with related topics that could include examples of cactus graphs. However, we prefer to not include more references that are not essentially connected with this article.

We hence now begin to formalize all the required notations and terminologies that shall be used throughout the document. To this end, for the whole exposition, let G be a connected simple graph with vertex set $V(G)$. For two adjacent vertices $x, y \in V(G)$, we use the notation $x \sim y$. For a vertex x of G, $N_G(x)$ denotes the set of neighbors that x has in G, i.e., $N_G(x) = \{y \in V(G) : y \sim x\}$. The set $N_G(x)$ is called the *open neighborhood of a vertex* x in G and $N_G[x] = N_G(x) \cup \{x\}$ is called the *closed neighborhood of a vertex* x in G. The *degree* of the vertex x is $\delta_G(x) = |N_G(x)|$. The diameter of G is defined as $D(G) = max_{x,y \in V(G)}\{d_G(x, y)\}$, where $d_G(x, y)$ is the length of a shortest path between x and y (a shortest x, y path). Two vertices x, y are called *diametral* if $d_G(x, y) = D(G)$. For a set $S \subset V(G)$, by $\langle S \rangle$ we represent the subgraph induced by S in G.

1.1. Strong Metric Dimension of Graphs

For two distinct vertices $u, v \in V(G)$, a vertex $w \in V(G)$ *strongly resolves* u, v if there is a shortest u, w path containing v, or a shortest v, w path containing u. Note that it could happen $w \in \{u, v\}$. A set S of vertices of G is a *strong resolving set* for G, if every two vertices of G are strongly resolved by some vertex of S. The smallest cardinality among all strong resolving sets for G is called the *strong metric dimension* of G, and is denoted by $dim_s(G)$. We say that a strong resolving set for G of cardinality $dim_s(G)$ is a *strong metric basis* of G. It next appears the value of the strong metric dimension of some basic graphs.

Observation 1. *Let G be a connected graph G of order $n \geq 2$.*

(a) *$dim_s(G) = n - 1$ if and only if $G \cong K_n$.*

(b) *If $G \ncong K_n$, then $dim_s(G) \leq n - 2$.*

(c) *$dim_s(G) = 1$ if and only if $G \cong P_n$.*

(d) *If $G \cong C_n$, then $dim_s(G) = \lceil n/2 \rceil$.*

(e) *If G is a tree with l leaves, $dim_s(G) = l - 1$.*

It is said that a vertex u of G is *maximally distant* from v if for every $w \in N_G(u)$, it happens $d_G(v, w) \leq d_G(u, v)$. If u is maximally distant from v and v is maximally distant from u, then u and v are *mutually maximally distant*, and we write that u, v are MMD in G. The set of MMD vertices of G is denoted by $\partial(G)$. Note that the set of MMD vertices of a graph G is also known as the *boundary of G*, as defined in [14,15]. An explanation on the equivalence of these two objects can be readily observed, but also found in [16]. From these definitions, the following remarks are straightforward to observe.

Remark 1. *Let G be a connected graph. Then every two vertices with degree 1 are MMD in G.*

For any two mutually maximally distant vertices in G, there is no vertex of G that strongly resolves them, except themselves. This allows to claim the following.

Remark 2. *For every pair of mutually maximally distant vertices x, y of a connected graph G, and for every strong metric basis S of G, it follows that $x \in S$ or $y \in S$.*

1.2. Strong Resolving Graph of a Graph

Given a connected graph G, the *strong resolving graph* of G, denoted by G_{SR}, has vertex set $\partial(G)$ and two vertices u, v are adjacent if and only if u and v are MMD in G. We must remark that the strong resolving graph of a graph G was defined in [7] as the graph with vertex set $V(G)$ and two vertices u, v are adjacent if and only if u and v are MMD in G. Observe that the difference between these two definitions is the existence of isolated vertices in the strong resolving graph from [7]. The main reason of using in this work the slightly different version is to have a simpler notation and more clarity while proving the results. Moreover, this fact does not influence on the computations we made.

For several basic families of graphs, describing their strong resolving graphs is a straightforward problem. We next recall some examples, which will maybe further useful, and to this end, we recall that a vertex v of a graph G is *simplicial*, if its closed neighborhood induces a complete graph, and also that a graph G is *2-antipodal* if every vertex of G is diametral with exactly one other vertex of G.

Observation 2.

(a) *If $\partial(G)$ equals the set of simplicial vertices of G, then $G_{SR} \cong K_{|\partial(G)|}$. In particular, $(K_n)_{SR} \cong K_n$ and for any tree T, $T_{SR} \cong K_{l(T)}$.*

(b) *For any 2-antipodal graph G of order n, $G_{SR} \cong \bigcup_{i=1}^{\frac{n}{2}} K_2$. In particular, $(C_{2k})_{SR} \cong \bigcup_{i=1}^{k} K_2$.*

(c) *For odd cycles $(C_{2k+1})_{SR} \cong C_{2k+1}$.*

(d) *For any complete k-partite graph $G = K_{p_1, p_2, \ldots, p_k}$ such that $p_i \geq 2$, $i \in \{1, 2, \ldots, k\}$, $G_{SR} \cong \bigcup_{i=1}^{k} K_{p_i}$.*

In [9], realization and characterization problems of the strong resolving graph of a graph as a graph transformation were firstly dealt with. That is, the following problems were studied.

- **Realization Problem.** Determine which graphs have a given graph as their strong resolving graphs.
- **Characterization Problem.** Characterize those graphs that are strong resolving graphs of some graphs.

For instance, in [9] was proved that complete graphs, paths and cycles of order larger than four are realizable as the strong resolving graph of other graphs. On the other hand, it was also proved in [9] that stars and cycles of order four are not realizable as strong resolving graphs. Based on these two facts, a conjecture concerning the not realization of complete bipartite graphs in general was pointed out. Such conjecture was recently shown in [10].

In connection with these comments, it would be desirable to continue obtaining some realization (and also characterization - although much more complicated) results for the strong resolving graphs of graphs. We are then aimed in this work to present some realization results which are involving cactus graphs.

1.3. Strong Metric Dimension of G versus Vertex Cover Number of G_{SR}

Oellermann and Peters-Fransen [7] showed that the problem of finding the strong metric dimension of graphs can be transformed into the well-known problem regarding the vertex cover of graphs. A set S of vertices of G is a *vertex cover* of G if every edge of G is incident with at least one vertex of S. The *vertex cover number* of G, denoted by $\beta(G)$, is the smallest cardinality of a vertex cover of G. We refer to a $\beta(G)$-set in a graph G as a vertex cover set of cardinality $\beta(G)$.

Theorem 1 ([7]). *For any connected graph G,*

$$dim_s(G) = \beta(G_{SR}).$$

Recall that the largest cardinality of a set of vertices of G, no two of which are adjacent, is called the *independence number* of G and is denoted by $\alpha(G)$. We refer to an $\alpha(G)$-set in a graph G as an independent set of cardinality $\alpha(G)$. The following well-known and useful result, due to Gallai, states the relationship between the independence number and the vertex cover number of a graph.

Theorem 2 (Gallai's theorem). *For any graph G of order n,*

$$\alpha(G) + \beta(G) = n.$$

Thus, by using Theorems 1 and 2 we immediately obtain the next result.

Corollary 1. *For any graph G,*
$$dim_s(G) = |\partial(G)| - \alpha(G_{SR}).$$

2. Cactus Graphs: General Issues

A *cactus graph* (also called a cactus tree) is a connected graph in which any two simple cycles have at most one vertex in common. Equivalently, every edge of the graph belongs to at most one simple cycle. Next we study the strong metric dimension of cactus graphs, and we first give some necessary terminology. Note that a cycle of two vertices is precisely a path on two vertices. A vertex belonging to at least two simple cycles is a *cut vertex*. A cycle having only one cut vertex is called a *terminal cycle*. In a terminal cycle A, every vertex being diametral, in the subgraph induced by A, with respect to the cut vertex of A is a *terminal vertex*. From now on, $\tau(G)$ denotes the set of terminal vertices of G. Also, $\varsigma_2(G)$ denotes the set of vertices v, of degree two, belonging to a cycle of order larger than two, being MMD only with vertices of the same cycle which v belongs. Moreover, $\iota_2(G)$ denotes the set of vertices u, of degree two, belonging to a cycle of order larger than two being MMD with at least one vertex of a different cycle which u belongs. The following remark can be easily observed.

Remark 3. *Let G be a cactus graph. Then, two vertices x, y are MMD in G if and only if $x, y \in \varsigma_2(G) \cup \iota_2(G) \cup \tau(G)$.*

Corollary 2. *For any cactus graph G, $\partial(G) = \varsigma_2(G) \cup \iota_2(G) \cup \tau(G)$.*

Theorem 3. *Let G be a cactus graph. Then*

$$|\tau(G)| + \left\lfloor \frac{|\varsigma_2(G)|}{2} \right\rfloor - 1 \le dim_s(G) \le |\tau(G)| + |\iota_2(G)| + \left\lfloor \frac{|\varsigma_2(G)|}{2} \right\rfloor.$$

Proof. The lower bound follows from the following facts. Any two terminal vertices of G are MMD on G, and thus, they induce a complete graph of order $|\tau(G)|$. Also, vertices of $\varsigma_2(G)$ induce at least a graph with $\left\lfloor \frac{|\varsigma_2(G)|}{2} \right\rfloor$ independent edges that need to be covered in G_{SR}. Thus, one needs at least $|\tau(G)| - 1 + \left\lfloor \frac{|\varsigma_2(G)|}{2} \right\rfloor$ to strongly resolve all the vertices of G.

To see the upper bound, it is only necessary to observe that the set $\tau(G) \cup \iota_2(G)$ together with half of vertices of the set $\varsigma_2(G)$ form a strong resolving set of G, and so, we are done. □

Despite the fact that the bounds above are easily proved, we might notice that the problem of describing the strong resolving graph, and similarly, of computing the strong metric dimension of cactus graphs seems to be very challenging based on the situation that we can not control things like the orders of the involved cycles, the number of terminal vertices and cut vertices, their adjacencies, etc. In this sense, it is desirable to introduce extra conditions on the cactus graphs to have more possibilities to give some practical results.

3. Strong Resolving Graphs

In this section we aim to describe the structure of the strong resolving graphs of several different families of cactus graphs. We specifically center our attention into unicyclic graphs, bouquet of cycles and chains of even cycles. With some of these results we contribute to the problem of realization of some graphs as strong resolving graphs, that is, to the problems previously presented.

3.1. Unicyclic Graphs

Given a unicyclic graph G different from a cycle, from now on we will denote by $C_r = v_1 v_2 \ldots v_r v_1$ the subgraph induced by the unique cycle of G. A vertex $v \in V(G)$ of degree one is a *terminal vertex* of G, and $T(G)$ is the set of terminal vertices of G. Note that the terminal vertices defined here represent a particular case of the terminal vertices defined for cactus graphs in general. If the vertex v_i of C_r has degree greater than two, then we say that u_i is a terminal vertex of v_i, if $d_G(u_i, v_i) = \min\{d_G(u_i, v_{j_r}) : v_j \neq v_i\}$. The set of terminal vertices of a vertex v_i is denoted by $t(v_i)$. We will denote by $c_2(G)$ the set of vertices of the cycle C_r having degree two. If $v \in c_2(G)$, then we will say that $t(v) = \emptyset$.

Notice that if the unicyclic graph G is isomorphic to the cycle C_n, then for n even $(C_n)_{SR} \cong \bigcup_{i=1}^{\frac{n}{2}} K_2$ and for n odd $(C_n)_{SR} \cong C_n$ as already presented in Observation 2. Thus, we will study the cases that $G \ncong C_n$.

We begin with the following straightforward observations that are useful to describe the strong resolving graph of any unicyclic graph.

Remark 4. *Let G be a unicyclic graph. For every vertex $x \in c_2(G)$ there exists at least one vertex $y \in c_2(G) \cup T(G)$ such that x, y are MMD in G.*

Remark 5. *Let G be a unicyclic graph. Then two vertices x, y are MMD in G if and only if $x, y \in c_2(G) \cup T(G)$.*

Corollary 3. *For any unicyclic graph G, $\partial(G) = c_2(G) \cup T(G)$.*

Notice that every two vertices $x, y \in T(G)$ are MMD. Also, every vertex $v \in c_2(G)$ is MMD with every vertex w satisfying one of the following conditions.

- w is a terminal vertex of a vertex u of C_r such that u, v are diametral vertices in C_r.
- w is a diametral vertex with v in C_r and $w \in c_2(G)$.

As a consequence of the above comments, we can deduce the structure of the strong resolving graph of any unicyclic graph G in the following way. First notice that, according to Corollary 3, G_{SR} has vertex set equal to $c_2(G) \cup T(G)$, and to describe the adjacency of vertices in G_{SR} we consider two cases.

G_{SR} for r even.

- The set $T(G)$ forms a clique in G_{SR} and each vertex of $T(G)$ has at most one neighbor in $c_2(G)$.
- If $x, y \in c_2(G)$ are diametral vertices in C_r, then $\langle \{x, y\} \rangle$ is a connected component of G_{SR} isomorphic to K_2.

- If x, y are diametral vertices in C_r, $x \in c_2(G)$ and $y \notin c_2(G)$, then $\{x\} \cup t(y)$ forms a subgraph of G_{SR} isomorphic to $K_{|t(y)|+1}$ and $N_{G_{SR}}(x) = t(y)$.

As a consequence of the description above, we can observe that $\beta(G_{SR}) \leq \frac{|c_2(G)|-1}{2} + |T(G)|$.

G_{SR} for r odd.

- The set $T(G)$ forms a clique in G_{SR} and each vertex of $T(G)$ has at most two neighbors in $c_2(G)$.
- Let $u \in c_2(G)$ and let x, y being diametral vertices with u in C_r.

  - If $x, y \in c_2(G)$, then $\langle\{u, x, y\}\rangle$ is a subgraph of G_{SR} isomorphic to P_3, $N_{G_{SR}}(u) = \{x, y\}$ and for every $w \in \{x, y\}, \delta_{G_{SR}}(w) \geq 2$.
  - If $x, y \notin c_2(G)$, then $\langle\{u\} \cup t(x) \cup t(y)\rangle$ is a subgraph of G_{SR} isomorphic to $K_{|t(x)|+|t(y)|+1}$, $N_{G_{SR}}(u) = t(x) \cup t(y)$ and for every $w \in t(x) \cup t(y), \delta_{G_{SR}}(w) \geq |t(x)| + |t(y)| + 1$ for $r \geq 5$ (notice that if $r = 3$, then $\delta_{G_{SR}}(w) = |t(x)| + |t(y)|$).
  - If $x \in c_2(G)$ and $y \notin c_2(G)$, then the set $\{u, x\} \cup t(y)$ form a subgraph (not induced) (Notice that the vertices $t(y)$ are adjacent between them in G_{SR}.) of G_{SR} isomorphic to a star graph $S_{1,|t(y)|+1}$ with central vertex u, $N_{G_{SR}}(u) = \{x\} \cup t(y)$, $\delta_{G_{SR}}(x) \geq 2$ and for every $w \in t(y)$, $\delta_{G_{SR}}(w) \geq |t(y)| + 1$.

Similarly to the case when r is even, we can observe here that $\beta(G_{SR}) \leq \frac{|c_2(G)|}{2} + |T(G)|$.

We define the *branch restricted unicyclic graph* $T(G)$ associated to a unicyclic graph G in the following way. We begin with taking the cycle C_r in G and removing the remaining vertices of G. Then we add $t(v_i)$ pendant edges to every vertex v_i in C_r. Figure 1 shows an example of a unicyclic graph, its branch restricted unicyclic graph and its strong resolving graph.

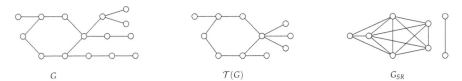

G $\qquad\qquad\qquad\qquad$ $T(G)$ $\qquad\qquad\qquad\qquad$ G_{SR}

Figure 1. A unicyclic graph G, $T(G)$ and G_{SR}.

Lemma 1. *Let G be a unicyclic graph and $T(G)$ be its branch restricted unicyclic graph. Then $(T(G))_{SR}$ is isomorphic to G_{SR}*

Proof. From Remarks 4 and 5, and by the definition of the branch restricted unicyclic graph, we deduce that $(T(G))_{SR}$ is isomorphic to G_{SR}. $\square$

Our next step is dedicated to present a realization result for some corona product graphs, where the solution precisely involves the use of unicyclic graphs. We first recall that the *corona product graph* $G \odot H$ is defined as the graph obtained from a graph G of order n and a graph H, by taking one copy of G and n copies of H, and then joining by an edge each vertex from the ith-copy of H with the ith-vertex of G.

Proposition 1. *For any integer $n \geq 3$, there exists a graph G such that $G_{SR} \cong K_n \odot K_1$.*

Proof. We consider the unicyclic graph G with a cycle $C_{2n} = v_1 v_2 \ldots v_{2n} v_1$ such that the vertices v_1, $v_2, \ldots, v_n$ form the set $c_2(G)$ and the remaining ones from the cycle have exactly one terminal vertex. Since $2n$ is an even number according to the Description of G_{SR} it clearly follows that G_{SR} is isomorphic to $K_{|T(G)|}$ where each vertex of $T(G)$ has exactly one neighbor in $c_2(G)$. $\square$

3.2. Bouquet of Cycles

Let $\mathcal{B}_{a,b,c}$ be a family of graphs obtained in the following way. Each graph $B \in \mathcal{B}_{a,b,c}$ is a bouquet of $a + b + c$ cycles where a of them are even cycles (of order at least four), b are odd cycles of order larger than three, c are cycles of order three, $a, b, c \geq 0$, and $a + b + c \geq 2$. All cycles of $B \in \mathcal{B}_{a,b,c}$ have the common vertex w. One example of a bouquet of cycles is given in Figure 2. Let $C_{r_1}, C_{r_2}, \ldots, C_{r_a}$ be the even cycles of order at least four in $B \in \mathcal{B}_{a,b,c}$ and $C_{s_1}, C_{s_2}, \ldots, C_{s_b}$ be the odd cycles of order larger than three in $B \in \mathcal{B}_{a,b,c}$.

Figure 2. A bouquet of cycles $B \in \mathcal{B}_{2,2,1}$ containing the cycles C_6, C_4, C_9, C_7 and C_3.

In [17], the authors have described the structure of the strong resolving graph of the graph $B \in \mathcal{B}_{a,b,c}$ as follows. By completeness of our exposition, we copy exactly the description presented there, since it makes no sense to do some changes on it, as it is fairly well written.

- The set of a vertices of the cycles $C_{r_1}, C_{r_2}, \ldots, C_{r_a}$ which are diametral with w induces a complete graph in B_{SR}. We denote such set as V_a (in Figures 2 and 3, the black colored vertices).
- The set of $2b$ vertices of the cycles $C_{s_1}, C_{s_2}, \ldots, C_{s_b}$ which are diametral with w induces a complete multipartite graph $K_{2,\ldots,2}$ with b bipartition sets each of cardinality two in B_{SR}. We denote such set as V_{2b} (in Figures 2 and 3, the red colored vertices).
- The set of $2c$ vertices of the cycles C_3 different from w induces a complete graph in B_{SR}. We denote such set as V_{2c} (in Figures 2 and 3, the blue colored vertices).
- The set of vertices of each odd cycle $C_{s_i}, i \in \{1, \ldots, b\}$, which are different from w induces a path of order $s_i - 1$, in B_{SR}, whose leaves are the two vertices that are diametral with w.
- The set of vertices of each cycle $C_{r_j}, j \in \{1, \ldots, a\}$, which are not diametral with w induces a graph isomorphic to the disjoint union of $(r_j - 2)/2$ complete graphs K_2 in B_{SR}.
- Every three vertices x, y, z such that $x \in V_a, y \in V_{2b}$ and $z \in V_{2c}$ are pairwise adjacent.

Figure 3 shows the strong resolving graph of the graph illustrated in Figure 2.

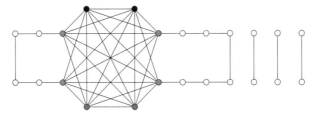

Figure 3. The strong resolving graph B_{SR} of the graph illustrated in Figure 2.

If we study the bouquet of cycles $B \in \mathcal{B}_{a,b,c}$ with $b = 0$ (or equivalently, B has not odd cycles of order larger than three), and $C_{r_1}, C_{r_2}, \ldots, C_{r_a}$ are the cycles of even order, then the strong resolving graph B_{SR} is composed by the complete graph K_{a+2c} and $\sum_{i=1}^{a} \frac{r_i - 2}{2}$ components isomorphic to K_2.

Now, we again give some realization results for strong resolving graphs. To this end, we need to define a graph structure which we call a *partial multisubdivided complete graph* $K_{2n}(p_1, p_2, \ldots, p_n)$. That is, a complete graph K_{2n} where each edge of a perfect matching of this graph is subdivided $p_i \geq 0$ times for $i \in \{1, 2, \ldots, n\}$ (the case when some $p_i = 0$ means that the edge corresponding to p_i is not subdivided). Moreover, recall that the *cocktail party graph* R_n, also called the hyperoctahedral graph, is a $n-2$ regular graph on n vertices.

Proposition 2. *For any integer $n \geq 2$, there exists a graph G such that G_{SR} is isomorphic to $K_{2n}(p_1, p_2, \ldots, p_n)$.*

Proof. We consider the bouquet of cycles $B \in \mathcal{B}_{a,b,c}$ with $a, c = 0$, $b = n$ and $C_{p_1+3}, C_{p_2+3}, \ldots, C_{p_n+3}$ are the cycles of odd order larger than three. According to the construction of the strong resolving graph B_{SR}, the subgraph $\langle V_b \rangle$ is isomorphic to R_{2n} and the set of vertices of each odd cycle C_{p_i+3}, $i \in \{1, \ldots, b\}$, which are different from w induces a path of order $p_i + 2$, in B_{SR}, whose leaves are the two vertices of this cycle that are not adjacent in R_{2n}. $\square$

Corollary 4. *For any integer $n \geq 2$, there exists a graph G such that G_{SR} contains the cocktail party graph R_{2n} as an induced subgraph.*

3.3. Chains of Even Cycles

A *chain of cycles* is a cactus graph in which, every cycle has order at least three and there are only two terminal cycles. Notice that in such case every non-terminal cycle has exactly two cut vertices, such that each cut vertex belongs to exactly two cycles. We next center our attention into the case of chains of even cycles. To this end, we need some terminology and notation. A chain of even cycles is a *straight chain*, if the cut vertices of every cycle in the chain are diametral in the cycle. Note that each straight chain contains two diametral vertices, which are the unique terminal vertices of this chain.

For the purposes of simplifying, given an integer $k \geq 0$, we shall define the next family $\mathcal{F}_k$ of graphs. Each graph $F \in \mathcal{F}_k$ is a chain of even cycles constructed as follows.

- We begin with $k+1$ straight chains of even cycles, say $G_0, \ldots, G_k$, satisfying that the last cycle of the straight chain G_i is isomorphic to the first cycle of the straight chain G_{i+1} for every $i \in \{0, \ldots, k-1\}$.
- Assume that the last cycle of each straight chain G_i is $C_r^i = v_0^i v_1^i \cdots v_{r-1}^i v_0^i$, for every $i \in \{0, \ldots, k\}$. By the item above, this C_r^i (in G_i) is isomorphic to the first cycle of the straight chain G_{i+1} with $i \in \{0, \ldots, k-1\}$.
- Assume also that the terminal vertices of each straight chain G_i are a_i, b_{k-i}, for every $i \in \{0, \ldots, k\}$.
- To construct our chain of even cycles $F \in \mathcal{F}_k$, for every $i \in \{0, \ldots, k-1\}$, we identify the last cycle C_r^i of G_i with the first cycle C_r^{i+1} of G_{i+1} (that are isomorphic) as follows. Every vertex v_j^i of C_r^i is identified with the vertex v_{j+t}^{i+1} for some $t \neq 0$ and every $j \in \{0, r-1\}$ (operations with the subindex of v are done modulo r).

Notice that for instance, for the chain of even cycles $F \in \mathcal{F}_k$ described above, the two terminal vertices of it are a_0 and b_0. Figure 4 shows a fairly representative example of a chain of even cycles. Recall that the way of drawing such graph (with respect to directions of the "turns" in the chain) does not influence in our purposes. The chain of even cycles $F \in \mathcal{F}_k$ presented in the Figure 4 has four straight chains of even cycles: G_0 contains C^1 and C^2, G_1 contains C^2, C^3 and C^4, G_2 contains C^4, C^5 and C^6, and G_3 contains C^6, C^7 and C^8.

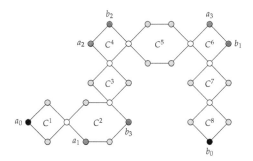

Figure 4. A chain of cycles $F \in \mathcal{F}_3$ containing six cycles C_4 and two cycles C_6.

We next describe the strong resolving graph of a chain of even cycles $F \in \mathcal{F}_k$. We need first the following observations.

Remark 6. *For any chain of even cycles $F \in \mathcal{F}_k$, a vertex x belongs to $\partial(F)$ if and only if x has degree two.*

Remark 7. *In a straight chain of cycles, the two terminal vertices form a pair of MMD vertices, as well as each pair of diametral vertices in each cycle.*

Observation 3. *For a chain of even cycles $F \in \mathcal{F}_k$, and for every $i \in \{0, \ldots, k\}$ and $j \in \{i, \ldots, k\}$ it follows.*

- *The terminal vertex a_i of the straight chain G_i is MMD with every vertex b_{k-j} of the straight chain G_j.*
- *The terminal vertex b_i of the straight chain G_{k-i} is MMD with every vertex a_{k-j} of the straight chain G_{k-j}.*
- *In any cycle of F, any pair of diametral (in the cycle) vertices being not cut nor terminal vertices of F are MMD.*

For instance, in Figure 4, the red vertex a_1 is MMD with the blue vertices b_2, b_1, b_0, while the blue vertex b_1 is MMD with the red vertices a_2, a_1, a_0. Moreover, again in Figure 4, any pair of green diametral vertices belonging to the same cycle are MMD in F.

With these observations above, we are able to describe the structure of F_{SR} for every chain of even cycles $F \in \mathcal{F}_k$. To do so, we shall need the following construction, which represents a bipartite graph J_r of order $2r + 2$ for some $r \geq 3$. The two bipartition sets of the bipartite graph J_r are the sets $U = \{a_0, \ldots, a_r\}$ and $V = \{b_0, \ldots, b_r\}$. The edges of J_r are as follows. For every $i \in \{0, \ldots, \lfloor r/2 \rfloor\}$ and every $j \in \{0, \ldots, r - i\}$, there exist the edges $a_i b_j$ and $b_i a_j$.

- *The set of vertices a_i and b_i, with $i \in \{0, \ldots, k\}$, forms a component of the graph F_{SR} isomorphic to a bipartite graph J_k.*
- *In each cycle of F, each pair of diametral vertices in the cycle, not including terminal nor cut vertices, induces a graph isomorphic to K_2 in F_{SR}.*

We may remark that, the strong resolving graph of a straight chain of cycles is simply a union of several complete graphs K_2. The strong resolving graph of the chain of even cycles shown in Figure 4 is drawn in Figure 5.

Figure 5. The strong resolving graph F_{SR} of the graph illustrated in Figure 4.

We end this subsection by giving a realization result for strong resolving graphs involving chains of even cycles.

Corollary 5. *For any integer $k \geq 2$, there exists a chain of even cycles $F \in \mathcal{F}_k$ such that F_{SR} contains the bipartite graph J_k as a component.*

4. The Strong Metric Dimension

We are next centered into computing or bounding the strong metric dimension of the cactus graphs which we have studied in the previous section.

4.1. Unicyclic Graphs

Our first results shows the relationship between the strong metric dimension of a unicyclic graph and that of its branch restricted unicyclic graph.

Lemma 2. *Let G be a unicyclic graph and $\mathcal{T}(G)$ be its branch restricted unicyclic graph. Then*

$$dim_s(G) = dim_s(\mathcal{T}(G)).$$

Proof. By Lemma 1 and Theorem 1, we derive that $dim_s(G) = \beta(G_{SR}) = \beta((\mathcal{T}(G))_{SR}) = dim_s(\mathcal{T}(G))$ and the proof is complete. □

Theorem 4. *Let G be a unicyclic graph with unique cycle C_r. Then*

$$\max\left\{\left\lceil \frac{r}{2} \right\rceil, |T(G)| - 1\right\} \leq dim_s(G) \leq |T(G)| + \left\lfloor \frac{|c_2(G)|}{2} \right\rfloor.$$

Proof. From Remark 1 we have that every strong resolving basis must contain at least $|T(G)| - 1$ vertices of degree one. So, $dim_s(G) \geq |T(G)| - 1$. On the other hand, for every vertex $i \in \{1, \ldots, r\}$ there exists at least a vertex $w_i \in t(v_i) \cup \{v_i\}$ such that $w_i \in \partial(G)$ (notice that it could happen $w_i = v_i$). Thus we have that $dim_s(G) = \beta(G_{SR}) \geq \frac{|\partial(G)|}{2} \geq \lceil \frac{r}{2} \rceil$.

On the other side, since $T(G)$ forms a clique in G_{SR} and for every $u \in c_2(G)$ there exists at least one vertex $v \in \partial(G)$ such that they are MMD, according to the description of G_{SR} presented in the previous section, we have $dim_s(G) = \beta(G_{SR}) \leq |T(G)| + \left\lfloor \frac{|c_2(G)|}{2} \right\rfloor$. Therefore the proof is complete. □

As we can see in the following, the bounds above are tight. In particular, we characterize all the unicyclic graphs having a unique cycle of even order that are attaining the upper bound.

Theorem 5. *Let G be a unicyclic graph with a unique cycle C_r of even order. Then $dim_s(G) = |T(G)| + \left\lfloor \frac{|c_2(G)|}{2} \right\rfloor$ if and only if $|c_2(G)| = r - 1$.*

Proof. ($\Leftarrow$) We assume $|c_2(G)| = r - 1$. Let v be the only vertex of C_r with degree greater than two, and let u be the diametral vertex with v in C_r. So, every two vertices in $t(v) \cup \{u\}$ are MMD. Also, every two diametral vertices in $c_2(G) - \{u\}$ are MMD. Thus, G_{SR} is formed by $\frac{r-2}{2} = \frac{|c_2(G)|-1}{2}$ connected components isomorphic to K_2 and one component isomorphic to $K_{|t(v)|+1}$. Since $T(G) = t(v)$, we have that

$$dim_s(G) = \beta(G_{SR}) = \beta(K_{|T(G)|+1}) + \beta\left(\bigcup_{t=1}^{\frac{|c_2(G)|-1}{2}} K_2\right) = |T(G)| + \frac{|c_2(G)| - 1}{2} = |T(G)| + \left\lfloor \frac{|c_2(G)|}{2} \right\rfloor.$$

($\Rightarrow$) We assume now that $dim_s(G) = |T(G)| + \left\lfloor \frac{|c_2(G)|}{2} \right\rfloor$ is satisfied. If $|c_2(G)| < r - 1$, then there are at least two vertices x, y such that $t(x) \geq 1$ and $t(y) \geq 1$. We consider two cases.

Case 1: x, y are diametral in C_r. Hence, $t(x) \cup t(y)$ forms a clique in G_{SR} of cardinality $|t(x)| + |t(y)|$. Also, the vertices in $t(x) \cup t(y)$ have no neighbor from $c_2(G)$ in G_{SR}. Note that, there could be some other vertices in $T(G)$ having neighbors from $c_2(G)$ in G_{SR}, and if there is one of such vertices, say z, then $|t(z)| \geq 1$ and $t(x) \cup t(y) \cup t(z)$ is also a clique in G_{SR}. However, this will not influence on the fact that, in order to cover the edges of G_{SR}, one can leave one vertex w of $t(x) \cup t(y)$ outside of the vertex cover set, by simply taking $T(G) \setminus \{w\}$ as a part of such vertex cover set. Thus, we have that $\beta(G_{SR}) \leq |T(G)| - 1 + \left\lfloor \frac{|c_2(G)|}{2} \right\rfloor$, a contradiction.

Case 2: x, y are not diametral in C_r. Let $x', y' \in c_2(G)$ being diametral vertices with x, y, respectively. Hence, $t(x) \cup t(y)$, $t(x) \cup \{x'\}$ and $t(y) \cup \{y'\}$ form cliques in G_{SR}. Also, x', y' have no neighbor in G_{SR} other than that ones in $t(x), t(y)$, respectively. Thus, in order to cover the edges of G_{SR}, we can leave outside of the vertex cover set both vertices x', y', by simply taking $T(G)$ in such vertex cover set. On the other hand, to cover the remaining vertices in $c_2(G) \setminus \{x', y'\}$ we will need at most $\left\lfloor \frac{|c_2(G)|-2}{2} \right\rfloor$. We then deduce that $\beta(G_{SR}) \leq |T(G)| + \frac{|c_2(G)|-2}{2} = |T(G)| - 1 + |c_2(G)|/2 - 1$, a contradiction again.

Since we have contradiction on both cases above, it must happen that $|c_2(G)| = r - 1$, and the proof is completed. $\square$

Note that the upper bound of Theorem 4 is also tight when the unique cycle of G is odd, but the characterization of the limit case seems to be a hard working task. For instance, if G has a unique cycle of odd order and $|c_2(G)| = r - 1$, then a "relatively" similar argument to the first part of the proof of Theorem 5 leads to conclude that $dim_s(G) = |T(G)| + \left\lfloor \frac{|c_2(G)|}{2} \right\rfloor$. Other cases, when $|c_2(G)| < r - 1$ can be hand computed, and we leave this to the reader.

Proposition 3. *Let G be a unicyclic graph with a unique cycle C_r of even order. Then $dim_s(G) = \frac{r}{2}$ if and only if the following items hold.*

(i) $|t(x)| \leq 1$ for every x of C_r.

(ii)   There is at most one pair of diametral vertices in C_r each one having one terminal vertex.

Proof. ($\Rightarrow$) Assume $dim_s(G) = \frac{r}{2}$. If $|t(x)| > 1$ for some x of C_r, then let x' be the vertex of C_r being diametral with x in C_r. Hence, $t(x) \cup t(x')$ (or $t(x) \cup \{x'\}$ if $x' \in c_2(G)$) is a clique in G_{SR}, and so, in order to cover the edges of G_{SR}, we need at most $\frac{r}{2}$ in connection with pairs of diametral vertices in C_r together with at least one extra vertex from $t(x)$, since $|t(x)| > 1$ (there are at least two MMD vertices in $t(x)$). Thus, (i) follows.

Now, let a be the number of pairs of diametral vertices in C_r each one having one terminal vertex. Suppose that $a \geq 2$. Also, let b be the number of pairs of diametral vertices in C_r, in which one of them has one terminal vertex and the other one belongs to $c_2(G)$, and let c be the number of pairs of diametral vertices in C_r, each one belonging to $c_2(G)$. Note that the $a + b + c = \frac{r}{2}$ and that $|T(G)| = 2a + b$. Also, the $2a$ vertices and the b vertices of $T(G)$, corresponding to that pairs mentioned above, form a clique in G_{SR} such that the $2a$ vertices has no neighbors other than that ones in such clique, and such that each of the b vertices has exactly one other neighbor from $c_2(G)$ in G_{SR}. Moreover, the c pairs of vertices also mentioned above, form c components of G_{SR} isomorphic to K_2. In consequence, we observe that $\beta(G_{SR}) = 2a - 1 + b + c = \frac{r}{2} - 1 + a \geq \frac{r}{2} + 1$. This is a contradiction, and the proof of (ii) is complete.

($\Leftarrow$) Assume on the other hand that G satisfies (i) and (ii). We shall use the same notation of a, b and c from the implication above. By (ii), $0 \leq a \leq 1$. If $a = 1$, then $dim_s(G) = \beta(G_{SR}) = 2a - 1 + b + c = \frac{r}{2} - 1 + a = \frac{r}{2}$ (note that the equality $\beta(G_{SR}) = 2a - 1 + b + c$ follows by using (i)). Also, if $a = 0$, then $dim_s(G) = \beta(G_{SR}) = b + c = \frac{r}{2}$ (we again use (i) as explained before). $\square$

To conclude this section, we next show that the differences between the lower (partially) and upper bounds of Theorem 4, and the real value of the strong metric dimension of some unicyclic graphs can be as large as possible.

We consider the unicyclic graph G^k with a cycle $C_{2n} = v_1 v_2 \cdots v_{2n} v_1$ and $1 \le k \le n$ such that the vertices $v_{k+1}, v_{k+2}, \ldots, v_{2n}$ form the set $c_2(G)$, and each vertex v_i for $i \in \{1, \ldots, k\}$ has one terminal vertex denoted by x_i. Since $2n$ is an even number, and according to the description of the strong resolving graph of a unicyclic graph, it clearly follows that $(G^k)_{SR}$ consists of a graph isomorphic to $K_{|T(G)|} \odot K_1$ and $\left\lfloor \frac{|c_2(G)|-k}{2} \right\rfloor$ graphs isomorphic to K_2. Thus, $dim_s(G^k) = |T(G)| + \left\lfloor \frac{|c_2(G)|-k}{2} \right\rfloor$. Since $1 \le k \le |c_2(G)|$, we can easily observe that $|T(G)| + \left\lfloor \frac{|c_2(G)|}{2} \right\rfloor - dim_s(G^k)$ and $dim_s(G^k) - (|T(G)| - 1)$ can be arbitrarily large.

4.2. Bouquet of Cycles

For the results of this subsection, we use the terminology and notations given in Section 3.2.

Theorem 6. *For any bouquet of cycles $B \in \mathcal{B}_{a,b,c}$,*

$$dim_s(B) = a + \sum_{i=1}^{a} \frac{r_i - 2}{2} + 2b + \sum_{j=1}^{b} \frac{s_j - 3}{2} + 2c - 1.$$

Proof. According to the description of B_{SR} presented before, it follows that B_{SR} consist of a graph isomorphic to $K_{a+2b+2c}(s_1 - 3, s_2 - 3, \ldots, s_b - 3, 0, 0, \ldots, 0)$ and $\sum_{i=1}^{a} \frac{r_i - 2}{2}$ graphs isomorphic to K_2. First we consider the subgraph H induced by $N_{B_{SR}}[V_a \cup V_{2b} \cup V_{2c}]$. Notice that $\beta(H) = a + 2b + 2c - 1$. In order to compute $\beta(K_{a+2b+2c}(s_1 - 3, s_2 - 3, \ldots, s_b - 3, 0, 0, \ldots, 0))$ we need to cover the remaining edges in B_{SR} corresponding to edges of the odd cycles in B. Since for each odd cycle C_{s_i} for $i \in \{1, \ldots, b\}$, two edges of it are already considered in H, it remains to cover $s_i - 4$ edges which are inducing a path of order $s_i - 3$. Thus, to cover each cycle C_{s_i} we need $\frac{s_i - 3}{2}$ vertices.

On the other hand, to cover the $\sum_{i=1}^{a} \frac{r_i - 2}{2}$ graphs isomorphic to K_2, $\sum_{i=1}^{a} \frac{r_i - 2}{2}$ extra vertices are needed. The sum of these three quantities above gives the vertex cover number of B_{SR}, and also the strong metric dimension of B, by using Corollary 1, which completes the proof. $\square$

4.3. Chains of Even Cycles

In order to give a formula for the strong metric dimension of chains of even cycles, we need to first compute the value of the vertex cover number of a bipartite graph J_r as described in Section 3.3.

Lemma 3. *For any bipartite graph J_r, $\beta(J_r) = r + 1$.*

Proof. We first note that if r is an even integer, then the set of edges $E_r = \{a_0 b_r, a_1 b_{r-1}, \ldots, a_{r/2} b_{r/2}\} \cup \{b_0 a_r, b_1 a_{r-1}, \ldots, b_{r/2-1} a_{r/2+1}\}$ is a maximum matching in J_r of cardinality $r/2 + 1 + r/2 = r + 1$.

On the other hand, if r is odd, then the set of edges $E_r = \{a_0 b_r, a_1 b_{r-1}, \ldots, a_{(r-1)/2} b_{(r+1)/2}\} \cup \{b_0 a_r, b_1 a_{r-1}, \ldots, b_{(r-1)/2} a_{(r+1)/2}\}$ is a maximum matching in J_r of cardinality $(r - 1)/2 + 1 + (r - 1)/2 + 1 = r + 1$.

Thus, since J_r is bipartite, by using the famous Kőnig's Theorem, we obtain the required result. $\square$

Theorem 7. *For any chain of even cycles $F \in \mathcal{F}_k$ of order n with c cut vertices,*

$$dim_s(F) = \frac{n - c}{2}.$$

Proof. According to the description of F_{SR} presented before, the vertices a_i and b_i, with $i \in \{0, \ldots, k\}$, forms a component of the graph F_{SR} isomorphic to a bipartite graph J_k of order $2k + 2$. For completing the graph F_{SR}, we need to add $\frac{n-c-2k-2}{2}$ graphs isomorphic to K_2. Hence, by using Theorem 1, Lemma 3 and Observation 1, we have $dim_s(F) = \beta(J_k) + \frac{n-c-2k-2}{2}\beta(K_2) = \frac{n-c}{2}$. $\square$

5. Concluding Remarks

We have studied the strong metric dimension of cactus graphs in this work. Along the way, we have given several contributions to the realization and characterization results of strong resolving graphs involving cactus graphs. The results shown allow to observe that working in this topic for the specific case of cactus graphs is very challenging, although some particular structures of such graphs can be easier handled. These are the cases of unicyclic graphs, chains of even cycles and bouquet of cycles, for which we have given the constructions of their strong resolving graphs and bounds or closed formulas for the values of their strong metric dimensions. As a consequence of this study, the following open questions are raised.

- Describe the structure of the strong resolving graphs of some classes of cactus graphs, and compute the strong metric dimension of the graphs in such families.
- Apply the results concerning the descriptions of the strong resolving graphs of the graphs given in the work to other problems, like for instance computing the strong partition dimension (see [4]) of such graphs.
- Continue the lines of this study for other more general families that cactus graphs. This could include for instance, planar graphs or chordal graphs.

Funding: This research received no external funding.

Conflicts of Interest: The author declares no conflict of interest.

References

1. Kelenc, A.; Tratnik, N.; Yero, I.G. Uniquely identifying the edges of a graph: The edge metric dimension. *Discret. Appl. Math.* **2018**, *251*, 204–220. [CrossRef]
2. Kelenc, A.; Kuziak, D.; Taranenko, A.; Yero, I.G. Mixed metric dimension of graph. *Appl. Math. Comput.* **2017**, *314*, 429–438.
3. Trujillo-Rasúa, R.; Yero, I.G. *k*-metric antidimension: A privacy measure for social graphs. *Inform. Sci.* **2016**, *328*, 403–417. [CrossRef]
4. Yero, I.G. On the strong partition dimension of graphs. *Electron. J. Combin.* **2014**, *21*, P3.14.
5. Gil-Pons, R.; Ramírez-Cruz, Y.; Trujillo-Rasua, R.; Yero, I.G. Distance-based vertex identification in graphs: The outer multiset dimension. *Appl. Math. Comput.* **2019**, *363*, 124612. [CrossRef]
6. Simanjuntak, R.; Siagian, P.; Vetrik, T. The multiset dimension of graphs. *arXiv* **2019**, arXiv:1711.00225v2.
7. Oellermann, O.R.; Peters-Fransen, J. The strong metric dimension of graphs and digraphs. *Discret. Appl. Math.* **2007**, *155*, 356–364. [CrossRef]
8. Kuziak, D. Strong Resolvability in Product Graphs. Ph.D. Thesis, Universitat Rovira i Virgili, Catalonia, Spain, 2014.
9. Kuziak, D.; Puertas, M.L.; Rodríguez-Velázquez, J.A.; Yero, I.G. Strong resolving graphs: The realization and the characterization problems. *Discret. Appl. Math.* **2018**, *236*, 270–287. [CrossRef]
10. Lenin, R. A short note on: There is no graph G with $G_{SR} \cong K_{r,s}$, $r, s \geq 2$. *Discrete Appl. Math.* **2019**, *265*, 204–205. [CrossRef]
11. Kuziak, D.; Yero, I.G.; Rodríguez-Velázquez, J.A. On the strong metric dimension of corona product graphs and join graphs. *Discrete Appl. Math.* **2013**, *161*, 1022–1027. [CrossRef]
12. Kuziak, D.; Yero, I.G.; Rodríguez-Velázquez, J.A. Strong metric dimension of rooted product graphs. *Int. J. Comput. Math.* **2016**, *93*, 1265–1280. [CrossRef]
13. Yi, E. On strong metric dimension of graphs and their complements. *Acta Math. Sin. (Engl. Ser.)* **2013**, *29*, 1479–1492. [CrossRef]
14. Brešar, B.; Klavžar, S.; Tepeh Horvat, A. On the geodetic number and related metric sets in Cartesian product graphs. *Discret. Math.* **2008**, *308*, 5555–5561. [CrossRef]

15. Cáceres, J.; Puertas, M.L.; Hernando, C.; Mora, M.; Pelayo, I.M.; Seara, C. Searching for geodetic boundary vertex sets. *Electron. Notes Discret. Math.* **2005**, *19*, 25–31. [CrossRef]
16. Rodríguez-Velázquez, J.A.; Yero, I.G.; Kuziak, D.; Oellermann, O.R. On the strong metric dimension of Cartesian and direct products of graphs. *Discret. Math.* **2014**, *335*, 8–19. [CrossRef]
17. Kuziak, D.; Yero, I.G. Further new results on strong resolving partitions for graphs. *Open Math.* **2020**, to appear. [CrossRef]

Article

Removing Twins in Graphs to Break Symmetries

Antonio González [1] and María Luz Puertas [2,*]

[1]   Departamento de Didáctica de las Matemáticas, Universidad de Sevilla, 41013 Sevilla, Spain;
       gonzalezh@us.es
[2]   Departamento de Matemáticas and Agrifood Campus of International Excellence (ceiA3),
       Universidad de Almería, 04120 Almería, Spain
*   Correspondence: mpuertas@ual.es

Received: 7 October 2019; Accepted: 14 November 2019; Published: 15 November 2019

Abstract: Determining vertex subsets are known tools to provide information about automorphism groups of graphs and, consequently about symmetries of graphs. In this paper, we provide both lower and upper bounds of the minimum size of such vertex subsets, called the determining number of the graph. These bounds, which are performed for arbitrary graphs, allow us to compute the determining number in two different graph families such are cographs and unit interval graphs.

Keywords: graph; automorphism group; determining number; cograph; unit interval graph

MSC: 05C25; 05C76

---

1. Introduction and Preliminaries

The graph isomorphism problem is not known to be solvable in polynomial time nor to be NP-complete (see [1]) and moreover, it is well known that constructing the automorphism group is at least as difficult (in terms of computational complexity) as solving the graph isomorphism problem (see [2]). Therefore, it is interesting to provide tools that give information about such automorphism groups.

Determining sets were introduced simultaneously by Boutin [3] and Erwin and Harary [4] (they called them fixing sets) in 2006, to deal with the problem of identifying the automorphism group of a graph. These sets are a generalization of resolving sets, independently introduced by Slater [5] and Harary and Melter [6], motivated by the problem of identifying the location of an intruder in a network, by means of distances. Resolving sets and some related sets were recently studied in [7–12]. Determining sets and resolving sets were jointly studied (see [13,14]). Furthermore, determining sets are closely related to the notion of "symmetry breaking", firstly studied by Alberson and Collins [15] in 1996. The interest of this notion, beyond the information it provides about the automorphism group, was pointed out by Bailey and Cameron in their survey paper [16] of 2011, citing Babai's words [17]:

> "In fact, breaking regularity is one of the key tools in the design of algorithms for graph isomorphism; the graph isomorphism problem has therefore been one of the strongest motivators of the study of all sorts of resolving/discriminating sets, and perhaps the only deep motivator of the study of those in contexts where no group is present."

In this paper, we deepen the study of determining sets of general graphs, providing both lower and upper bounds of this parameter in terms of the so-called twin graph. We follow the same spirit as other works that find general bounds involving other aspects of graphs, such as the number of automorphisms [3] or the number of orbits [4]. Furthermore, our bounds allow us to obtain the determining number of some graph classes (cographs and unit interval graphs), which is a problem of interest due to the NP-hardness of the computation of this parameter in arbitrary graphs [18]. Indeed, many papers in the literature are devoted to study the determining number of specific graph families: trees [4,13], Cartesian products [4,13,19], Kneser and Johnson graphs [3,20], twin-free graphs [14], and Cayley graphs [21]; among others.

We now introduce the definitions and notations that we shall need throughout the rest of the paper. All graphs considered here are finite, simple and undirected. An *automorphism* of a graph G is a bijective mapping $\phi : V(G) \longrightarrow V(G)$ so that $\phi(u)\phi(v) \in E(G)$ if and only if $uv \in E(G)$. The set Aut(G) of all automorphisms of G forms a group under composition, and its identity element is denoted by id_G. We recall the definition of determining set and determining number from [3].

Definition 1 ([3]). *A subset S of the vertices of a graph G is called a determining set if whenever $g, h \in$ Aut(G) agree on the vertices of S, they agree on all vertices of G. That is, S is a determining set if whenever g and h are automorphisms with the property that $g(s) = h(s)$ for all $s \in S$, then $g = h$. The determining number of a graph G is the smallest integer r so that G has a determining set of size r. Denote this by Det(G).*

We quote from [3] the following example illustrating this concept.

Example 1. *The Petersen graph is shown in Figure 1, where the vertices are identified with the 2-subsets of a 5-set. The Persersen graph has a determining number equal to three and examples of minimum determining sets of this graph are $S = \{\{1,2\}, \{2,4\}, \{2,5\}\}$ and $T = \{\{1,2\}, \{2,3\}, \{3,4\}\}$ (see [3]).*

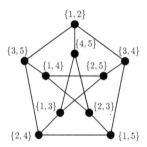

Figure 1. The Petersen graph.

The following useful characterization of determining sets, in terms of the stabilizer of a vertex subset, can be also found in [3]. The *stabilizer* of a vertex subset $S \subseteq V(G)$ is the automorphism subset Stab$_G(S) = \{\phi \in$ Aut(G) : $\phi(u) = u, \forall u \in S\}$. Observe that Stab$_G(S) = \cap_{s \in S}$ Stab$_G(\{s\})$, and moreover $S \subseteq T$ implies that Stab$_G(T) \subseteq$ Stab$_G(S)$.

Proposition 1 ([3]). *Let S be a subset of the vertices of a graph G. Then S is a determining set of G if and only if Stab$_G(S) = \{id_G\}$.*

We now quote from [22] the construction of the twin graph G^1 associated with a given graph G. This graph will be the main tool to obtain our new bounds. For a vertex $u \in V(G)$, the open and the closed neighborhood of u are respectively denoted by $N(u)$ and $N[u]$ and the degree of u is $deg(u) = |N(u)|$. We say that two different vertices $u, v \in V(G)$ are *twins* when $N(u) = N(v)$ or $N[u] = N[v]$. This notion induces the following equivalence relation on $V(G)$: $u \equiv v$ if and only if either $u = v$ or u and v are twins. This allows defining the *twin class* of u as $[u] = \{v \in V(G) : u \equiv v\}$. We say that a twin class is *trivial* if it contains just one vertex and *non-trivial* in other case. When each twin class is trivial, we say that G is *twin-free* For $S \subseteq V(G)$, we write $[S] = \cup_{u \in S}[u]$.

Assuming that there are exactly $n^{(1)}$ different equivalence classes, we can consider the partition $[u_1], \dots, [u_{n^{(1)}}]$ of $V(G)$ induced by them, where every u_i is a representative of $[u_i]$. The twin graph of G, denoted by G^1, is the graph with vertex set the set of equivalence classes of G. The vertex of G^1

representing the equivalence class $[u]$ is denoted by u^1. The edge set is $E(G^1) = \{u^1v^1 : uv \in E(G)\}$. For $S \subseteq V(G)$, we denote $S^1 = \{u^1 \in V(G^1) : u \in S\}$.

Please note that G^1 is well defined, as shown in the following lemma.

Lemma 1 ([22]). *Let G^1 be the twin graph of a graph G. Then, $u^1v^1 \in E(G^1)$ if and only if $xy \in E(G)$ for all $x \in [u], y \in [v]$.*

We illustrate the construction of the twin graph of a given graph G with the following example.

Example 2. *A graph G and its twin graph G^1 are shown in Figure 2a,b, respectively. Please note that u_2 and u_4 are twin vertices of G, so $u_2^1 = u_4^1$ in G^1.*

(a) A graph G (b) The graph G^1

Figure 2. A graph G and its twin graph G^1.

This paper is organized as follows. In Section 2 we use the twin graph G^1 to provide a lower bound of the determining number of an arbitrary graph G, whereas in Section 3 we use similar tools to give an upper bound. Section 4 is devoted to use these bounds to compute the determining number of cographs and unit interval graphs. We conclude the paper in Section 5 with some remarks and future work.

2. A Lower Bound of Det(G) from Removing Twins

In this section, we present a new lower bound of the determining number of a graph. A lower bound in terms of both orders of G and G^1 is already known (see [14]).

Lemma 2 ([14]). *Let G be a graph of order n such that G^1 has order $n^{(1)}$. Then,*

$$n - n^{(1)} \leq \text{Det}(G).$$

We present a different approach that relates the determining numbers of G and G^1. To this end, we need to define the following natural mapping between the automorphism groups of both G and G^1:

$$\widetilde{\mathcal{T}} : \text{Aut}(G) \to \text{Aut}(G^1)$$

given by $\widetilde{\mathcal{T}}(\phi)(u^1) = \phi(u)^1$. In the following lemma, we show that this mapping is a well-defined group automorphism.

Lemma 3. *For every graph G, the mapping $\widetilde{\mathcal{T}}$ satisfies the following properties:*

1. *$\widetilde{\mathcal{T}}$ is well-defined.*
2. *$\widetilde{\mathcal{T}}$ is a group homomorphism.*

Proof.   1. Firstly, we have to check that $\widetilde{\mathcal{T}}(\phi)(u^1)$ does not depend on the choice of the representative of u^1. By definition of graph automorphism, it is clear that $N(u) = N(v)$ if and only if $N(\phi(u)) = N(\phi(v))$, and also $N[u] = N[v]$ if and only if $N[\phi(u)] = N[\phi(v)]$, so u, v are twin vertices if and only if $\phi(u), \phi(v)$ are twin vertices. Let $u, v \in V(G)$ be two different vertices such that $v^1 = u^1$, then u, v are twin vertices and $\phi(v), \phi(u)$ are also twin vertices, that means that $\phi(v)^1 = \phi(u)^1$. Therefore $\widetilde{\mathcal{T}}_G(\phi)(u^1) = \phi(u)^1 = \phi(v)^1 = \widetilde{\mathcal{T}}(\phi)(v^1)$.

On the other hand, for $u^1, v^1 \in V(G^1)$, Lemma 1 yields $u^1 v^1 \in E(G^1)$ if and only if $uv \in E(G)$, or equivalently $\phi(u)\phi(v) \in E(G)$, that is $\phi(u)^1 \phi(v)^1 = \widetilde{\mathcal{T}}(\phi)(u^1)\widetilde{\mathcal{T}}(\phi)(v^1) \in E(G^1)$, as desired.

2. Clearly $\widetilde{\mathcal{T}}(\phi \circ \phi')(u^1) = (\phi \circ \phi')(u)^1 = \phi(\phi'(u))^1 = \widetilde{\mathcal{T}}(\phi)(\phi'(u)^1) = \widetilde{\mathcal{T}}(\phi) \circ \widetilde{\mathcal{T}}(\phi')(u^1)$, so $\widetilde{\mathcal{T}}(\phi \circ \phi') = \widetilde{\mathcal{T}}(\phi) \circ \widetilde{\mathcal{T}}(\phi')$. □

We will also need the following definition of a special type of vertex subset. We say that a set $\Omega \subseteq V(G)$ is a *plenty twin set* if no pair of vertices of $V(G) \setminus \Omega$ are twins. Equivalently, Ω is a plenty twin set if it contains all but at most one vertices of every non-trivial twin class. In particular, this gives that every determining set is a plenty twin set (see [14], proof of Lemma 3.3). However, there are plenty twin sets that are not determining sets, as we show with the following example.

Example 3. *The graph G in Figure 3 has exactly two non-trivial twin classes, $[u_1] = \{u_1, v_1\}$, $[u_2] = \{u_2, v_2\}$, therefore $\{u_1, u_2\}$ is a plenty twin set. Moreover, the mapping ϕ satisfying $\phi(w) = w$ for every vertex $w \in \{u, u_1, v_1, u_2, v_2\}$, $\phi(a_1) = a_2, \phi(a_2) = a_1, \phi(b_1) = b_2, \phi(b_2) = b_1$ is a non-trivial graph automorphism fixing both u_1, u_2, so $\{u_1, u_2\}$ is not a determining set of G.*

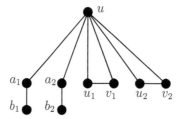

Figure 3. $\{u_1, u_2\}$ is a plenty twin set but it is not a determining set.

A basic property of plenty twin sets is the following.

Lemma 4. *If Ω is a plenty twin set of a graph G, then Ω^1 is a plenty twin set of G^1.*

Proof. On the contrary, let us assume that there is a pair of twins $x^1, y^1 \in V(G^1) \setminus \Omega^1$. Thus, we have that $x, y \in V(G) \setminus [\Omega]$, and so $[x] = \{x\}$ and $[y] = \{y\}$, because Ω is a plenty twin set.

In particular, x, y are not twins in G, and so we may assume without loss of generality the existence of a vertex $z \in V(G) \setminus \{x, y\}$ such that $z \in N_G(x)$ and $z \notin N_G(y)$. By Lemma 1, $z^1 \in N_{G^1}(x^1)$ and $z^1 \notin N_{G^1}(y^1)$. This contradicts the fact that x^1 and y^1 are twins. □

In the following lemma, we present the general behaviour of the stabilizer of a vertex subset under the mapping $\widetilde{\mathcal{T}}$ and also the special situation of plenty twin sets.

Lemma 5. *Let G be a graph. For any subset $S \subseteq V(G)$, it holds that*

$$\widetilde{\mathcal{T}}(\text{Stab}_G(S)) \subseteq \text{Stab}_{G^1}(S^1).$$

Furthermore, if S is a plenty twin set, then the equality holds.

Proof. Let $\phi \in \text{Aut}(G)$ such that $\psi(u) = u$ for all $u \in S$. Thus, $\widetilde{\mathcal{T}}(\phi)(u^1) = \phi(u)^1 = u^1$, and so $\widetilde{\mathcal{T}}(\phi) \in \text{Stab}_{G^1}(S^1)$, which gives the desired inclusion.

Now, assume that S is a plenty twin set and let $\psi \in \text{Stab}_{G^1}(S^1)$, and let us construct the mapping $\phi : V(G) \longrightarrow V(G)$ in the following way. If $u \in V(G)$ satisfies $u^1 \in S^1$ then we define $\phi(u) = u$ (in particular $\phi(u) = u$ for all $u \in S$). In this case, it is clear that $\psi(u^1) = u^1 = \phi(u)^1$. On the other hand, if $u \in V(G)$ satisfies $u^1 \in V(G^1) \setminus S^1$ then, $\psi(u^1) \in V(G^1) \setminus S^1$, because $\psi \in \text{Stab}_{G^1}(S^1)$. Thus there exists $v^1 \in V(G^1) \setminus S^1$ such that $\psi(u^1) = v^1$. Using that S is a plenty twin set, we obtain that $[v] = \{v\}$, and we define $\phi(u) = v$. Please note that in this case, again $\psi(u^1) = v^1 = \phi(u)^1$.

Let us check that ϕ is an automorphism of G. Indeed, $uv \in E(G)$ if and only if $u^1 v^1 \in E(G^1)$, which is equivalent to $\phi(u)^1 \phi(v)^1 = \psi(u^1)\psi(v^1) \in E(G^1)$ since ψ is an automorphism of G^1. Again, this is equivalent to $\phi(u)\phi(v) \in E(G)$, by Lemma 1. This proves that $\phi \in \text{Aut}(G)$.

By construction, $\psi(u^1) = \phi(u)^1 = \tilde{\mathcal{T}}(\phi)(u^1)$ for all $u \in V(G)$, and so $\psi = \tilde{\mathcal{T}}(\phi)$. Furthermore, ϕ fixes each element of S, which means $\phi \in \text{Stab}_G(S)$. Therefore, $\tilde{\mathcal{T}}(\text{Stab}_G(S)) \supseteq \text{Stab}_{G^1}(S^1)$. □

We now present the announced lower bound of the determining number of a graph, in terms of the corresponding parameter of its twin graph.

Theorem 1. *If S is a determining set of a graph G then S^1 is a determining set of the twin graph G^1. Consequently, $\text{Det}(G^1) \leq \text{Det}(G)$ and this bound is tight.*

Proof. Let S be a determining set of G. Thus, S is a plenty twin set and Lemma 5 gives

$$\tilde{\mathcal{T}}_G(\text{Stab}_G(S)) = \text{Stab}_{G^1}(S^1). \tag{1}$$

On the other hand, $\tilde{\mathcal{T}}$ is a group homomorphism and $\text{Stab}_G(S) = \{id_G\}$, which implies that $\tilde{\mathcal{T}}(\text{Stab}_G(S)) = \tilde{\mathcal{T}}(\{id_G\}) = \{id_{G^1}\}$. Combining this with Equality (1), we obtain that $\text{Stab}_{G^1}(S^1) = \{id_{G^1}\}$ and S^1 is a determining set of G^1. Furthermore, $|S^1| \leq |S|$ and therefore $\text{Det}(G^1) \leq \text{Det}(G)$.

To prove the tightness of the bound, let H_s, with $s \geq 1$, be a graph with vertex set $V(H_s) = \{u, u_0\} \cup \{u_1, v_1, \ldots, u_s, v_s\}$ and edge set $E(H_s) = \{uu_i : 0 \leq i \leq s\} \cup \{uv_i : 1 \leq i \leq s\} \cup \{u_iv_i : 1 \leq i \leq s\}$; its twin graph H_s^1 is a star on $s + 2$ vertices (see Figure 4). It is easy to check that $S = \{u_1, \ldots, u_s\}$ and $S^1 = \{u_1^1, \ldots, u_s^1\}$ are minimum determining sets of H_s and H_s^1, respectively, and so $\text{Det}(H_s) = \text{Det}(H_s^1) = s$. □

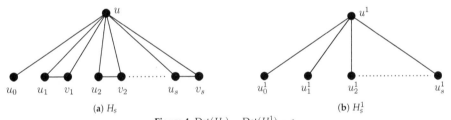

(a) H_s (b) H_s^1

Figure 4. $\text{Det}(H_s) = \text{Det}(H_s^1) = s$.

In order to compare our new lower bound with that showed in Lemma 2, we provide the following two examples.

Example 4. *Consider the graph G with $s + 2$ vertices consisting of a complete graph with $s \geq 3$ vertices, a vertex v that is not a neighbor of any vertex in the complete graph and a vertex u which is a neighbor of v and of every vertex in the complete graph (see Figure 5a). Clearly G^1 is a path with three vertices (see Figure 5b), so $n^{(1)} = 3$ and $\text{Det}(G^1) = 1$. Therefore $\text{Det}(G^1) = 1 < n - n^{(1)} = s + 2 - 3 = s - 1$ and in this case, the lower bound in Lemma 2 is greater than the new one.*

(a) G (b) G^1

Figure 5. $\mathrm{Det}(G^1) = 1 < n - n^{(1)} = s - 1$.

Example 5. *Consider the graph G, with $n = 3s + 3$ vertices ($s \geq 3$), shown in Figure 6a, whose twin graph G^1 is depicted in Figure 6b. In this case, $n^{(1)} = n - 1$ and $S = \{u_1^1, u_2^1, \ldots u_{s-1}^1\}$ is a minimum determining set of G^1, so $\mathrm{Det}(G^1) = s - 1$. Therefore $n - n^{(1)} = 1 < \mathrm{Det}(G^1)$ and our new lower bound is a better option than the old one.*

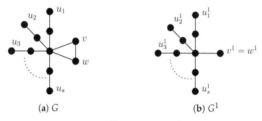

(a) G (b) G^1

Figure 6. $n - n^{(1)} = 1 < \mathrm{Det}(G^1) = s - 1$.

Therefore, both lower bounds are independent and we obtain the following corollary.

Corollary 1. *Let G be a graph. Then, it holds that*

$$\max\{n - n^{(1)}, \mathrm{Det}(G^1)\} \leq \mathrm{Det}(G).$$

3. An Upper Bound on Det(G) from Removing Twins

In the previous section, we explored the relationship between the determining number of graphs G and G^1, and thereby providing a new general lower bound for the determining number of a graph. We now focus on using such relationship to obtain an upper bound for the determining number.

Our strategy is now to obtain a twin-free graph by iterating the process of building G^1 from G. Contrary to what one might think, the twin graph G^1 of a graph G is not twin-free in general (see Figure 7).

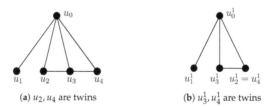

(a) u_2, u_4 are twins   (b) u_3^1, u_4^1 are twins

Figure 7. G^1 is not necessarily a twin free graph.

This fact suggests the iterative process of defining, for any integer $i \geq 2$, the graph G^i as the twin graph of G^{i-1}; its order is denoted by $n^{(i)}$. So, having in mind that G is a finite graph, we can iterate this process thus obtaining a graph sequence $G = G^0, G^1, \ldots, G^r$, where G^r is the only twin-free graph of the sequence. Clearly, if G is a non twin-free graph with n vertices, then $1 \leq r \leq n - 1$. The following example illustrates the extreme case $r = n - 1$.

Example 6. *In Figure 8 we show a graph G with $n = 5$ vertices, and its sequence of twin graphs G^1, G^2, G^3, G^4. Please note that G, G^1, G^2, G^3 are not twin-free whereas G^4 is, so $r = 4 = 5 - 1 = n - 1$.*

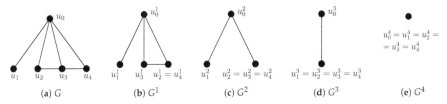

Figure 8. The sequence of twin graphs obtained from G.

We denote by $\mathcal{T}^i \colon V(G^{i-1}) \to V(G^i)$ the natural projection of G^{i-1} onto its twin graph G^i, for any $1 \leq i \leq r$. Let us denote $u^i = (\mathcal{T}^i \circ \mathcal{T}^{i-1} \circ \ldots \circ \mathcal{T}^1)(u)$ and $[u]^i = \{v \in V(G) : u^i = v^i\}$ for any vertex $u \in V(G)$. In general, for any subset $S \subseteq V(G)$, we denote by $S^i = \{u^i \in V(G^i) : u \in S\}$, note that it is a vertex subset of G^i, and by $[S]^i = \{u \in V(G) : u^i \in S^i\}$, note that it is a vertex subset of G.

The proof of the following properties is trivial.

Lemma 6. *Let G be a graph, let $u \in V(G)$ and let $S \subseteq V(G)$. Then, the following statements hold*

1. $[u]^1 = [u]$ and $[S]^1 = [S]$.
2. $[u] \subseteq [u]^i$ and this inclusion is not an equality in general, for $i \geq 2$.
3. $S \subseteq [S]^1 \subseteq [S]^2 \subseteq \ldots \subseteq [S]^r \subseteq V(G)$. In particular, if S is a plenty twin set, then $[S]^i$ is also a plenty twin set, for every i.

Remark 1. *In Figure 8 we can see an example of the second property of Lemma 6. In this case* $[u_4]^1 = \{u_2, u_4\} \subsetneq [u_4]^2 = \{u_2, u_3, u_4\} \subsetneq [u_4]^3 = \{u_1, u_2, u_3, u_4\} \subsetneq [u_4]^4 = \{u_0, u_1, u_2, u_3, u_4\}$.

The iterated application of the construction process of the twin graph easily provides this straightforward generalization of Lemma 4.

Lemma 7. *If Ω is a plenty twin set of a graph G, then Ω^i is a plenty twin set of G^i, for $i \geq 1$.*

We now present three technical lemmas that will be useful to obtain the main result of this section. These lemmas collect the behavior of plenty twin sets and their stabilizers under the successive twin graph operations.

Lemma 8. *Let Ω be a plenty twin set of a graph G, and let $x \in V(G)$. If $x \in V(G) \setminus [\Omega]^i$ for some $i \geq 1$, then $[x]^i = \{x\}$.*

Proof. We proceed by induction on $i \geq 1$. For $i = 1$, let $x \in V(G) \setminus [\Omega]^1 = V(G) \setminus [\Omega]$; in particular, $x \notin \Omega$. Suppose on the contrary that there exists $y \neq x$ such that $y \in [x]^1 = [x]$. Then, x and y are twin vertices of G, and using that Ω is a plenty twin set, we obtain that $y \in \Omega$. However, this means $x \in [y] \subseteq [\Omega]$, which is a contradiction.

Our inductive hypothesis is the following: if $x \in V(G) \setminus [\Omega]^{i-1}$ then $[x]^{i-1} = \{x\}$. Suppose now that $x \in V(G) \setminus [\Omega]^i$ (and so $x^i \notin \Omega^i$ by definition of Ω^i); in particular, by Statement 3 of Lemma 6, $x \notin [\Omega]^{i-1}$ (and so $x^{i-1} \notin \Omega^{i-1}$) and by the inductive hypothesis $[x]^{i-1} = \{x\}$. Assume that there exists $y \neq x$ such that $y \in [x]^i$, which yields $x^i = y^i$. This implies that x^{i-1} and y^{i-1} are twins in G^{i-1}. We know that $[x]^{i-1} = \{x\}$, so $y^{i-1} \neq x^{i-1}$. On the other hand, Ω^{i-1} is a plenty twin set because of Lemma 7, so $y^{i-1} \in \Omega^{i-1}$. Finally, this gives that $x^i = y^i \in \Omega^i$, a contradiction. $\square$

Lemma 9. *Let Ω be a plenty twin set of a graph G. Then, for every $i \geq 1$,*

$$\mathrm{Stab}_{G^{i-1}}(\Omega^{i-1}) = \mathrm{Stab}_{G^{i-1}}((\mathcal{T}^i)^{-1}(\Omega^i)).$$

Proof. Recall that $G^0 = G$ and $\Omega^0 = \Omega$. We only have to prove the inclusion $\mathrm{Stab}_{G^{i-1}}(\Omega^{i-1}) \subseteq \mathrm{Stab}_{G^{i-1}}((\mathcal{T}^i)^{-1}(\Omega^i))$, so let $\phi \in \mathrm{Stab}_{G^{i-1}}(\Omega^{i-1})$ and let $u^{i-1} \in (\mathcal{T}^i)^{-1}(\Omega^i)$. We need to show that $\phi(u^{i-1}) = u^{i-1}$. If $u_{i-1} \in \Omega^{i-1}$, then $\phi(u^{i-1}) = u^{i-1}$, by hypothesis about ϕ. Assume now that $u_{i-1} \in (\mathcal{T}^i)^{-1}(\Omega^i) \setminus \Omega^{i-1}$. Then $\mathcal{T}^i(u^{i-1}) = u^i \in \Omega^i$.

On the other hand, $\phi \in \mathrm{Stab}_{G^{i-1}}(\Omega^{i-1})$ implies that $\tilde{\mathcal{T}}^i(\phi) \in \tilde{\mathcal{T}}^i(\mathrm{Stab}_{G^{i-1}}(\Omega^{i-1})) = \mathrm{Stab}_{G^i}(\Omega^i)$, by Lemma 5, and so $\tilde{\mathcal{T}}^i(\phi)(u^i) = u^i$. Moreover, by definition, $\tilde{\mathcal{T}}^i(\phi)(u^i) = (\phi(u^{i-1}))^1$, and this means that $(\phi(u^{i-1}))^1 = u^i$. In other words, $\phi(u^{i-1})$ and u^{i-1} belong to the same twin class in G^{i-1}.

Finally, if $\phi(u^{i-1}) \neq u^{i-1}$, using that Ω^{i-1} is a plenty twin set not containing u^{i-1}, we have that $\phi(u^{i-1}) \in \Omega^{i-1}$, however this is not possible because ϕ is a bijective mapping that fixes every vertex in Ω^{i-1}, and no vertex outside Ω^{i-1} have its image in Ω^{i-1}. So $\phi(u^{i-1}) = u^{i-1}$, as desired. $\square$

Lemma 10. *Let G be a graph, and let $\Omega \subseteq V(G)$ be a plenty twin set. Then, for each $i \geq 1$:*

$$\mathrm{Stab}_G(\Omega) = \mathrm{Stab}_G([\Omega]^i).$$

Proof. We proceed by induction on $i \geq 1$. Firstly, for $i = 1$, Lemma 9 gives $\mathrm{Stab}_G(\Omega) = \mathrm{Stab}_G((\mathcal{T}^1)^{-1}(\Omega^1))$ and $(\mathcal{T}^1)^{-1}(\Omega^1) = [\Omega]^1$, by definition.

We now assume that $\mathrm{Stab}_G(\Omega) = \mathrm{Stab}_G([\Omega]^{i-1})$. Let $\phi \in \mathrm{Stab}_G(\Omega) = \mathrm{Stab}_G([\Omega]^{i-1})$. We need to prove that $\phi \in \mathrm{Stab}_G([\Omega]^i)$. Indeed, the iteration of Lemma 5 on the plenty twin set $[\Omega]^{i-1}$ gives $\tilde{\mathcal{T}}^{i-1} \circ \ldots \circ \tilde{\mathcal{T}}^1(\mathrm{Stab}_G([\Omega]^{i-1}) = \mathrm{Stab}_{G^{i-1}}(\mathcal{T}^{i-1} \circ \ldots \circ \mathcal{T}^1([\Omega]^{i-1})) = \mathrm{Stab}_{G^{i-1}}(\Omega^{i-1})$. Furthermore, by using again Lemma 9, we obtain that $\mathrm{Stab}_{G^{i-1}}(\Omega^{i-1}) = \mathrm{Stab}_{G^{i-1}}((\mathcal{T}^i)^{-1}(\Omega^i))$. This means that $\tilde{\mathcal{T}}^{i-1} \circ \ldots \circ \tilde{\mathcal{T}}^1(\phi) \in \mathrm{Stab}_{G^{i-1}}(\Omega^{i-1}) = \mathrm{Stab}_{G^{i-1}}((\mathcal{T}^i)^{-1}(\Omega^i))$.

Let $x \in [\Omega]^i \setminus [\Omega]^{i-1}$. This implies that $x^{i-1} \notin \Omega^{i-1}$ but $x^i \in \Omega^i$, so $x^{i-1} \in (\mathcal{T}^i)^{-1}(\Omega^i)$. Hence, $\tilde{\mathcal{T}}^{i-1} \circ \ldots \circ \tilde{\mathcal{T}}^1(\phi)(x^{i-1}) = x^{i-1}$. On the other hand, $\tilde{\mathcal{T}}^{i-1} \circ \ldots \circ \tilde{\mathcal{T}}^1(\phi)(x^{i-1}) = \phi(x)^{i-1}$ by definition. Thus, $\phi(x)^{i-1} = x^{i-1}$, which implies that $\phi(x) \in [x]^{i-1} = \{x\}$, by Lemma 8, so $\phi(x) = x$. Hence, $\phi \in \mathrm{Stab}_G([\Omega]^i)$. $\square$

We finally present the main result of this section, that provides an upper bound for $\mathrm{Det}(G)$.

Theorem 2. *Let G be a graph of order n, and let r be the smallest integer such that G^r is twin-free. Then,*

$$\mathrm{Det}(G) \leq n - n^{(1)} + \mathrm{Det}(G^r)$$

and moreover, this bound is tight.

We first prove the following assertion.
Claim 1. For any plenty twin set Ω of G, we have that

$$\mathrm{Stab}_G([\Omega]^r) \cap \mathrm{Ker}(\tilde{\mathcal{T}}^r \circ \ldots \circ \tilde{\mathcal{T}}^1) = \{id_G\}.$$

Proof. (Proof of Claim 1)
Let $\phi \in \mathrm{Stab}_G([\Omega]^r) \cap \mathrm{Ker}(\tilde{\mathcal{T}}^r \circ \ldots \circ \tilde{\mathcal{T}}^1)$ and let $u \in V(G)$. We need to prove that $\phi(u) = u$. Clearly, we may assume that $u \in V(G) \setminus [\Omega]^r$. Since $\phi \in \mathrm{Ker}(\tilde{\mathcal{T}}^r \circ \ldots \circ \tilde{\mathcal{T}}^1)$, we have that $\tilde{\mathcal{T}}^r \circ \ldots \circ \tilde{\mathcal{T}}^1(\phi)(u^r) = u^r$, but $\tilde{\mathcal{T}}^r \circ \ldots \circ \tilde{\mathcal{T}}^1(\phi)(u^r) = \phi(u)^r$ by definition. Thus, $\phi(u)^r = u^r$, or equivalently $\phi(u) \in [u]^r = \{u\}$, where the last equality is a consequence of Lemma 8, as $[\Omega]^r$ is a plenty set. Therefore, $\phi(u) = u$ and this proves the claim.

Let R be a minimum determining set of G^r, and let $S \subseteq V(G)$ be a subset of cardinality $|R|$ such that $S^r = R$. By Lemma 5, we have that $\tilde{\mathcal{T}}(\mathrm{Stab}_G(S)) \subseteq \mathrm{Stab}_{G^1}(S^1)$, and therefore we obtain that

$\tilde{\mathcal{T}}^2 \circ \tilde{\mathcal{T}}(\text{Stab}_G(S)) \subseteq \tilde{\mathcal{T}}^2(\text{Stab}_{G^1}(S^1)) \subseteq \text{Stab}_{G^2}(S^2)$, where the last inclusion is given again by the same lemma. Thus, iterating this process yields

$$\tilde{\mathcal{T}}^r \circ \ldots \circ \tilde{\mathcal{T}}^1(\text{Stab}_G(S)) \subseteq \text{Stab}_{G^r}(S^r) = \text{Stab}_{G^r}(R) = \{id_{G^r}\}$$

since R is a determining set of G^r. Hence, $\text{Stab}_G(S) \subseteq \text{Ker}(\tilde{\mathcal{T}}^r \circ \ldots \circ \tilde{\mathcal{T}}^1)$.

On the other hand, let $\Omega \subseteq V(G)$ be a vertex subset composed by all but one vertices of each twin class in G. Clearly, Ω is a plenty twin set and $|\Omega| = n - n^{(1)}$. Lemma 10 yields $\text{Stab}_G(\Omega) = \text{Stab}_G([\Omega]^r)$, and Claim 1 yields $\text{Stab}_G([\Omega]^r) \cap \text{Ker}(\tilde{\mathcal{T}}^r \circ \ldots \circ \tilde{\mathcal{T}}^1) = \{id_G\}$. Therefore, we obtain that $\text{Stab}_G(\Omega) \cap \text{Ker}(\tilde{\mathcal{T}}^r \circ \ldots \circ \tilde{\mathcal{T}}^1) = \{id_G\}$ but $\text{Stab}_G(\Omega) \cap \text{Stab}_G(S) \subseteq \text{Stab}_G(\Omega) \cap \text{Ker}(\tilde{\mathcal{T}}^r \circ \ldots \circ \tilde{\mathcal{T}}^1) = \{id_G\}$. This means that $\text{Stab}_G(S \cup \Omega) = \text{Stab}_G(S) \cap \text{Stab}_G(\Omega) = \{id_G\}$ and so $S \cup \Omega$ is a determining set of G. This gives the desired bound, since $|S| = \text{Det}(G^r)$ and $|\Omega| = n - n^{(1)}$.

To show the tightness of the bound, we consider the graph G in Figure 9a, with $2s + 4$ vertices ($s \geq 2$). Clearly, G^1 (see Figure 9b) is not twin-free whereas G^2 is (see Figure 9c). Moreover, $S = \{u_1, u_2, \ldots, u_{s-1}, w\}$ is a minimum determining set of G, so $\text{Det}(G) = s$. On the other hand, $R = \{u_1^2, u_2^2, \ldots, u_{s-1}^2\}$ is a minimum determining set of G^2 and $\text{Det}(G^2) = s - 1$. Finally, note that $n - n^{(1)} = 1$ and therefore $\text{Det}(G) = n - n^{(1)} + \text{Det}(G^2)$. $\square$

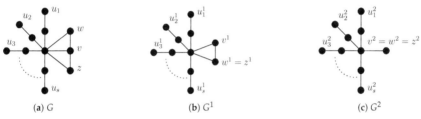

(a) G (b) G^1 (c) G^2

Figure 9. $\text{Det}(G) = n - n^{(1)} + \text{Det}(G^2)$.

Corollary 2. *Let r be the smallest integer such that G^r is twin-free. Then,*

$$\max\{n - n^{(1)}, \text{Det}(G^1)\} \leq \text{Det}(G) \leq n - n^{(1)} + \text{Det}(G^r).$$

Remark 2. *It is proved in [14] that a twin-free graph has determining number at most the half of its order. Then, $\max\{n - n^{(1)}, \text{Det}(G^1)\} \leq \text{Det}(G) \leq n - n^{(1)} + \dfrac{n^{(r)}}{2}$.*

4. Determining Number of Cographs and Unit Interval Graphs

As an application of the bounds obtained in the previous sections, we can compute the determining number of cographs and unit interval graphs. A *cograph* is a graph that can be constructed from the single-vertex graph K_1 by complementation and disjoint union. This graph class was independently described by several authors (see [23–26]). Examples of cographs are, among others, the complete graphs, the complete bipartite graphs, the cluster graphs and the threshold graphs.

Proposition 2. *Let G be a cograph of order n with twin graph G^1 of order $n^{(1)}$, then*

$$\text{Det}(G) = n - n^{(1)}.$$

Proof. Cographs are precisely the graphs without an induced P_4 as a subgraph (see [27,28]), and so the resulting graph from removing any vertex of a cograph is also a cograph. Thus, given a cograph G, G^1 can be seen as a graph obtained by deletion of vertices of G, so it is clear that G^1 is also a cograph. Iterating this argument we obtain that G^i is a cograph, for any index i; in particular, if r is the smallest integer such that G^r is twin-free, then G^r is a cograph.

It is known that a non-trivial cograph has at least a pair of twins (see [27]), hence G' is necessarily isomorphic to K_1, and so $\text{Det}(G') = \text{Det}(K_1) = 0$. Finally, by Corollary 2, we obtain that $n - n^{(1)} \leq \max\{n - n^{(1)}, \text{Det}(G^1)\} \leq \text{Det}(G) \leq n - n^{(1)} + \text{Det}(G') = n - n^{(1)}$, and $\text{Det}(G) = n - n^{(1)}$, as desired. □

Please note that the proof of Theorem 2 and Proposition 2 give that minimum determining sets of cographs are exactly plenty twin sets with $n - n^{(1)}$ vertices, that is, containing exactly all but one vertices of every non-trivial twin class. In the following example we illustrate this property of cographs.

Example 7. *The graph in Figure 10a is a cograph (see [29]) with $n = 7$ vertices and its twin graph, that is shown in Figure 10b, has $n^{(1)} = 4$ vertices. Therefore, $\text{Det}(G) = n - n^{(1)} = 3$ and $\Omega = \{a, c, e\}$ is a minimum determining set of G because it is composed by all but one vertices of each non-trivial twin class of G.*

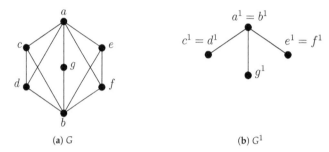

(a) G (b) G^1

Figure 10. A cograph G and its twin graph G^1.

We now focus on unit interval graphs. A graph is a *unit interval graph* if it is possible to assign to each of its vertices a unit interval of the real line in such a way that two vertices are adjacent exactly if the associated intervals intersect (see [30]). We will apply again our previous results to bound the determining number of these graphs, and we first need the following technical lemma.

Lemma 11. *Let S be a vertex subset of a graph G, and let $x \in V(G) \setminus S$ be such that for every $y \in V(G) \setminus (S \cup \{x\})$ either $deg(x) \neq deg(y)$ or $(N(x) \setminus N(y)) \cap S \neq \emptyset$. Then, $\text{Stab}_G(S) = \text{Stab}_G(S \cup \{x\})$.*

Proof. Clearly we just need to prove that $\text{Stab}_G(S) \subseteq \text{Stab}_G(S \cup \{x\})$. To this end, let $\phi \in \text{Stab}_G(S)$, which means that $\phi(u) = u$, for every $u \in S$. Let us see that $\phi(x) = x$. Suppose, on the contrary, that $\phi(x) = y \neq x$, (note that $y \notin S$, because if $y \in S$ then, $y = \phi(y)$). Clearly $deg(x) = deg(\phi(x)) = deg(y)$, because automorphisms preserve degrees of vertices, so $(N(x) \setminus N(y)) \cap S \neq \emptyset$, by hypothesis. Let $z \in (N(x) \setminus N(y)) \cap S$. Then, $z \in N(x)$ and $\phi(z) \in N(\phi(x)) = N(y)$. On the other hand, $z \in S$ implies that $\phi(z) = z$, a contradiction with $z \notin N(y)$. □

Proposition 3. *Let G be a connected unit interval graph of order n with twin graph G^1 of order $n^{(1)}$. Then, $\text{Det}(G) \in \{n - n^{(1)}, n - n^{(1)} + 1\}$.*

Proof. It is well known that unit interval graphs and indifference graphs are equivalent graphs classes (see [31]), so the vertices of G can be represented as real numbers $\{x_1, \ldots, x_n\}$, with $x_i < x_j$ when $i < j$, and $E(G) = \{x_i x_j \colon |x_i - x_j| \leq 1\}$.

We first consider the particular case when G is a connected unit interval twin-free graph. Let us see that, in this case, $\text{Stab}_G(\{x_1, \ldots, x_{i-1}\}) = \text{Stab}_G(\{x_1, \ldots, x_{i-1}, x_i\})$, for every $i \in \{2, \ldots n\}$. If $i = n$, clearly $\text{Stab}_G(\{x_1, \ldots, x_{n-1}\}) = \text{Stab}_G(\{x_1, \ldots, x_{n-1}, x_n\})$. We now fix $i \in \{2, \ldots n - 1\}$, and suppose that $(N(x_i) \setminus N(x_j)) \cap \{x_1, \ldots, x_{i-1}\} \neq \emptyset$, for every $j \in \{i + 1, \ldots, n\}$. Then, by Lemma 11, we obtain $\text{Stab}_G(\{x_1, \ldots, x_{i-1}\}) = \text{Stab}_G(\{x_1, \ldots, x_{i-1}, x_i\})$.

Assume now that there exits $j > i$ such that $N(x_i) \cap \{x_1, \ldots, x_{i-1}\} \subseteq N(x_j) \cap \{x_1, \ldots, x_{i-1}\}$. Since G is twin-free, there is $x_k \in (N(x_i) \setminus N(x_j)) \cup (N(x_j) \setminus N(x_i))$. Please note that $N(x_i) \cap \{x_1, \ldots, x_{i-1}\} \neq \varnothing$, since G is connected, and the hypothesis of this case $N(x_i) \cap \{x_1, \ldots, x_{i-1}\} \subseteq N(x_j) \cap \{x_1, \ldots, x_{i-1}\}$ gives that $|x_i - x_j| \leq 1$. This also means that $N(x_i) \cap \{x_{i+1}, \ldots, x_n\} \subseteq N(x_j) \cap \{x_{i+1}, \ldots, x_n\}$ and therefore, $N[x_i] \subseteq N[x_j]$. This means that $deg(x_i) \leq deg(x_j)$. In addition, $x_k \in N(x_j) \setminus N(x_i)$ gives that $deg(x_i) < deg(x_j)$. Again, by Lemma 11, $\text{Stab}_G(\{x_1, \ldots, x_{i-1}\}) = \text{Stab}_G(\{x_1, \ldots, x_{i-1}, x_i\})$.

Applying repeatedly this condition we obtain that $\text{Stab}_G(\{x_1\}) = \text{Stab}_G(\{x_1, \ldots, x_n\}) = \text{Stab}_G(V(G))$. So $\{x_1\}$ is a determining set of G and $\text{Det}(G) \in \{0, 1\}$, whenever G is a connected unit interval twin-free graph.

Finally, let us consider the general case and let G be any connected unit interval graph. Observe that every G^i is also a connected unit interval graph. In particular, if r is the smallest integer such that G^r is twin-free, then $\text{Det}(G^r) \in \{0, 1\}$. Finally, by Corollary 2, we obtain that $n - n^{(1)} \leq \text{Det}(G) \leq n - n^{(1)} + \text{Det}(G^r) \leq n - n^{(1)} + 1$, as desired. $\square$

We illustrate the behavior of minimum determining sets of unit interval graphs with the following examples.

Example 8. *We show a unit interval graph G and its representation through intersections of intervals of length one (see [32]) in Figure 11a. The twin graph of G is in Figure 11b and it is clearly a twin-free graph satisfying $\text{Det}(G^1) = 1$. Proposition 3 gives $\text{Det}(G) \in \{n - n^{(1)}, n - n^{(1)} + 1\} = \{5 - 4, 5 - 4 + 1\} = \{1, 2\}$. In this case, it is easy to check that $\text{Det}(G) = n - n^{(1)} = 1$ and both $\{b\}$ and $\{c\}$ are minimum determining sets of G.*

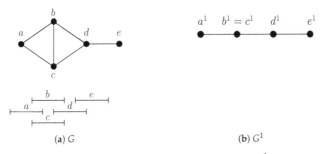

(a) G (b) G^1

Figure 11. A unit interval G and its twin graph G^1.

Example 9. *We now show a unit interval graph G and its representation through intersections of intervals of length one in Figure 12a. The twin graph of G (see Figure 12b) is a twin-free graph satisfying $\text{Det}(G^1) = 1$. In this case, it is easy to check that $\text{Det}(G) = n - n^{(1)} + 1 = 2$ and $\{b, f\}$ is an example of minimum determining set of G.*

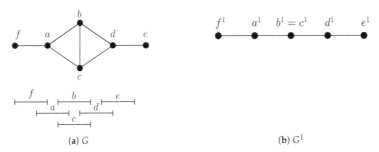

(a) G (b) G^1

Figure 12. A unit interval G and its twin graph G^1.

5. Concluding Remarks

In this paper, we provided a lower bound and an upper bound, each of them being tight, of the determining number of general graphs. We also showed that our lower bound is independent from the one obtained in [14]. The main tool that we used is the twin graph, defined in [22] to study the metric dimension of graphs, and which has proven to be also useful for obtaining determining sets and for computing the determining number. Indeed, as an application of our bounds, we computed the exact value of the determining number of cographs. In the case of unit interval graphs, we placed this parameter in an set of two consecutive integers. In both cases, the obtained values depend only on the number of vertices of both graphs G and its twin graph G^1.

We think that our bounds could be useful to deal with other graph families (e.g., distance-hereditary graphs or parity graphs) in order to obtain the exact value of their determining numbers, or at least to bound the range of possible values. Actually, we could find other techniques, different from twin deletion, to provide new bounds of the determining number of a graph: addition of vertices or edges, vertex contraction, etc. Furthermore, it could be of interest to apply all those techniques to other types of sets different from determining sets such as dominating sets, cut sets, and independent sets.

Author Contributions: All authors contributed equally to this work. Conceptualization, A.G. and M.L.P.; methodology, A.G. and M.L.P.; formal analysis, A.G. and M.L.P.; validation, A.G. and M.L.P.; writing—original draft preparation, A.G. and M.L.P.; writing-review and editing, A.G. and M.L.P.

Funding: The second author is partially supported by grants MTM2015-63791-R (MINECO/FEDER) and RTI2018-095993-B-100.

Conflicts of Interest: The authors declare no conflict of interest.

References

1. Garey, M.R.; Johnson, D.S. *Computers and Intractability: A Guide to the Theory of NP-Completeness*; W. H. Freeman & Co.: New York, NY, USA, 1979.
2. Luks, E.M. Isomorphism of Graphs of Bounded Valence Can Be Tested in Polynomial Time. *J. Comput. Syst. Sci.* **1982**, *25*, 42–65. [CrossRef]
3. Boutin, D.L. Identifying Graph Automorphisms Using Determining Sets. *Electron. J. Combin.* **2006**, *13*, 78.
4. Erwin, D.; Harary, F. Destroying automorphisms by fixing nodes. *Discret. Math.* **2006**, *306*, 3244–3252. [CrossRef]
5. Slater, P.J.; Leaves of trees. *Congr. Numer.* **1975**, *14*, 549–559.
6. Harary, F.; Melter, R. On the metric dimension of a graph. *Ars Combin.* **1976**, *2*, 191–195.
7. Barragán-Ramírez, G.A.; Estrada-Moreno, A.; Ramírez-Cruz, Y.; Rodríguez-Velázquez, J. The Simultaneous Local Metric Dimension of Graph Families. *Symmetry* **2017**, *9*, 132. [CrossRef]
8. Imran, S.; Siddiqui, M.K.; Imran, M.; Hussain, M.; Bilal, H.M.; Cheema, I.Z.; Tabraiz, A.; Saleem, Z. Computing the Metric Dimension of Gear Graphs. *Symmetry* **2018**, *10*, 209. [CrossRef]
9. Imran, S.; Siddiqui, M.K.; Imran, M.; Hussain, M. On Metric Dimensions of Symmetric Graphs Obtained by Rooted Product. *Mathematics* **2018**, *6*, 191. [CrossRef]
10. Hussain, Z.; Munir, M.; Chaudhary, M.; Kang, S.M. Computing Metric Dimension and Metric Basis of 2D Lattice of Alpha-Boron Nanotubes. *Symmetry* **2018**, *10*, 300. [CrossRef]
11. Liu, J.-B.; Kashif, A.; Rashid, T.; Javaid, M. Fractional Metric Dimension of Generalized Jahangir Graph. *Mathematics* **2019**, *7*, 100. [CrossRef]
12. Wang, J.; Miao, L.; Liu, Y. Characterization of n-Vertex Graphs of Metric Dimension n - 3 by Metric Matrix. *Mathematics* **2019**, *7*, 479. [CrossRef]
13. Cáceres, J.; Garijo, D.; Puertas, M.L.; Seara, C. On the determining number and the metric dimension of graphs. *Electron. J. Combin.* **2010**, *17*, 63.
14. Garijo, D.; González, A., Márquez, A. The difference between the metric dimension and the determining number of a graph. *Appl. Math. Comput.* **2014**, *249*, 487–501. [CrossRef]
15. Albertson, M.O.; Collins, K.L. Symmetry Breaking in Graphs. *Electron. J. Combin.* **1996**, *3*, R18.

16. Bailey, R.F.; Cameron, P.J. Base size, metric dimension and other invariants of groups and graphs. *Bull. Lond. Math. Soc.* **2011**, *43*, 209–242. [CrossRef]

17. Babai, L. On the complexity of canonical labeling of strongly regular graphs. *SIAM J. Comput.* **1980**, *9*, 212–216. [CrossRef]

18. Blaha, K.D. Minimum Bases for Permutation Groups: The Greedy Approximation. *J. Algorithms* **1992**, *13*, 297–306. [CrossRef]

19. Boutin, D.L. The Determining Number of a Cartesian Product. *J. Graph Theory* **2009**, *61*, 77–87. [CrossRef]

20. Cáceres, J.; Garijo, D.; González, A.; Márquez, A.; Puertas, M.L. The determining number of Kneser graphs. *Discret. Math. Theor. Comput. Sci.* **2013**, *15*, 1–14.

21. Javaid, I.; Azhar, M.N.; Salman, M. Metric Dimension and Determining Number of Cayley Graphs. *World Appl. Sci. J.* **2012**, *18*, 1800–1812.

22. Hernando, C.; Mora, M.; Pelayo, I.M.; Seara, C.; Wood, D.R. Extremal Graph Theory for Metric Dimension and Diameter. *Electron. J. Combin.* **2010**, *17*, 30. [CrossRef]

23. Lerchs, H. *On Cliques and Kernels*; Technical Report; Department of Computer Science, University of Toronto: Toronto, ON, USA, 1971.

24. Seinsche, D. On a property of the class of n-colorable graphs. *J. Comb. Theory (B)* **1974**, *16*, 191–193. [CrossRef]

25. Sumner, D.P. Dacey graphs. *J. Austral. Math. Soc.* **1974**, *18*, 492–502. [CrossRef]

26. Jung, H.A. On a class of posets and the corresponding comparability graphs. *J. Comb. Theory (B)* **1978**, *24*, 125–133. [CrossRef]

27. Corneil, D.G.; Lerchs, H.; Stewart-Burlingham, L. Complement reducible graphs. *Discret. Appl. Math.* **1981**, *3*, 163–174. [CrossRef]

28. Corneil, D.G.; Perl, Y.; Stewart, L. Cographs: recognition, application and algorithms. *Congr. Numer.* **1984**, *43*, 249–258.

29. Randerath, B.; Schiermeyer, I. Vertex Colouring and Forbidden Subgraphs—A Survey. *Graphs Combin.* **2004**,*20*, 1–40. [CrossRef]

30. Fishburn, P.C. Interval graphs and interval orders. *Discret. Math.* **1985**, *55*, 135–149. [CrossRef]

31. Roberts, F.S. Indifference graphs. In *Proof Techniques in Graph Theory (Proceedings of the Second Ann Arbor Graph Theory Conference, Ann Arbor, MI, USA, 1968)*; Academic Press: New York, NY, USA, 1969; pp. 139–146.

32. Hanlon, P. Counting Interval Graphs. *Trans. Amer. Math. Soc.* **1982**, *272*, 383–426. [CrossRef]

Article

The Simultaneous Strong Resolving Graph and the Simultaneous Strong Metric Dimension of Graph Families

Ismael González Yero

Departamento de Matemáticas, Universidad de Cádiz, EPS, 11202 Algeciras, Spain; ismael.gonzalez@uca.es

Received: 5 December 2019; Accepted: 10 January 2020; Published: 14 January 2020

Abstract: We consider in this work a new approach to study the simultaneous strong metric dimension of graphs families, while introducing the simultaneous version of the strong resolving graph. In concordance, we consider here connected graphs G whose vertex sets are represented as $V(G)$, and the following terminology. Two vertices $u, v \in V(G)$ are strongly resolved by a vertex $w \in V(G)$, if there is a shortest $w - v$ path containing u or a shortest $w - u$ containing v. A set A of vertices of the graph G is said to be a strong metric generator for G if every two vertices of G are strongly resolved by some vertex of A. The smallest possible cardinality of any strong metric generator (SSMG) for the graph G is taken as the strong metric dimension of the graph G. Given a family $\mathcal{F}$ of graphs defined over a common vertex set V, a set $S \subset V$ is an SSMG for $\mathcal{F}$, if such set S is a strong metric generator for every graph $G \in \mathcal{F}$. The simultaneous strong metric dimension of $\mathcal{F}$ is the minimum cardinality of any strong metric generator for $\mathcal{F}$, and is denoted by $\mathrm{Sd}_s(\mathcal{F})$. The notion of simultaneous strong resolving graph of a graph family $\mathcal{F}$ is introduced in this work, and its usefulness in the study of $\mathrm{Sd}_s(\mathcal{F})$ is described. That is, it is proved that computing $\mathrm{Sd}_s(\mathcal{F})$ is equivalent to computing the vertex cover number of the simultaneous strong resolving graph of $\mathcal{F}$. Several consequences (computational and combinatorial) of such relationship are then deduced. Among them, we remark for instance that we have proved the NP-hardness of computing the simultaneous strong metric dimension of families of paths, which is an improvement (with respect to the increasing difficulty of the problem) on the results known from the literature.

Keywords: simultaneous strong resolving set; simultaneous strong metric dimension; simultaneous strong resolving graph

MSC: 05C12

1. Introduction

Topics concerning distances in graphs are widely studied in the literature, and a high number of applications to real life problems can be found in the literature. As a sporadic example of a work that gives some ideas on the vastness of this topic we cite, for instance [1]. Metric graph theory is a significant area in graph theory that deals with distances in graphs, and a large number of works on this topic is nowadays being developed. One of the lines belonging to metric graph theory is that of the metric dimension parameters. Such topic is indeed a huge area of research that is lastly intensively dealt with. It is then not our goal to enter into citing several articles which are not connected exactly with our exposition. To those readers interested in metric dimension things, we suggest for instance the Ph.D. dissertation [2] (and references cited therein), which contains a good background on the topic.

For any given simple and connected graph G whose vertex set is represented as $V(G)$ and its edge set by $E(G)$, while considering it as a metric space, several styles of metrics over the vertex set V, provided with the standard vertex distance, are nowadays defined and studied in the literature.

For instance, the metric $d_G : V(G) \times V(G) \to \mathbb{N} \cup \{0\}$, where $\mathbb{N}$ represents the set of positive integers numbers, and $d_G(x, y)$ is taken as the length of a shortest $u - v$ path, is one of the most commonly studied. In this sense, the pair $(V(G), d_G)$ is clearly a metric space. Concerning such a metric space, it is said that a vertex $v \in V(G)$ distinguishes (recognizes or determines are also used terms) two vertices x and y if $d_G(v, x) \neq d_G(v, y)$. A set $S \subset V(G)$ is said to be a *metric generator* for the graph G if it is satisfied that any pair of vertices of G is uniquely determined by some element of S. Consider that $S = \{w_1, w_2, \ldots, w_k\}$ is an ordered subset of vertices of G. The *metric vector* (or metric representation) of a given vertex $v \in V(G)$, with respect to S, is the vector of distance $(d(v, w_1), d(v, w_2), \ldots, d(v, w_k))$. In this sense, the subset of vertices S is called a *metric generator* for the graph G, if any two distinct vertices produce distinct metric vectors relative to such set S. A metric generator of G having the minimum possible cardinality is called a *metric basis*, and its cardinality is precisely the *metric dimension* of G, which is usually denoted by $\dim(G)$. The definitions of these concepts (for general metric spaces) are coming from the earliest 1950s from the work [3], although its popularity was not developed until relatively recently (about 15 years before). On the other hand, for the specific case of graphs, and motivated by a problem of uniquely recognizing intruder's locations in networks, these concepts were presented and studied by Slater in [4]. In such work, metric generators were called *locating sets*. On the other hand, Harary and Melter (see [5]) also independently came out with the same concept. In such work, metric generators were called *resolving sets*. It is interesting to remark that some examples of applications of the metric dimension concern navigation of robots in networks as discussed in the work [6], or to chemistry as appearing in [7–9].

An interesting variant of metric dimension in graphs was described by Sebö and Tannier in [10], where they have asked the following question. "*For a given metric generator T of a graph H, whenever H is a subgraph of a graph G, and the metric vectors of the vertices of H relative to T agree in both H and G, is H an isometric subgraph of G?*" The situation is that, despite the fact that metric vectors of all vertices of a graph G (relative to a given metric generator) distinguish all pairs of vertices in such graph, it happens that they do not always uniquely recognize all distances in this graph, a fact that was already shown in [10]. Addressed to give a positive answer to their own question, the authors of [10] replaced the notion of "metric generator" by a stronger one. This is described next.

Given a pair of vertices $u, v \in V(G)$, the *interval* $I_G[u, v]$ between such two vertices u and v is defined as the collection of all vertices that belong to some shortest $u - v$ path. In this sense, a vertex w *strongly resolves* two other different vertices u and v, if it is satisfied that $v \in I_G[u, w]$ or $u \in I_G[v, w]$, or equivalently, if $d_G(u, w) = d_G(u, v) + d_G(v, w)$ or $d_G(v, w) = d_G(v, u) + d_G(u, w)$. In connection with this, it is also said that u, v are *strongly resolved* by w. From now on, all graphs considered are connected. A set S of vertices of G is a *strong metric generator* for G if any two distinct vertices x, y of such graph are strongly resolved by some vertex $u \in S$ (it could happen that u equals x or y). Then, the smallest possible cardinality of any set being a strong metric generator for G is called the *strong metric dimension* of G, and this cardinality is denoted by $\dim_s(G)$. In addition, a strong metric generator for G whose cardinality is precisely equal to $\dim_s(G)$ is called a *strong metric basis* of G. It is now readily observed that any strong metric generator of G also satisfies the property of being a metric generator for G. The computational problem concerning finding the strong metric dimension of a given graph is now relatively well studied, and one can find a rich literature concerning it. For more information on this issue, we suggest, for instance, the articles [11,12], the Ph.D. Thesis [13], the survey [14], and references cited therein.

More recently, an extension of the notion of the strong metric dimension of graphs to families of graphs was presented in [15]. The following was stated: Consider that $\mathcal{G} = \{G_1, G_2, \ldots, G_k\}$ is a family of connected graphs $G_i = (V, E_i)$ having a common vertex set V. Note that the edge sets of the graphs belonging to the family are not necessarily edge-disjoint, and also that the union of their edge sets is not necessarily the complete graph. Concerning such family, it was said in [15] that a *simultaneous strong metric generator* (SSMG for short) for the family $\mathcal{G}$ is taken as a set $S \subset V$ with the property that S forms a strong metric generator for every graph G_i of the family. As usual, an SSMG having the minimum possible cardinality for $\mathcal{G}$ is called a *simultaneous strong metric basis* of $\mathcal{G}$. This smallest cardinality is then precisely called the *simultaneous strong metric dimension* of $\mathcal{G}$, and this is denoted by $\mathrm{Sd}_s(\mathcal{G})$, or by $\mathrm{Sd}_s(G_1, G_2, ..., G_t)$ when it is necessary to clarify the graphs of the family. It is worthwhile mentioning that such concepts arise from a related version of simultaneity for the standard metric dimension studied in [16,17].

The notion of the simultaneous metric dimension of graphs families (and its strong related version) was first studied in the Ph.D. thesis [18], based on the following problem, which arises in relation with a similar problem for the standard metric dimension. It is assumed that the topology of robots navigation network changes within some amount of possible simple networks, say a set (or family) of graphs $\mathcal{F}$. Nodes of the networks remain the same, but their links could appear or disappear. This setting could require the use of a dynamic network whose links change over the time. In this sense, the problem concerning uniquely identifying the robots (by using the smallest resources) navigating in such a "variable" network can be understood as the problem of determining the minimum cardinality of a set of vertices that is simultaneously a metric generator for each graph belonging to this set $\mathcal{F}$. That is, if a set of vertices S gives a solution to this problem, then the position of a robot can be uniquely determined by the distance to the elements of S, independently of the graph which is being used in each moment in this dynamic network.

We now present some basic terminology and notation to beused throughout our exposition. Given a vertex v of a graph G, $N_G(v)$ denotes the *open neighborhood* of v in G, while the *closed neighborhood* is represented by $N_G[v]$ and it equals $N_G(v) \cup \{v\}$. If there is no confusion, we then simply use $N(v)$ or $N[v]$. Two vertices $x, y \in V(G)$ are called *twins* if they satisfy $N_G[x] = N_G[y]$ or $N_G(x) = N_G(y)$. Specifically, when $N_G[x] = N_G[y]$, they are known as *true twins*, and similarly whether $N_G(x) = N_G(y)$, they are called *false twins*. Now, if the open neighborhood $N(v)$ of a vertex v induces a complete graph, then such v is known as an *extreme vertex*. The set of extreme vertices of G is denoted by $\sigma(G)$. The largest possible distance between any two vertices of G is denoted by $D(G)$, also called the *diameter* of G. In this sense, a graph G is called 2-antipodal if, for every vertex $x \in V(G)$, there is exactly one other vertex $y \in V(G)$ satisfying the fact that $d_G(x, y) = D(G)$. Examples of 2-antipodal graphs are, for instance, even cycles C_{2k}, and the hypercubes Q_r. Finally, for a given set $W \subset V(G)$, by $\langle W \rangle_G$, we represent the subgraph of G induced by W. Any other definition used shall be introduced whenever a concept is firstly needed.

Since all the definitions above require the connectedness of the graph in question, throughout the whole exposition, we will consider that our graphs are connected; even so, we will not explicitly mention this fact.

2. The Simultaneous Strong Resolving Graph

In this section, we describe an approach which was first presented in [19], in order to transform the problem of finding the strong metric dimension of a graph to computing the vertex cover number of another related graph. To this end, we need some terminology and notation. A vertex u of G is said to be *maximally distant* from other v, if every vertex $w \in N_G(u)$ satisfies that $d_G(v, w) \leq d_G(u, v)$. For a pair of vertices, u, v, if it happens that u is maximally distant from v and v is also maximally distant from u, then these u and v are called a pair of *mutually maximally distant vertices* (MMD for short). The set of vertices of G that are MMD with at least one other vertex of G is denoted by $\partial(G)$. The *strong resolving graph* of G, which is denoted by G_{SR}, is another graph whose vertex set is $V(G_{SR}) = V(G)$. In addition, there is an edge between two vertices u, v in G_{SR} if such vertices u and v are mutually maximally distant in the original graph G. Clearly, those vertices which are not MMD with any other vertex of G are isolated vertices in G_{SR}. The recent work [20] (a kind of survey) contains a number of results concerning characterizations, realizability, and several other properties of the strong resolving graphs of graphs.

Now, by a *vertex cover* set of a graph G, we mean a set of vertices S of G satisfying that every edge of G has at least one end vertex in the set S. The *vertex cover number* of G, which is denoted by

$\alpha(G)$, is taken as the smallest possible cardinality of a subset of vertices of G being a vertex cover set of G. By an $\alpha(G)$-set, we represent a vertex cover set of cardinality $\alpha(G)$. In connection with this concept, the authors Oellermann and Peters-Fransen (see [19]) have proved that finding the strong metric dimension of a connected graph G is equivalent to finding the vertex cover number of G_{SR}, which is the next result.

Theorem 1 ([19]). *For any connected graph G, $\dim_s(G) = \alpha(G_{SR})$.*

There are several different and non trivial families of connected graphs for which the strong resolving graphs can relatively easily be obtained. We next mention some of these cases, mainly based on the fact that we further on shall refer to them. Such following observations have already appeared (in an identical presentation) in other works like, for instance [20].

Observation 1.

(a) If $\partial(G) = \sigma(G)$, then $G_{SR} \cong K_{|\partial(G)|} \cup \left(\bigcup_{i=1}^{n-|\partial(G)|} K_1 \right)$. In particular, $(K_n)_{SR} \cong K_n$ and for any tree T of order n with $l(T)$ leaves, $(T)_{SR} \cong K_{l(T)} \cup \left(\bigcup_{i=1}^{n-l(T)} K_1 \right)$.

(b) For any 2-antipodal graph G of order n, $G_{SR} \cong \bigcup_{i=1}^{\frac{n}{2}} K_2$. Even cycles are 2-antipodal. Thus, $(C_{2k})_{SR} \cong \bigcup_{i=1}^{k} K_2$.

(c) For odd cycles, $(C_{2k+1})_{SR} \cong C_{2k+1}$.

We now turn our attention to the simultaneous strong metric dimension of graph families and look for an equivalent version of the strong resolving graph in a simultaneous version. That is, given a family of graphs $\mathcal{G} = \{G_1, G_2, ..., G_k\}$ defined over the set of vertices V (as described above), we say that the *simultaneous strong resolving graph* of G, denoted by $\mathcal{G}_{SSR}$, is a graph whose vertex set is $V(\mathcal{G}_{SSR}) = V$. In addition, two vertices u, v are adjacent in $\mathcal{G}_{SSR}$ if the vertices u and v are mutually maximally distant in some graph $G_i \in \mathcal{G}$. It is readily seen that $\mathcal{G}_{SSR}$ can be obtained from the overlapping of the strong resolving graphs of the graphs $G_1, G_2, \ldots, G_k$. An equivalent result to that of Theorem 1 can be then derived for the simultaneous case. To this end, the next remarks make an important role.

Remark 1. *Let G be any connected graph. For any two vertices $x, y \in V(G)$, there are two MMD vertices x', y' of G, such that a shortest $x' - y'$ path contains the vertices x, y.*

We must recall that at least one of the vertices x, y in the result above could precisely be at least one of the vertices x', y', respectively (this could happen in case x, y are MMD or whether one of them is maximally distant from the other).

Theorem 2. *For any family of graphs, $\mathcal{G} = \{G_1, G_2, ..., G_k\}$, $Sd_s(\mathcal{G}) = \alpha(\mathcal{G}_{SSR})$.*

Proof. We shall prove that any set is an SSMG for $\mathcal{G}$ if and only if it is a vertex cover of $\mathcal{G}_{SSR}$. Assume each graph of $\mathcal{G}$ is defined over the set of vertices V. Let $W \subset V$ be an SSMG of $\mathcal{G}$ and let uv be an edge of $\mathcal{G}_{SSR}$. By the definition of $\mathcal{G}_{SSR}$, there is a graph $G_i \in \mathcal{G}$ such that u, v are MMD in G_i. Thus, $W \cap \{u, v\} \neq \emptyset$, which means that the edge uv is covered by W in $\mathcal{G}_{SSR}$. Thus, W is a vertex cover of $\mathcal{G}_{SSR}$.

On the other hand, let $W' \subset V$ be a vertex cover of $\mathcal{G}_{SSR}$ and let x, y be any two different vertices of V. If x, y are MMD in some $G_j \in \mathcal{G}$, then xy is an edge of $\mathcal{G}_{SSR}$, which means that $W' \cap \{x, y\} \neq \emptyset$, since such edge must be covered by W'. Assume $x \in W'$. Thus, the pair of vertices x, y is strongly resolved by x in every $G_i \in \mathcal{G}$. On the contrary, if x, y are not MMD in every $G_i \in \mathcal{G}$, then the edge xy does not exist in $\mathcal{G}_{SSR}$. Moreover, by Remark 1, in every graph $G_l \in \mathcal{G}$, there are two MMD vertices x_l, y_l such that a shortest $x_l - y_l$ path of G_l contains x and y. Clearly, for every $G_l \in \mathcal{G}$, the edge

$x_l y_l$ belongs to G_{SSR} and so, $W' \cap \{x_l, y_l\} \neq \emptyset$. Hence, for any $G_l \in \mathcal{G}$, we observe that x, y are strongly resolved by x_l or by y_l. As a consequence, W' is a strong resolving set for any $G_i \in \mathcal{G}$ and therefore W' is a simultaneous strong resolving set of $\mathcal{G}$, which completes the proof of the equality $Sd_s(\mathcal{G}) = \alpha(\mathcal{G}_{SSR})$. $\square$

3. Realization of the Simultaneous Strong Resolving Graphs with Some Consequences

In the recent work [20], several results concerning the realization of the strong resolving graphs of graphs were presented. For instance, there was proved that there is not any graph G whose strong resolving graph is isomorphic to a complete bipartite graph $K_{2,r}$ for every $r \geq 2$. In contrast with these facts, we shall prove that every graph G can represent the simultaneous strong resolving graph of some family of graphs.

Proposition 1. *For any graph G of order n and size m with vertex set V, there exist a family of m paths $\mathcal{P} = \{P_n^1, P_n^2, \ldots, P_n^m\}$ defined over the set of vertices V such that $\mathcal{P}_{SSR}$ is isomorphic to G.*

Proof. Let $V = \{v_1, v_2, \ldots, v_n\}$ be the vertex set of G. For any edge $e_{ij} = v_i v_j$ of G, consider a path P_n^{ij} whose leaves are v_i and v_j and the remaining vertices are $V - \{v_i, v_j\}$. Since the strong resolving graph of P_n^{ij} is formed by a graph K_2 on the vertices $\{v_i, v_j\}$ and the $n - 2$ isolated vertices $V - \{v_i, v_j\}$, it is readily seen that the union (overlapping) of the m paths P_2 constructed in this way, corresponding to the edges of G, together with the other $n - 2$ isolated vertices, is precisely the graph G. $\square$

Since the realization family given above is formed only by paths, one may now wonder if a given graph can be realized as the simultaneous strong resolving graph of a family of other graphs different from paths. For instance, the following two results show two other different realizations. To this end, a *multisubdivided star* $S_{r,t}$ of order $r + t + 1$ is obtained from a star $S_{1,t}$ by subdividing some edges with some vertices until we have a graph of order $r + t + 1$ (clearly r vertices were used in this multisubdivision process). In addition, a *comet graph* $C_{r,t}$ (where $r \geq 4$ is an even integer and $t \geq 0$) is a unicyclic graph of order $r + t$ whose unique cycle has order r, and there is at most one vertex of degree three and at most one leaf. Note that this comet graph can be a cycle graph when $t = 0$ (in such case an even cycle indeed). In other words, a comet graph is obtained from a cycle C_r by attaching a path of order $t \geq 0$ to one of its vertices.

Proposition 2. *For any graph G of order n with vertex set V, there exists a family of multisubdivided star graphs $\mathcal{F} = \{G_1, G_2, \ldots, G_k\}$ defined over the set of vertices V such that $\mathcal{F}_{SSR}$ is isomorphic to G.*

Proof. Let $V = \{v_1, v_2, \ldots, v_n\}$ be the vertex set of G. Now, for every clique Q_j of G of cardinality j, consider a multisubdivided star graph $S_{j,t}$ such that $j + t + 1 = n$ whose leaves are the vertices of Q_j, and the remaining vertices are $V - Q_j$ (taken in any order). Since the strong resolving graph of every multisubdivided star graph $S_{j,t}$ is formed by a complete graph K_j on the vertices of Q_j and the $n - |Q_j|$ isolated vertices in $V - Q_j$ (by using Observation 1), it is readily seen that the overlapping of the strong resolving graphs of the graphs belonging to this set of multisubdivided star graphs constructed in this way, corresponding to the cliques of G, together with the other corresponding isolated vertices, gives precisely the graph G. $\square$

In order to present our next construction, we remark (which can be easily observed) that the strong resolving graph of a comet graph is given by the disjoint union of r graphs K_2 and t isolated vertices. We also need the following terminology. A *matching* in a graph G is a set of pairwise disjoint edges in the graph, and a *maximum matching* is a matching M such that the inclusion of any other edge of G to M leads to at least two not disjoint edges.

Proposition 3. *For any graph G of order n with vertex set V, there exist a family $\mathcal{F} = \{G_1, G_2, \ldots, G_k\}$ containing comet graphs and paths, defined over the set of vertices V such that $\mathcal{F}_{SSR}$ is isomorphic to G.*

Proof. Let $V = \{v_1, v_2, \ldots, v_n\}$ be the vertex set of G. We consider all possible maximum matchings of G. If there is a maximum matching which has only one edge $e = uv$, then we consider a path graph P_n, for the family $\mathcal{F}$, whose leaves are u and v. Clearly, the strong resolving graph of this path is the graph K_2 on the vertex set $\{u, v\}$ and $n - 2$ isolated vertices. Next, we take every other maximum matching M_i of G having $i \geq 2$ edges. Now, consider a comet graph $C_{2i,t}$ with $2i + t = n$, such that any two vertices being an edge of M_i are diametral in the cycle C_{2i} of $C_{2i,t}$, and the remaining vertices are $V - M_i$ (taken in any order) forming the path of $C_{2i,t}$ of order t that are attached to one vertex of C_{2i}. Note that the strong resolving graph of any comet graph is given by the disjoint union of i graphs K_2 and t isolated vertices. Thus, by using all the graphs constructed as mentioned above for all the maximum matchings of G, it is readily seen that the overlapping of the strong resolving graphs of the graphs belonging to this set constructed in this way, corresponding to the maximum matchings of G, together with the other corresponding isolated vertices, gives precisely the graph G. □

Based on the constructions above, it looks like several different families of graphs can produce the same simultaneous strong resolving graph. In this sense, it is natural to raise the following question, which roughly speaking, seems to be very challenging.

Open question: Given a graph G, is it possible to characterize all the possible families of graphs $\mathcal{F} = \{G_1, G_2, \ldots, G_k\}$ such that $\mathcal{F}_{SSR}$ is isomorphic to G?

It was proved in [15] that computing the simultaneous strong metric dimension of graph families is NP-hard, even when restricted to families of trees. An interesting consequence of Proposition 1 shows that such problem, which next appears, remains NP-hard, even when restricted to a couple of simpler families.

Simultaneous Strong Metric Dimension Problem (SSD Problem for Short)

INSTANCE: A graph family $\mathcal{G} = \{G_1, G_2, \ldots, G_k\}$ defined on a common vertex set V and an integer k, $1 \leq k \leq |V| - 1$.
PROBLEM: Deciding whether $Sd_s(\mathcal{G})$ is less than k.

By using Proposition 1, we next present a reduction of the problem of computing the vertex cover number of graph to the problem of computing the simultaneous strong metric dimension of families of paths.

Theorem 3. *The SSD problem is NP-complete for families of paths or multisubdivided star graphs.*

Proof. The problem is clearly in NP since verifying that a given set of vertices is indeed an SSMG for a graph family can be done in polynomial time. Now, let G be any graph with vertex set V of order n and size m. From Proposition 1 (resp. Proposition 2), we know there is a family of m paths $\mathcal{P} = \{P_n^1, P_n^2, \ldots, P_n^m\}$ (resp. of multisubdivided star graphs) defined over the set of vertices V such that $\mathcal{P}_{SSR}$ is isomorphic to G. Therefore, from Theorem 2, we have that $Sd_s(\mathcal{P}) = \alpha(\mathcal{P}_{SSR}) = \alpha(G)$, which completes the NP-completeness reduction based on the fact that the decision problem concerning the vertex cover number of graphs is an NP-complete problem (see [21]). □

Another interesting consequence of Theorem 2 concerns the approximation of computing the simultaneous strong metric dimension of graphs families. We first note that finding the simultaneous strong resolving graph of a graph family can be polynomially done. This fact, together with the fact that computing the vertex cover number of graphs admits a polynomial-time 2-approximation, allows for claiming that computing the simultaneous strong metric dimension of graphs families also admits a polynomial-time 2-approximation.

4. Applications of the Simultaneous Strong Resolving Graph

Since computing the simultaneous strong metric dimension of graph families is NP-hard even when restricted to very specific families, it is then desirable to describe as many families as possible for which its simultaneous strong metric dimension can be computed. In this sense, from now on in this section we are devoted to make this so, and a fundamental tool for it shall precisely be the simultaneous strong resolving graph and, connected with it, Theorem 2.

Proposition 4. *If $\mathcal{F}$ is a family of bipartite graphs, each of them is defined over the common bipartition sets U, V, then $\mathrm{Sd}_s(\mathcal{F}) \leq |U| + |V| - 2$.*

Proof. If any two vertices are MMD in some graph $G_i \in \mathcal{F}$, then they belong to the same bipartition set of G_i. Thus, it must happen that $\mathcal{F}_{SSR}$ is a subgraph of a graph with two connected components isomorphic to $K_{|U|}$ and $K_{|V|}$. By using Theorem 2, we obtain that $\mathrm{Sd}_s(\mathcal{F}) = \alpha(\mathcal{F}_{SSR}) \leq \alpha(K_{|U|} \cup K_{|V|}) = |U| + |V| - 2$. $\square$

Next, we particularize the result above and show that such bound is achieved in several situations.

Proposition 5. *If $\mathcal{F}$ is a family of bipartite graphs, each of them is defined over the common bipartition sets U, V, and such that it contains the complete bipartite graph $K_{|U|,|V|}$, then $\mathrm{Sd}_s(\mathcal{F}) = |U| + |V| - 2$.*

Proof. The result directly follows from the fact that, if $K_{|U|,|V|} \in \mathcal{F}$, then $(\mathcal{F})_{SR}$ is isomorphic to $K_{|U|} \cup K_{|V|}$. Thus, from Theorem 2, we get the desired result, since $\alpha(K_{|U|} \cup K_{|V|}) = |U| + |V| - 2$. $\square$

Let $C_r = v_0 v_1 \ldots v_{r-1}$, with $r \geq 4$ and even be a cycle. Then, let $\mathcal{F}_C$ be a family of cycles defined on a common vertex set with $C_r \in \mathcal{F}_C$, and every other cycle $C \in \mathcal{F}_C$ is obtained from C_r, by making a permutation of two vertices v_i, v_j of C_r such that either $i, j \in \{0, \ldots, r/2 - 1\}$ or $i, j \in \{r/2, \ldots, r-1\}$.

Proposition 6. *If $\mathcal{F}_C$ is a family of cycles obtained from a cycle C_r as described above, then $\mathrm{Sd}_s(\mathcal{F}_C) = \frac{r}{2}$.*

Proof. We first note (by Observation 1) that the strong resolving graph of any cycle $C_r^{(j)} \in \mathcal{F}_C$ is isomorphic to $\bigcup_{i=1}^{r/2} K_2$. Now, since any cycle of $\mathcal{F}_C$ is obtained from C_r, by making a permutation of two vertices v_i, v_j of C_r such that either $i, j \in \{0, \ldots, r/2 - 1\}$ or $i, j \in \{r/2, \ldots, r-1\}$, we deduce that there are no edges in $(\mathcal{F}_C)_{SSR}$ between any two vertices of the set $\{v_0, v_1, \ldots, v_{r/2-1}\}$, in addition to no edges between any two vertices of the set $\{v_{r/2}, v_{(r/2+1)}, \ldots, v_{r-1}\}$. Moreover, for any vertex of the set $v_j \in \{v_0, v_1, \ldots, v_{r/2-1}\}$, there is an edge joining v_j with a vertex $v_k \in \{v_{r/2}, v_{r/2+1}, \ldots, v_{r-1}\}$ and vice versa. As a consequence of such facts, we obtain that $(\mathcal{F}_C)_{SSR}$ is a bipartite graph, which is a subgraph of the complete bipartite graph $K_{r/2,r/2}$. Since $\alpha(K_{r/2,r/2}) = r/2$, by using Theorem 2, we have $\mathrm{Sd}_s(\mathcal{F}_C) = \alpha((\mathcal{F}_C)_{SSR}) \leq \alpha(K_{r/2,r/2}) = \frac{r}{2}$. On the other hand, since $C_r \in \mathcal{F}_C$, the edges $v_0 v_{r/2}, v_1 v_{r/2+1}, \ldots, v_{r/2-1} v_{r-1}$ belong to $(\mathcal{F}_C)_{SSR}$. Consequently, in order to cover such edges, it must happen $\alpha((\mathcal{F}_C)_{SSR}) \geq r/2$. Therefore, by using again Theorem 2, we complete the proof. $\square$

Let T be a tree having all the vertices with a degree larger than two unless they are leaves. Hence, let $\mathcal{F}_T$ be the family of trees defined on a common vertex set with $T \in \mathcal{F}_T$, and every other tree $T' \in \mathcal{F}_T$ is obtained from T, by making a permutation of two vertices u, v of T such that u is a leaf of T and v is not a leaf.

Proposition 7. *If $\mathcal{F}_T$ is a family of trees obtained from a tree T with t leaves as described above, then $t - 1 \leq \mathrm{Sd}_s(\mathcal{F}_T) \leq t$. Moreover, $\mathrm{Sd}_s(\mathcal{F}_T) = t$ if and only if every leaf of T has been used to make a permutation with other non leaf vertex of T in order to obtain another tree of $\mathcal{F}_T$.*

Proof. By Observation 1, the strong resolving graph of the tree $T \in \mathcal{F}_T$ is isomorphic to the complete graph K_t together with $n - t$ isolated vertices. Thus, K_t is a subgraph of the graph $(\mathcal{F}_T)_{SSR}$ and so, by using Theorem 2, we obtain $\mathrm{Sd}_s(\mathcal{F}_T) = \alpha((\mathcal{F}_T)_{SSR}) \geq \alpha(K_t) = t - 1$, which is the lower bound. Now, observe that the strong resolving graph of any tree, other than T, is obtained from the strong resolving graph of T by removing all edges incident to one vertex, say y, corresponding to a leaf of T, choosing an isolated vertex x corresponding to a non leaf of T, and adding all the possible edges between x and the vertices corresponding to leaves of T other than y. Moreover, since there are no edges between any two of such chosen isolated vertices mentioned above, it is clear that the set of t vertices corresponding to the leaves of T represents a vertex cover set of $(\mathcal{F}_T)_{SSR}$. By using again Theorem 2, we obtain $\mathrm{Sd}_s(\mathcal{F}_T) = \alpha((\mathcal{F}_T)_{SSR}) \leq t$, which is the upper bound.

On the other hand, in order for this set of t vertices to correspond to the leaves of T, which will represent a vertex cover set of minimum cardinality in $(\mathcal{F}_T)_{SSR}$, it is required that all such vertices will have a neighbor not in this set of leaves. This means that every leaf of T has been used to make a permutation with another non leaf vertex of T in order to obtain a tree of $\mathcal{F}_T$ other than T. The opposite direction is straightforward to observe. Therefore, the proof is complete. $\square$

Again, let T be a tree having all the vertices with a degree larger than two unless they are leaves. Let $\mathcal{H}_T$ be the family of at least two unicyclic graphs H defined on a common vertex set such that every graph $H \in \mathcal{H}_T$ is obtained from T, by adding an edge between any two vertices u, v of T. Before studying the simultaneous strong metric dimension of $\mathcal{H}_T$, we introduce some terminology and basic properties of the strong resolving graph of unicyclic graphs. Given a unicyclic graph $G = (V, E)$ with the unique cycle C_r, we denote by $c_2(G)$ the set of vertices of the cycle C_r having degree two. By $T(G)$, we represent the set of vertices of degree one in G.

Remark 2. *Let G be a unicyclic graph. For every vertex $x \in c_2(G)$, there exists at least one vertex $y \in c_2(G) \cup T(G)$ such that x, y are mutually maximally distant in G.*

Remark 3. *Let G be a unicyclic graph. Then, two vertices x, y are mutually maximally distant in G if and only if $x, y \in c_2(G) \cup T(G)$.*

We note that any graph $H \in \mathcal{H}_T$ satisfies that $c_2(H)$ is empty (whether the unicyclic graph H has been obtained from T by adding an edge between two non leaf vertices of T), or has cardinality 1 (whether H has been obtained from T by adding an edge between a leaf a non leaf vertex of T), or cardinality 2 (whether H has been obtained by an added edge between two leaves of T).

Proposition 8. *If $\mathcal{H}_T$ is a family of unicyclic graphs obtained from a tree T with t leaves as described above, then $\mathrm{Sd}_s(\mathcal{H}_T) = t - 1$.*

Proof. By Remarks 2 and 3, and the fact that $0 \leq |c_2(H)| \leq 2$, we deduce that, for any graph $H \in \mathcal{H}_T$, it follows that H_{SR} contains $|V(G)| - t$ isolated vertices together with either

(i) a subgraph isomorphic to K_t or,

(ii) a subgraph isomorphic to K_{t-1} and one extra vertex adjacent to a subset of vertices of the subgraph K_{t-1} or,

(iii) a subgraph isomorphic to K_{t-2} and two extra vertices (in which case such two vertices are not adjacent), which are adjacent to two different subsets of vertices of the subgraph K_{t-2}.

We note that these, one or two, extra vertices are precisely the leaves of T, for which an incident edge has been added to the tree T in order to obtain H. According to these facts, the simultaneous strong resolving graph $(\mathcal{H}_T)_{SSR}$ has a connected component which is a subgraph of a complete graph K_t whose vertex set is precisely the set of leaves of T. In this sense, by using Theorem 2, we obtain $\mathrm{Sd}_s(\mathcal{H}_T) = \alpha((\mathcal{H}_T)_{SSR}) \leq t - 1$.

On the other hand, consider Q is the subgraph induced by the set of vertices corresponding to the leaves of T. If item (i) above occurs for every $H \in \mathcal{H}_T$, then clearly $(\mathcal{H}_T)_{SSR} \cong K_t$ and so

$\mathrm{Sd}_s(\mathcal{H}_T) = \alpha((\mathcal{H}_T)_{SSR}) = t - 1$. Suppose now that $\mathrm{Sd}_s(\mathcal{H}_T) < t - 1$. This means that there are two vertices x, y corresponding to two leaves of T which are not adjacent in $(\mathcal{H}_T)_{SSR}$. In consequence, there is a unicyclic graph $G_{x,y} \in \mathcal{H}_T$ which was obtained from T by adding the edge xy. However, since $\mathcal{H}_T$ has at least two graphs, there is at least a graph $G' \in \mathcal{H}_T$, other than $G_{x,y}$ in which the vertices x, y are not adjacent. Thus, x, y are MMD in G' and so the edge xy exists in $(\mathcal{H}_T)_{SSR}$, a contradiction with our supposition. Therefore, $\mathrm{Sd}_s(\mathcal{H}_T) \geq t - 1$ and we have the desired equality. $\square$

A similar process as described above can be developed in order to get families of graphs for which the simultaneous strong metric dimension of graphs can be computed. However, one may need to use several assumptions while constructing such families. This is based on the fact that computing the simultaneous strong metric dimension is NP-complete for several "very simple" families of graphs (like families of paths, for instance). In connection with this, it would be desirable to find some "properties" satisfied by a graph family in order to decide if it is "easy" to compute its simultaneous strong metric dimension or not.

5. The Particular Case of Cartesian Product Graphs Families

Given two graph families $\mathcal{F}_1 = \{G_1, \ldots, G_r\}$ and $\mathcal{F}_2 = \{H_1, \ldots, H_t\}$ defined over the common sets of vertices V_1 and V_2, respectively, the *Cartesian product graph family* $\mathcal{F}_1 \square \mathcal{F}_2$ is given by the family $\{G_i \square H_j \ : \ G_i \in \mathcal{F}_1, \ H_j \in \mathcal{F}_2\}$. In order to study the simultaneous strong metric dimension of Cartesian product graphs families, we also need the following definition. The *direct product graph family* $\mathcal{F}_1 \times \mathcal{F}_2$ is given by the family $\{G_i \times H_j \ : \ G_i \in \mathcal{F}_1, \ H_j \in \mathcal{F}_2\}$.

We shall next need the following definitions. Given two graphs G and H, the *Cartesian product graph* of G and H is a graph, denoted by $G \square H$, having vertex set $V(G \square H) = V(G) \times V(H)$. In addition, there is an edge between two vertices $(a, b), (c, d) \in V(G \square H)$ if it is satisfied that either $(a = c$ and $bd \in E(H))$ or $(b = d$ and $ac \in E(G))$. In a similar way, the direct product of graphs can be defined. That is, the *direct product graph* of G and H is a graph, denoted by $G \times H$, having vertex set $V(G \times H) = V(G) \times V(H)$. Now, two vertices $(a, b), (c, d)$ are adjacent in the direct product $G \times H$ whenever $ac \in E(G)$ and $bd \in E(H)$.

The first result concerning Cartesian product graphs families is a relationship between the simultaneous strong resolving graph of Cartesian product graphs families and that of its factors. The following equivalent result for the strong metric dimension of graph was given in [22].

Theorem 4 ([22]). *Let G and H be two connected graphs. Then, $(G \square H)_{SR} \cong G_{SR} \times H_{SR}$.*

By using the result above and the fact that the simultaneous strong resolving graph of a graph family equals the union (overlapping) of the strong resolving graph of each graph of the family, we deduce the next result.

Theorem 5. *Let $\mathcal{F}_1 = \{G_1, \ldots, G_r\}$ and $\mathcal{F}_2 = \{H_1, \ldots, H_t\}$ be two graph families defined over the common sets of vertices V_1 and V_2, respectively. Then, $(\mathcal{F}_1 \square \mathcal{F}_2)_{SSR} \cong (\mathcal{F}_1)_{SSR} \times (\mathcal{F}_2)_{SSR}$.*

Proof. Since $(\mathcal{F}_1 \square \mathcal{F}_2)_{SSR}$ is given by $\bigcup_{G_i \in \mathcal{F}_1, H_j \in \mathcal{F}_2} (G_i \square H_j)_{SR}$ and $(G_i \square H_j)_{SR} \cong (G_i)_{SR} \times (H_j)_{SR}$ (by Theorem 4), we get that

$$(\mathcal{F}_1 \square \mathcal{F}_2)_{SSR} \cong \bigcup_{G_i \in \mathcal{F}_1, H_j \in \mathcal{F}_2} (G_i \square H_j)_{SR} \cong \bigcup_{G_i \in \mathcal{F}_1, H_j \in \mathcal{F}_2} (G_i)_{SR} \times (H_j)_{SR} \cong (\mathcal{F}_1 \times \mathcal{F}_2)_{SSR},$$

which gives our claim. $\square$

We next give several results concerning the simultaneous strong metric dimension of Cartesian product graph families. In this sense, the result above plays an important role. Now, our next result, which is obtained by using Theorem 2 and Theorem 5, shall be used as an important tool to develop our exposition.

Corollary 1. *Let $\mathcal{F}_1 = \{G_1, \ldots, G_r\}$ and $\mathcal{F}_2 = \{H_1, \ldots, H_t\}$ be two graph families defined over the common sets of vertices V_1 and V_2, respectively. Then, $\mathrm{Sd}_s(\mathcal{F}_1 \square \mathcal{F}_2) = \alpha((\mathcal{F}_1)_{SSR} \times (\mathcal{F}_2)_{SSR})$.*

Due to the similarity of the results above (in this section) with those obtained in [22] concerning the strong metric dimension of graphs, we note that some analogous reasonings as that ones in [22] shall lead to several results concerning the simultaneous strong metric dimension of graph families. In this sense, we now close our exposition with some problems that are of interest in our point of view.

6. Conclusions and Open Problems

A new approach to study the simultaneous strong metric dimension of graphs families has been presented in this work. That is, we have introduced the notion of simultaneous strong resolving graph of graphs families, and proved the computing the simultaneous strong metric dimension of a family of graphs is equivalent to compute the vertex cover number of this newly introduced simultaneous strong resolving graph. Based on this equivalence, several computational and combinatorial results have been deduced. For instance, we have proved that computing the simultaneous strong metric dimension of families of paths and families of multisubdivided star graphs is NP-hard. As a consequence of the study, a number of open questions have been raised. We next point out several of the most interesting ones:

- Since finding the simultaneous strong metric dimension of graph families is NP-hard, even for relatively simple families of graphs (like families of paths for instance), it would be desirable to describe several other graph families in which this problem could be solved in polynomial time.
- Based on the fact that computing the simultaneous strong metric dimension is NP-hard for several "very simple" families of graphs (like families of paths for instance), it would be desirable to find some structural properties satisfied by a graph family in order to claim that computing its simultaneous strong metric dimension can be efficiently done.
- One of the families studied in [15] was that one containing a graph G and its complement $\overline{G}$. In this sense, it would be interesting to consider the problem of describing the strong resolving graph of $\overline{G}$ and its possible relationship with the strong resolving graph of G, in order to construct the simultaneous strong resolving graph of $\{G, \overline{G}\}$ and thus study its simultaneous strong metric dimension. With this problem, we would also contribute to some open problem presented in [20] concerning describing the structure of the strong resolving graph of several graphs.

Funding: This research received no external funding.

Conflicts of Interest: The author declares no conflict of interest.

References

1. Goddard, W.; Oellermann, O.R. Distance in Graphs. In *Structural Analysis of Complex Networks*; Dehmer, M., Ed.; Birkhäuser: Boston, MA, USA, 2011; pp. 49–72.
2. Estrada-Moreno, A. On the (k, t)-Metric Dimension of a Graph. Ph.D. Thesis, Universitat Rovira i Virgili, Catalonia, Spain, 2016.
3. Blumenthal, L.M. *Theory and Applications of Distance Geometry*; University Press: Oxford, UK, 1953.
4. Slater, P.J. Leaves of trees. *Congr. Numer.* **1975**, *14*, 549–559.
5. Harary, F.; Melter, R.A. On the metric dimension of a graph. *ARS Comb.* **1976**, *2*, 191–195.
6. Khuller, S.; Raghavachari, B.; Rosenfeld, A. Landmarks in graphs. *Discret. Appl. Math.* 1996, *70*, 217–229. [CrossRef]
7. Chartrand, G.; Eroh, L.; Johnson, M.A.; Oellermann, O.R. Resolvability in graphs and the metric dimension of a graph. *Discret. Appl. Math.* **2000**, *105*, 99–113. [CrossRef]

8. Johnson, M. Structure-activity maps for visualizing the graph variables arising in drug design. *J. Biopharm. Stat.* **1993**, *3*, 203–236. [CrossRef] [PubMed]

9. Johnson, M. Browsable structure-activity datasets. In *Advances in Molecular Similarity*; Chap. 8; Carbó-Dorca, R., Mezey, P., Eds.; JAI Press Inc.: Stamford, CT, USA, 1998; pp. 153–170.

10. Sebö, A.; Tannier, E. On metric generators of graphs. *Math. Oper. Res.* **2004**, *29*, 383–393. [CrossRef]

11. Kuziak, D.; Yero, I.G.; Rodríguez-Velázquez, J.A. Strong metric dimension of rooted product graphs. *Int. J. Comput. Math.* **2016**, *93*, 1265–1280. [CrossRef]

12. Kuziak, D.; Yero, I.G.; Rodríguez-Velázquez, J.A. On the strong metric dimension of corona product graphs and join graphs. *Discret. Appl. Math.* **2013**, *161*, 1022–1027. [CrossRef]

13. Kuziak, D. Strong Resolvability in Product Graphs. Ph.D. Thesis, Universitat Rovira i Virgili, Catalonia, Spain, 2014.

14. Kratica, J.; Kovačević-Vujčić, V.; Čangalović, M.; Mladenović, N. Strong metric dimension: A survey. *Yugosl. J. Oper. Res.* **2014**, *24*, 187–198. [CrossRef]

15. Estrada-Moreno, A.; García-Gómez, C.; Ramírez-Cruz, Y.; Rodríguez-Velázquez, J.A. The simultaneous strong metric dimension of graph families. *Bull. Malays. Math. Sci. Soc.* **2016**, *39*, 175–192. [CrossRef]

16. Ramírez-Cruz, Y.; Oellermann, O.R.; Rodríguez-Velázquez, J.A. The simultaneous metric dimension of graph families. *Discret. Appl. Math.* **2016**, *198*, 241–250. [CrossRef]

17. Ramírez-Cruz, Y.; Oellermann, O.R.; Rodríguez-Velázquez, J.A. Simultaneous resolvability in graph families. *Electron. Notes Discret. Math.* **2014**, *46*, 241–248. [CrossRef]

18. Ramírez-Cruz, Y. The Simultaneous (strong) Metric Dimension of Graph Families. Ph.D. Thesis, Universitat Rovira i Virgili, Catalonia, Spain, 2016.

19. Oellermann, O.R.; Peters-Fransen, J. The strong metric dimension of graphs and digraphs. *Discret. Appl. Math.* **2007**, *155*, 356–364. [CrossRef]

20. Kuziak, D.; Puertas, M.L.; Rodríguez-Velázquez, J.A.; Yero, I.G. Strong resolving graphs: The realization and the characterization problems. *Discret. Appl. Math.* **2018**, *236*, 270–287. [CrossRef]

21. Garey, M.R.; Johnson, D.S. Computers and Intractability: A Guide to the Theory of NP-Completeness; W. H. Freeman & Co.: New York, NY, USA, 1979.

22. Rodríguez-Velázquez, J.A.; Yero, I.G.; Kuziak, D.; Oellermann, O.R. On the strong metric dimension of Cartesian and direct products of graphs. *Discret. Math.* **2014**, *335*, 8–19. [CrossRef]

MDPI

St. Alban-Anlage 66

4052 Basel

Switzerland

Tel. +41 61 683 77 34

Fax +41 61 302 89 18

www.mdpi.com

Mathematics Editorial Office

E-mail: mathematics@mdpi.com

www.mdpi.com/journal/mathematics

Lightning Source UK Ltd.
Milton Keynes UK
UKHW052329020223
416374UK00004B/120